Trauma-Informed Mindfulness

Trauma-Informed Mindfulness

A Practitioner's Guide
for One-to-One Work

by
Nikki Kiyimba

University of Chester Press

First published 2020
by University of Chester Press
University of Chester
Parkgate Road
Chester CH1 4BJ

Printed and bound in the UK by the
TJ International
Padstow PL28 8RW

Cover designed by the
LIS Graphics Team
University of Chester

A catalogue record for this book is available
from the British Library

ISBN 978-1-908258-36-6

CONTENTS

ACKNOWLEDGEMENTS

I would like to express my appreciation for the foundation in mindfulness practice provided by my teacher Suryacitta. Thanks also to Ian Lowens who generously shared his knowledge and ideas about compassion focused therapy and to Lynda Coley for her insights about developing cultural safety. Thank you to Ian Woollams, Christina Buxton, Eryn Donnally and Daniel Crossley for being inspirational friends and for commenting on earlier drafts.

In helping me develop and refine this model of Trauma-Informed Mindfulness, I am indebted to my incredible students on the doctoral and postgraduate programmes in psychological trauma. Thank you for your openness and honesty in sharing your own experiences, for participating wholeheartedly, and giving me great feedback in the development of this approach. I owe a great deal to your breadth of professional and personal experience.

I am also grateful to my colleagues in the Centre for Research and Education in Psychological Trauma and the Department of Social and Political Science at the University of Chester for their passion and commitment to excellence in research and teaching practice, and to Sarah Griffiths at the University of Chester Press for your support in bringing this text into print.

Thanks also to Rae and Carole for always providing smiles and treats along the way!

Finally, thank you to all the clients who have worked patiently with me, teaching me what to do and not do, sharing what has been helpful and not helpful in applying mindfulness practice to their lives. You have been my ultimate inspiration and motivation to make this book a reality.

INTRODUCTION

Chapter contents
• Introduction to Trauma-Informed Mindfulness (TIM)   • Reflexive statement   • Chapter overview   • Guide to using this book

Post-traumatic stress disorder (PTSD) is the most widely known trauma-related mental health difficulty. However, many other psychological, emotional and behavioural difficulties are also arguably better understood as trauma-related. In light of this, a new movement of trauma-informed care has begun to make an impact in a number of countries, leading several large institutions such as schools and prisons to reconsider the way that they work with their service users to be aware of how traumatic experiences can be the cause of a number of behavioural difficulties. In parallel, the increase in the use of mindfulness, and the research evidence supporting its efficacy, have transformed the way that psychological interventions, particularly for anxiety and depression have been practiced.

The model of TIM that is presented in this book is born out of research and experience of both of these movements. It is an offering to all practitioners working with traumatised individuals, to help to provide a simple framework for introducing and utilising mindfulness practices safely and effectively in one-to-one interactions. This introduction provides a context for using mindfulness exercises in a specifically trauma-informed way, and also gives an overview of each component of TIM. A simple summary of each chapter gives an indication of how each of the TIM components relate together, and how a working knowledge of both psychological trauma, and mindfulness practices are needed as a foundation to working with this model.

Introduction to TIM

TIM is a model that has been developed initially as a response to the need for individual exercises that can be used in a variety of settings to support traumatised individuals in a one-to-one setting in learning to focus, to concentrate, to be more self-compassionate and less self-critical. Consideration has been given to the ways that mindfulness practices can be implemented in the most beneficial and least harmful way for people who have experienced trauma, and are still experiencing trauma-related symptoms. It is not an adaptation of traditional mindfulness group-based interventions, but is a different kind of model that utilises the principles of mindfulness and compassion in a way that can be flexibly adapted and titrated for the particular needs of individual clients.

It is intended that TIM can be used as an adjunctive or integrated component alongside a range of other psychotherapeutic models that may be used in individual one-to-one counselling, psychology and psychotherapy sessions. It is an approach that is very flexible in that it can be tailored to address specific client needs, and for those using phased-based treatment protocols, is most likely to be of particular use in relation to the stabilisation and resourcing phase of treatment. However TIM is a model that could also be learned and utilised in a much wider range of settings, such as schools, prisons, drug and alcohol services, and for staff in a range of other workplace settings. A particular emphasis of TIM is the importance of taking a self-compassionate stance in relation to the growing development of awareness that mindfulness practice facilitates. This is vital for those who have experienced trauma, especially where the trauma has been interpersonal, has involved shame or physical violence, or has been over a long period of time. There are seven characteristics that make up the model of TIM, which are:

Introduction

1. Psychological trauma knowledge
2. Mindfulness knowledge
3. Personal practice of mindfulness and self-compassion
4. Prioritisation of client safety and choice
5. Avoidance of harm
6. Work with titration
7. Dynamic stabilisation and integration

The full TIM model is explained in detail in chapter one, so that you can gain an immediate sense of exactly what the model is and how it fits together. Each of the seven characteristics has been allocated a separate chapter, so as to provide more detail about what they are, and how they fit within a trauma-informed approach. The application of the model in practice primarily relates to the characteristic of 'work with titration', which refers to the gradual and incremental introduction of mindfulness practices in a way that is tolerable and beneficial for the particular client. An introduction to psychological trauma (TIM characteristic 1. Psychological trauma knowledge) is explained in chapter two: TIM characteristic 2. Knowledge of mindfulness is presented in chapter three. TIM characteristic 3. Personal practice of mindfulness and self-compassion is described in chapter four. Chapter five addresses TIM characteristic 4. Prioritisation of client safety and choice, and chapter six covers TIM characteristic 5. Avoidance of harm. TIM characteristic 6. Work with titration is discussed in chapter seven, and the last TIM characteristic: Dynamic stabilisation and integration is detailed in chapter eight. The final chapter (chapter nine), Integrating TIM into your current practice, concludes the book.

Each of the TIM characteristics is addressed in such a way as to explain the role they play and how they interact with one another to form this holistic system of trauma-informed practice. In addition, you will be guided to an appreciation and understanding of what the particular vulnerabilities of this client group are, and therefore what the risks might be in relation to their additional needs for establishing safety and choice. The book contains practical examples of how to engage in titrated, individually focused mindfulness practices throughout; however, it is intended to be a practitioner guide rather than a self-help book. If you are seeking to use the exercises in this book for yourself, take care to ensure that you are being kind, taking things slowly at your own speed and ensuring that you are careful not to trigger any adverse reactions. You may also benefit from working together with a trained practitioner to support you.

Reflexive statement

I have developed this model as a result of my own therapeutic experience as a Clinical Psychologist in the UK, and also as a University Lecturer in Psychological Trauma. What I have found is that standard mindfulness protocols can sometimes be triggering for people who have experienced trauma. A simple example would be that a typical exercise in mindfulness is to do a 'body scan' where the client brings their conscious attention to each part of their body in turn. What I have found is that people who have experienced physical and/or sexual violence are often reminded of their abuse when their awareness reaches the part of their body where they were assaulted or injured. This can trigger a relapse, de-compensation or an abreaction. Another issue is that people who have experienced interpersonal abuse such as rape or sexual violence often have very high levels of shame and guilt. Although there have been some very good recent adaptations, standard mindfulness practice does not always sufficiently address the extra need for developing self-compassion for people who have experienced interpersonal, developmental or complex trauma. In TIM I draw both on my own clinical experience of working with many individuals who have experienced trauma, as well as experience of teaching about psychological trauma to a wide range of professionals from different backgrounds. The particular third wave therapeutic interventions that I have found most helpful in developing this model of TIM are:

- Mindfulness Based Stress Reduction (MBSR)
- Compassion Focused Therapy (CFT)
- Dialectical Behaviour Therapy (DBT)

These therapies are sometimes referred to as 'third wave' because they share a mindfulness component. The mindfulness skills taught in DBT tend to be shorter and more 'external'. By this I mean that the exercises involve activities such as drawing or describing objects in the outside world, rather than solely focusing on inner processes and sensations within the body. People who have not experienced trauma are usually able to notice body sensations without negative effect. However, people who have experienced trauma often use dissociation as a defence against connecting with painful internal emotions, thoughts or bodily sensations. For example, someone who has suffered physical violence may learn to cope with the intense physical pain by 'shutting off' their awareness of their physical body.

Traditional mindfulness practices generally encourage people to be 'embodied' by being more aware of, and less disconnected from, their physical body. Whilst this is often an important part of an intervention, for those people who have protected themselves from feeling things in their body through dissociation for many years, this can be really challenging. TIM therefore offers strategies for practitioners to titrate the exercises in various ways, including starting with external observations before and moving towards internal mindfulness exercises at a speed and level that the client can tolerate safely. In presenting this model of working with individual clients I want to acknowledge the considerable input from clients and students alike in forming, shaping and honing these ideas, as well as their invaluable patience and willingness to experiment and practice the techniques advised here.

Chapter overview
In order to get a sense of how TIM might differ from or complement other modalities of mindfulness that you have studied before, the following section offers a brief summary of each chapter, with an explanation of how it fits within the overall structure of the model. Bear in mind that TIM is an approach to mindfulness training that is designed as an individual intervention that can be used as a stand-alone model or adopted as an adjunct to other one-to-one approaches.

- **Chapter one – Overview of Trauma-Informed Mindfulness (TIM)**

This chapter explains in detail the whole TIM model. The model is comprised of three sets of seven elements each. The three elements are, the 'characteristics', the 'attitudes' and the 'skills'. A rationale is offered for each of the **seven TIM characteristics** of: 1. Psychological trauma knowledge; 2. Mindfulness knowledge; 3. Personal practice of mindfulness and self-compassion; 4. Prioritisation of client safety and choice; 5. Avoidance of harm; 6. Work with titration; and 7. Dynamic stabilisation and integration. In addition, the **seven TIM attitudes** are introduced here and described in turn. These attitudes are the ways in which the mindfulness practical exercises are to be approached, and are: 1. Being present; 2. Having hope; 3. Self-compassion; 4. Having patience; 5. Being honest; 6. Being courageous; and 7. Accepting what is. Finally the **seven TIM skills** are described in turn. TIM skills are those that form the focus of the practice exercises and are: 1. Curiosity; 2. Observation; 3. Factual description; 4. Non-judgement; 5. Non-resistance; 6. Turning towards; and 7. Letting go. These final skills are the actual assignments that are provided to the client during the 'setting intention' part of the practice, and are also the skills reported on during the inquiry phase after the practice session.

- **Chapter two – Psychological trauma knowledge**

The first of the characteristics of the model of TIM is psychological trauma knowledge. This chapter presents an overview of what trauma is, how it is defined medically, and how different 'types' of trauma are differentiated. It also gives an overview of the impact of trauma on people when they experience single or repeated traumatic events. In this chapter you will be given an overview of the classic symptom clusters used to diagnose Post Traumatic Stress Disorder (PTSD), which are intrusion, avoidance, negative alterations in cognitions and mood, and alterations in arousal and reactivity. It also considers the differences between PTSD and Complex PTSD by comparing the diagnoses of these two conditions as they appear in the fifth version of the *Diagnostic and Statistics Manual* (*DSM-5*) and the eleventh version of the *International Classification of Diseases* (*ICD-11*). As well as looking at the different ways in which a diagnosis of a mental health difficulty that is predominantly trauma-related might be made, this chapter also provides an overview of how the autonomic nervous system is designed to respond to stressors, and how this affects neurology.

- **Chapter three – Mindfulness knowledge**

This chapter provides an overview of the foundations of mindfulness, and will provide grounding in the basic tenets of mindfulness if you have never studied it before. If you have, this will be a valuable re-cap and prelude to looking at how mindfulness has been used in various 'third wave' therapies, including MBSR, DBT and ACT. You will be shown how mindfulness is practiced slightly differently in each of these therapies, within the context of the client presentations the therapies were designed to help. This chapter will also explain what the core principles of mindfulness are and offer you a summary of some of the research in this area. This foundational explanation of what mindfulness is and how it has been variously adapted according to different models of therapy in the West forms the basis for exploration of what kind of modifications of standard mindfulness practice may be necessary or desirable for use with clients who have experienced trauma.

- **Chapter four – Personal practice of mindfulness and self-compassion**

Once a foundational knowledge of psychological trauma and of mindfulness has been established, another key thread that is central to conducting TIM is to keep a watchful eye on self-criticism, blame and guilt in the client and yourself. Having compassion means to offer understanding and kindness to others when they fail or make mistakes, rather than judging them harshly. It also means to appreciate that suffering, failure and imperfection is part of the shared human experience. Self-compassion involves having this same attitude towards yourself if you make a mistake or notice something about yourself that you do not like, or when something you are experiencing feels difficult or painful. In Western culture people can tend to confuse self-compassion with self-indulgence or self-pity, which may lead to being hard on yourself. Rather than criticising, ignoring or condemning, self-compassion is a process of kindly allowing yourself to acknowledge that what you are experiencing is really difficult and asking how you might care for or comfort yourself at that moment. Self-compassion is a vital component of mindfulness. Many people who have experienced interpersonal trauma, in particular sexual abuse or domestic violence, feel very guilty and shamed by their experiences. Being the victim of this and other kinds of trauma can mean that people often blame themselves for what has happened, even though it is clearly inappropriate for them to be held accountable. Therefore, it is really important to validate their experience, and to take extra care to build into the treatment ways to help the client to learn to be more self-compassionate.

- **Chapter five – Prioritisation of client safety and choice**

What I have learned from working with clients who have experienced trauma, and from teaching students who work with traumatised groups of people, is that there are two main components of experiencing trauma that most affect people. These are having no control or choice over what is happening, and experiencing being unsafe. This knowledge therefore forms the basis of TIM, and provides an overarching framework to work within. This is a very practical chapter that builds on this underpinning explanation of why establishing a sense of safety and choice for the client is really important as a starting point, and as a continuous reference point throughout therapy. The chapter uses specific examples of how to help clients to feel safe, including agreeing ways to communicate when they need to stop or take a break. Safety can be considered environmentally, relationally, physically, culturally and in relation to the process of the intervention itself. Each of these will be explored in detail. The chapter also explains why feeling in control and having some elements of choice relating to aspects of the therapy are important, and so the chapter offers specific examples and direction about this issue.

- **Chapter six – Avoidance of harm**

This chapter initially introduces the concept of iatrogenesis, which is a term usually confined to medical situations where unintended harm is caused as the result of medical or surgical interventions. The concept of iatrogenic harm has been adopted by TIM to describe the harm that might happen unintentionally by those involved in providing services for people who have experienced trauma. Harm can be caused at an institutional level, where risk and behaviour management policies take priority over rehabilitation in a way that is not just delaying rehabilitation, but perhaps making rehabilitation more difficult due to implementing practices that are re-traumatising. Often these policies are based on a premise that the risky or undesirable behaviours of service users need to be 'controlled' or 'punished'. This chapter presents an alternative to the behaviourist approach by describing the value of trauma-informed models of care. This chapter also covers the important topics of vulnerability and resilience, including describing the stress-vulnerability model, and offering suggestions for strengthening and increasing resilience, particularly within vulnerable populations.

- **Chapter seven – Work with titration**

In traditional mindfulness, a lot of different exercises are used to help people to be 'in their body' rather than 'in their mind'. This can range from engaging in breathing exercises in order to increase focus and awareness of the physical sensations and movement in the chest and abdomen when breathing in and out, to eating something with intense awareness of all the senses of smell, taste, sight, touch. However, historically there has been little guidance provided or differentiation made with regard to titration of how, when or with whom they are used. For people who have experienced trauma, especially where the trauma has directly impacted on their body in some way, exercises where the person is required to relate to different parts of their body with intense focus, can be really challenging and may even trigger intense emotional reactions, flashbacks or dissociation. In TIM a more cautious titrated approach is taken to awareness building through mindfulness, starting with learning to focus on aspects of the external environment, moving on then to focus awareness on aspects of the physical body, and finally to learn to focus attention on more subtle internal processes such as how thoughts and emotions might be experienced physically. In TIM this is called 'proximity of practice'. When you are following the model of TIM, this will allow both you and your client collaboratively to be more in control of the process. Advice is also offered about how to negotiate moving through these stages or layers with your clients.

- **Chapter eight – Dynamic stabilisation and integration**

For many years, experts who work clinically with people who have experienced trauma have agreed that there is value to adopting a phased approach to trauma treatment interventions. Typically, this would consist of three phases: stabilisation, trauma processing and integration. Some therapeutic approaches concentrate primarily (or only) on supporting stabilisation, which is a term used to describe the phase of supporting a client to establish skills and techniques to maintain a level of equilibrium in relation to their affect regulation. Without the ability to utilise self-soothing strategies to calm the stress response, attempts to enter the trauma-processing phase of treatment can be thwarted, and the client caused undue and potentially completely unmanageable distress. Other primarily processing-focused interventions tend to concentrate more directly on trauma processing without as much concern for stabilisation. There is currently some debate in the field as to the evidence base to support the use of stabilisation as a discrete phase or dynamic process, or whether stabilisation can effectively be discarded. Previously, for many clients who had experienced severe, complex and/or repeated trauma, a long stabilisation phase of months or years was usually recommended as necessary before any processing could be started safely. The integration phase of the phased approach relates to the later stage in therapy after the trauma memories have been processed, to help a client learn to live a life with new beliefs about themselves and the world that may be very different to what they had pre-treatment. There is also usually a period of adjustment for family members and other close relationships as the social system flexes. The stage or phased-based approach, together with its criticisms is discussed in more detail in this chapter. Two propositions are made in this regard; the first being the potential to introduce a fourth pre-stabilisation phase based on the readiness for change model as a proposed solution to the challenges in trauma therapy work of non-engagement and dropout; and the second being a discussion of the concept of 'dynamic stabilisation and integration', which is an engagement with the phased approach in a more flexible way, so for example, in one treatment session readiness, stabilisation, processing and integration may be dynamically assessed and addressed through facilitator/client attunement.

- **Chapter nine – Integrating TIM into your professional practice**

Initially TIM was designed to support therapists, psychologists and counsellors to use as an integrative or adjunctive intervention to their current practice. However, TIM can be also used as a stand-alone intervention, and can also usefully be utilised by professionals from a wider reach of services. It may offer a helpful additional resource to enhance the work with your clients, in order to offer them the best possible service. Whatever your personal preference, this chapter will offer you some very practical guidance about both integrating TIM into your existing work, and using it as a completely 'stand-alone' technique. Additionally, there is immense value in practicing mindfulness for yourself, to help build your resilience to vicarious trauma, compassion fatigue or burnout. This chapter offers some very practical solutions to how professionals might add mindfulness into their work in a safe and considered way.

Guide to using this book

This book is designed as an accompaniment to practitioner training courses for therapists, counsellors, psychologists, doctors, nurses, occupational therapists, social workers and others who work therapeutically with people with complex trauma and PTSD. As such, it contains references to key literature in the field to provide an academic, theory and evidence-based foundation, as well as being very practical in relation to how the model can be implemented in practice. Secondary professions who may also practice mindfulness with their clients are those who work within religious organisations, peer support organisations, voluntary organisations and third sector charities, prison chaplains and sexual health advisors. TIM is designed to be a very accessible handbook for professionals who work with people who have experienced trauma and who would like to incorporate mindfulness into their work. Throughout, I have therefore used the terms 'client' and 'facilitator' to reference the scope of various professionals and service users who may access TIM. The main thing about TIM as an approach is that, unlike traditional mindfulness programmes that are designed as courses that run over a number of weeks, and are presented in group settings, it is designed for individual one-to-one work that can be tailored for the particular client. The exercises are best practiced together with a client during a planned appointment, but can also be set for homework. Within each chapter are distributed occasional 'practice it' boxes. These are designed to give you an opportunity to pause for a moment, reflect on what you have read so far, and in congruence with the ethos of mindfulness, to start to put into practice some of the concepts that you are learning about and to try it for yourself. It is easy to skip over these, but I do encourage you to make use of them along your journey.

CHAPTER ONE
OVERVIEW OF TRAUMA-INFORMED
MINDFULNESS (TIM)

Chapter contents
• Overview
• The seven characteristics of TIM
• The seven attitudes of TIM
• The seven skills of TIM
• Summary

Overview

In this chapter, the whole TIM model is presented according to the main elements of its structure. The model comprises three sets of seven elements. Overarching the whole model are the seven **characteristics** of the approach that are unique in classifying it as a trauma-informed model, and under which everything else falls. The characteristics of TIM are: 1. Psychological trauma knowledge; 2. Mindfulness knowledge; 3. Personal practice of mindfulness and self-compassion; 4. Prioritisation of client safety and choice; 5. Avoidance of harm; 6. Work with titration; and 7. Dynamic stabilisation and integration. These characteristics relate to the knowledge and skills required of the facilitator. As these are central to the model, separate chapters of this book have been devoted to each of them.

Within the overarching framework of these seven TIM characteristics within which the facilitator is trained, are two other sets of conditions that apply to the client; the first are the mindful **attitudes** that are important to relate to as you approach each of the practices. These are: 1. Being present; 2. Having hope; 3. Self-compassion; 4. Having patience; 5. Being honest; 6. Being courageous; and 7. Accepting what is. Each of these are introduced in this chapter and described in turn. These attitudes are key characteristics of TIM practice, and will be part of the initial psycho-education about TIM provided to the client. Although these attitudes are all very important for TIM, they are not the actual skills that are practiced specifically during the exercises.

The second set of conditions relates to the specific **skills** that are practiced in the mindfulness exercises. These are the skills that are taught, learned, discussed and monitored for progress. The seven TIM skills are: 1. Curiosity; 2. Observation; 3. Factual description; 4. Non-judgement; 5. Non-resistance; 6. Turning towards; and 7. Letting go. Each of these will be described and discussed in turn within this chapter, together with some practice exercises included throughout to help you to get to grips with the nature of these and to consolidate your learning. To begin, the whole model is represented graphically in the 'TIM 777 doughnut'. This is a simple figure (see figure 1.1) to help you remember that there are three elements to the TIM model, and each of the three components has seven aspects. Each of these three aspects of the TIM model is illustrated in figure 1.2 (on p. 18).

If you are familiar with other kinds of mindfulness practice, you will probably need to suspend what you already know, so that you can fully engage with the TIM model, as it differs in several ways from other mindfulness-based programmes.

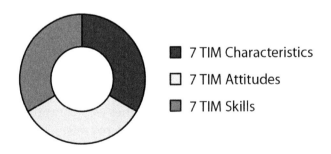

Figure 1.1: Trauma-Informed Mindfulness (TIM) 777 doughnut

- First, unlike most mindfulness interventions that are group-based, TIM is designed to be used predominantly in **one-to-one situations**. This does not preclude its use in groups, and in fact I have used it in groups. However, it is not a manualised programme that a group of people will work through over a number of weeks, with a predetermined list of exercises to cover in each week. Because trauma responses are individual, TIM is intentionally designed as a tailored approach that can be drawn upon flexibly to meet the very specific needs of an individual client

- Second, unlike many mindfulness practices, TIM emphasises the use of **very short exercises**. Typically, a person new to using TIM might be engaging in an exercise that is one minute in length. This may be built up to perhaps five minutes if that seems an appropriate titration for the client, but usually no longer. The crucial thing about TIM is not how long one practices, but how well. It would be far more typical in a TIM session for a client to repeat the same skills exercise three or four separate times in succession for one minute each, than to try to practice it once for a longer stretch. The reason for this is that when learning mindfulness it is difficult to sustain concentration for very long, especially with client groups who have complex trauma, attention deficit or psychosis

- Third, unlike some mindfulness approaches, there is a **wide range of exercises** that are used in mindfulness practice in TIM. Instead of long practices that predominantly use the breath as the main point of focus, the exercises in TIM are more similar to those used in the mindfulness skills training in DBT. Almost anything can become a TIM exercise. The choice of exercise itself will only be constrained by your own imagination, the setting you work in, and the resources available

- Fourth, there is a very clear focus on what mindfulness skill is being practiced during the short practice exercise. This is what is known in TIM as the intention. The **intention is set first** before the exercise is started, and will relate very clearly to one of the seven TIM skills. The intention is something that is discussed collaboratively and agreed between the facilitator and the client before the practice begins

- Fifth, a clear discussion and assessment of how well the client managed to achieve that skill will follow each skills practice during the inquiry. In TIM the **inquiry follows the practice** and refers to the moment when the facilitator asks the client a question that is very specifically related to the intention that was agreed before the practice. This specificity of inquiry in TIM differs from other mindfulness group approaches that tend to use more open questions for the inquiry

The characteristics relate to those features of the TIM model that essentially make it what it is. For anyone delivering TIM these are the key features that would be expected for the facilitator to learn, and to be recognisably present to be adherent to the model. Each of the characteristics is expanded in the next section to ensure clarification. As the flow chart in figure 1.2 indicates, from these characteristics arise the attitudes that are expected of the practitioner and client to approach the skills practice. Having these attitudes as a backdrop to the practice, the actual TIM skills are the focus of the TIM exercises. These are the things that the client is facilitated to use as the specific focus of their training, and can be used either individually or combined together, depending on the stage of development in their skills capability, and the level of titration that has been agreed collaboratively.

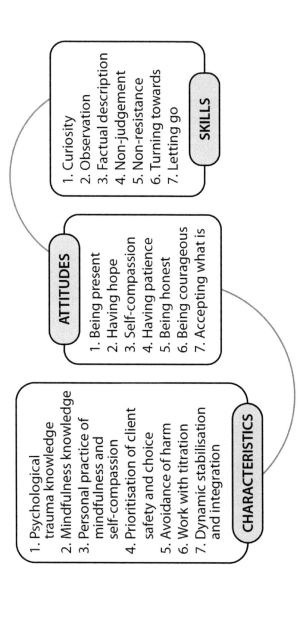

Figure 1.2: Trauma-Informed Mindfulness (TIM) 777 flow chart

The seven characteristics of TIM

As stated, TIM is primarily a model that is designed to be used flexibly with individual clients, rather than being a manualised programme for groups. It consists of seven characteristics that are introduced briefly and described in table 1.1. A brief overview is provided here by explaining how they relate to one another and the importance of maintaining the integrity of this as a holistic approach. The characteristics listed relate predominantly to the knowledge and skills required of a facilitator to engage effectively in a TIM intervention. The table breaks down each of the components more specifically into the knowledge of that area that would be expected. This table can therefore be used as a guideline for the development of any training that might be required to prepare facilitators for engaging in TIM practices with their clients.

Table 1.1: The seven characteristics of TIM

	TIM characteristic	Description
1.	Psychological trauma knowledge	• To have a foundational knowledge of how trauma affects the brain and how the autonomic nervous system operates to manage homeostasis • To understand the main symptom clusters for someone who is suffering from the lasting impact of having experienced trauma • To understand the risks for staff working with traumatised individuals of developing secondary traumatic stress
2.	Mindfulness knowledge	• To have a foundational knowledge of the history of mindfulness and how it has been adapted for Western use in third wave psychological therapies

		• To understand the aims of mindfulness practice and how mindfulness can achieve those goals • To learn and use a number of different mindfulness practice exercises
3.	Personal practice of mindfulness and self-compassion	• To appreciate the importance of a personal ongoing mindfulness practice • To engage in regular personal mindfulness practice for self-care and awareness building, and to manage the stress of working with traumatised individuals • To utilise personal self-compassion exercises for self-care and development • To draw on this experience reflexively to inform training with others
4.	Prioritisation of client safety and choice	• To appreciate the importance of safety and choice for people who have experienced trauma • To be familiar with ways of supporting and encouraging safety and choice for traumatised individuals • To understand that safety needs to be developed environmentally, relationally, culturally in the body and in relation to the intervention • To be aware of the impulse towards avoidance for traumatised clients, and to ensure that they feel safe and supported and sufficiently resourced to engage in practice • To be aware of the prevalence of dissociation within traumatised individuals, and to be able to use skills to avoid or manage dissociation
5.	Avoidance of harm	• To understand how trauma symptoms may present behaviourally and in which coping

		behaviours a traumatised person may engage
		• To have an awareness of vulnerability and resilience factors
		• To appreciate the possibility of iatrogenic effects from trauma treatments
		• To be aware of what it means to work in a trauma-informed way
		• To have an understanding of how and why using mindfulness could potentially re-traumatise someone if triggers are not carefully attended to, and safety procedures followed
6.	**Work with titration**	• To have an understanding of the need for titrating mindfulness practice at the pace of the individual, so as to minimise the risk of re-traumatisation
		• To commit to working collaboratively with a client always to establish titration levels and choice of practices
		• To understand the need to balance the dialectics of challenge and validation
		• To try to avoid working with too many skills of mindfulness in one practice, but to develop them incrementally
		• To take a strengths-based approach so that the individual is able to build mastery before moving to the next level
7.	**Dynamic stabilisation and integration**	• To understand the model of working in a phased way within a trauma treatment programme
		• To have a knowledge of the existing recommended phases of stabilisation, intervention and integration in trauma work

		• To be able to work dynamically within these phases and to work backwards and forwards between them when necessary • To critically assess the potential value of including a readiness for change pre-treatment phase

The first two TIM characteristics, psychological trauma knowledge and mindfulness knowledge, form an information base for the TIM facilitator. These two aspects can be learned by attending a training course, or through reading appropriate literature in each of these areas. Later chapters in this book are designed to give an introductory level knowledge in each of these domains for the would-be TIM facilitator. The third characteristic of the programme is a personal practice of mindfulness and self-compassion; and, in common with all other mindfulness training programmes, this is essential for anyone who is interested in using TIM as a helpful intervention with their clients. This characteristic is the one that will require a period of time to establish in your own personal life first before attempting to share its treasures with others. Not only are mindfulness and self-compassion extremely beneficial for a number of different client-groups, but are extremely valuable and beneficial for us as facilitators to have as a personal regular practice and way of life. Especially for professionals and carers who are involved with people who have experienced trauma, the need for self-awareness, self-compassion and the ability to have control over one's attention and reactivity is arguably essential.

The rest of the TIM characteristics: 4. Prioritisation of safety and choice; 5. Avoidance of harm; 6. Work with titration; and 7. Dynamic stabilisation and integration, involve a combination of knowledge and skills practice. It is first necessary to have an intellectual grasp of the concepts, but then equally if not more importantly, to be able to work with them in actual practice. It is only through repeatedly working with the practicalities of each of these characteristics that a level of expertise can be achieved. These four characteristics themselves are fairly simple in concept, but require skill to use well. For those readers who already have competencies in similar areas, it will probably be relatively straightforward to transfer those skills across to facilitation of TIM practice in your setting. For others, this is where face-to-face training and supervision in applying and using them will be necessary.

Before moving on to discuss the attitudes and skills that comprise TIM, it may be helpful to provide an illustrative example of the steps that you might go through in preparing for a typical TIM intervention. Figure 1.3 (overleaf) shows three steps to getting started. Step one is facilitator training and practice that includes education about psychological trauma, trauma-informed care and mindfulness. This step also includes getting established with your own self-compassion and mindfulness practice or lifestyle. Finally, step one also involves practicing the skills of working to create and maintain a felt experience of safety and choice for your client, and to practice the different kinds of titration of TIM exercises. Step two relates to the processes of introducing TIM to a new client by explaining the seven attitudes and skills, and then working on collaborative goal setting. The third step relates to the specific details of negotiating with your client on the first exercise, the level of titration and the skill to be practiced. It also is the step within which the actual TIM exercise is practiced with the client and the inquiry process is engaged.

In the third step, an important element is to set the initial level of skills practice titration. Titration is a term borrowed from the field of chemistry, and refers to the way that the exercises and skills are introduced in TIM in a way similar to the cognitive behavioural therapy (CBT) concept of graded exposure. The types of titration available will be covered in much more detail in a later

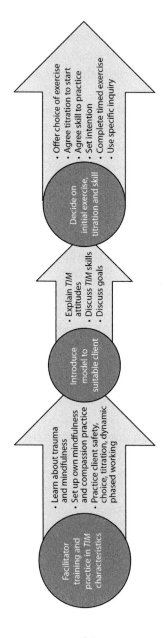

Figure 1.3: Trauma-Informed Mindfulness (TIM) process chart

chapter of this book. However, the basic options when thinking about how to grade or titrate the client's experience of any given TIM exercise are:

- **Length of time for practice.** As a suggestion, an initial time-frame of one minute is usually a good starting point. However, clients who struggle more with maintaining attention may wish to start with 30 seconds. It is best to have a timer set so that the time is measured accurately
- **Proximity of practice.** Proximity refers to whether the exercise is outside in the environment, relates to the body, or is an internal experience. Starting with an exercise that is outside in the environment, such as observing something nearby or engaging in an activity that is external to the body, is usually the best starting point with a new client

After a few practice sessions, exercises can be made more difficult by titrating either or both of these aspects. Always bear in mind though, that it is much better for the client to have the feeling of building mastery and succeeding in the skills practice chosen, than feeling they have not done well or have failed. Thus, the golden rule of titration is to set the challenge to a level that is within the client's ability to start with, so that the client quickly establishes a feeling of success. Do not be tempted to rush ahead and make the exercises more difficult too quickly, even if your client is keen. Slow and steady progress will ensure that progress is consolidated, that the skills are being practiced properly, and that any potential for dissociation, avoidance or abreaction is kept to the minimum.

As the TIM process chart in figure 1.3 shows, the next step after facilitator training and practice is step two, to introduce the model to a suitable client. In terms of deciding who a suitable client might be, some common sense and professional judgement may be needed, bearing in mind your particular setting and client group. In terms of contra-indications of TIM,[i] it has been designed to take into account a wide range of client presentations for those who have experienced trauma. Step two bears in mind the TIM characteristics of client safety and choice and expects these to be prioritised when engaging with the client in education about the TIM model. It is anticipated that it would make sense to explain briefly what the TIM attitudes are initially, using a visual aid if possible. The time spent on this will be variable depending on your client.

Next, you would discuss what the seven TIM skills are, ensuring that the client has a reasonable idea of what they each mean. It is best to think about your client, what their goals and expectations are, and how much time you have in deciding how long to spend on this stage. It will be necessary to balance carefully explaining the intervention sufficiently so they have enough information to make their own choices and provide consent to proceed, with allowing sufficient time to practice the skills. Also, depending on their capacity to retain information, you will need to think about not overloading them with lots of theory. It is a good time to discuss with the client what their goals might be for using TIM now that they have some information about the range of skills needed. For example, a client with poor impulse control might see the value of practicing the mindfulness skill of 'turning towards'. For the exercise, the intention agreed and set at the beginning might be to 'turn towards' any difficult feelings or impulses noticed during the practice. The key thing is to focus on one thing at a time. After the timed practice exercise, the facilitator could ask the client specifically whether any difficult feelings or urges arose, and how well they managed with their specific goal of turning towards those experiences.

---

[i] The topic of assessing for contra-indications will be revisited and discussed in more detail in chapter nine.

Titration helps your client to learn the basics and to succeed early on, **one** TIM skill at a time. This will help your client to focus completely on one thing at a time, and will also help you to be more focused in your inquiry.

The seven attitudes of TIM

In TIM there are seven attitudes in total, each of which will be discussed in turn to explain more fully. In summary they are: 1. Being present; 2. Having hope; 3. Self-compassion; 4. Having patience; 5. Being honest; 6. Being courageous; and 7. Accepting what is. When explaining a TIM practice to a client, it can be helpful to explain these seven attitudes, as they underpin all of the skills that are the focus of the practical exercises. However, there are probably too many to remember, to start with at least, and this is where having wisdom about titration is important. You might want to print out a list of what the attitudes are with an explanation, such as is provided in table 1.2 (overleaf).

As a conversation starter, it may help to explore which mindfulness attitudes your client thinks that they are good at already, and which ones perhaps may present more of a challenge. For example, someone who is quite self-critical might struggle initially with attitude 3. of 'being self-compassionate'. If that were the case, rather than trying to think about all of them at once, you might just focus on 'being self-compassionate' as the main attitude to hold in mind whilst engaging in the skills practice exercises. Similarly, if your client is either quite dissociative (you can use the Dissociative Experiences Scale (DES)[ii] to assess this if you are unsure), if they have a lot of anxious thoughts, or they are tied up

---

[ii] Dissociative Experiences Scale (DES) (Bernstem and Putnam, 1986; Ross et al., 1989) and adolescent version (ADES) (Armstrong et al., 1997).

in rumination about the past, then the TIM attitude of 'being present' (number 1.), might be the one to really encourage and focus on at the outset. The main thing to remember is that this is all new to your client and so gentle titration is key. It is far better to introduce concepts one at a time during each session if necessary, rather than all at once and then struggle to achieve any of them.

Table 1.2: Trauma-Informed Mindfulness (TIM) seven attitudes

	TIM Attitudes	Description
1.	Being present	• Know that even if you are thinking about the past or the future, you do it all in the present moment • Being present is about bringing awareness to what is right now • Being present is about focusing on one thing in this present moment
2.	Having hope	• Having hope is about holding an attitude of optimism that it is possible to have a life that is OK • Hope expects that there will be an improvement, and helps maintain motivation to keep going
3.	Self-compassion	• Self-compassion is an attitude that avoids being harsh and critical, even if you or others make mistakes • A self-compassionate attitude can help you feel kinder to yourself and others • Self-compassion means not using force, but having a gentle attitude
4.	Having patience	• Having an attitude of patience allows you to take your learning at your own speed • Practicing mindfulness takes time, and having a patient attitude with yourself can help you to avoid frustration

		• A patient attitude will allow you to be more self-compassionate
5.	**Being honest**	• Being honest means being willing to put preconceptions to one side • An honest attitude is to face the reality of a situation without bias • Honesty helps us to gain a more realistic perspective • Honesty helps to avoid cognitive distortions
6.	**Being courageous**	• Practicing mindfulness tends to reveal things about ourselves that we had not previously realised fully • Facing the reality of these things through mindful awareness requires an attitude of courage • Courage to do this needs to be acknowledged and validated
7.	**Accepting what is**	• By accepting what is, we can have more peace and less resistance and struggle • An attitude of acceptance is the starting point for making changes • Self-acceptance is the starting point for happiness and contentment

It might be that in the initial education phase before you start TIM with your client you choose to run through these seven attitudes, but then just put it to one side so that you can introduce the actual skills that will be used during the practice. Approaching it in this way will mean that you can refer back to your table of attitudes as and when they seem to come up naturally in conversation with your client. For example, if you have been using the exercise of touching the bark of a tree, and have been practicing skill three of 'Factual description' (in table 1.3 on p. 37), the client might say during the inquiry stage after the exercise that they found they kept thinking about what they needed to do when they got home. At that point, you might suggest they remember the TIM attitude of 'Being present', so that in the next exercise you do together, they can try to practice the skill of 'Factual description' and draw upon the attitude of 'Being present' to help them to engage with practicing that skill more fully. I have added in a few practice exercises that relate to each of the mindfulness skills presented. However, if you are new to mindfulness and have experienced trauma, please approach these carefully if you do decide to try them out. Sometimes mindfulness exercises can trigger physical or emotional trauma symptoms, so only do the practice exercises for a moment, and if you notice any adverse reactions, give yourself permission to stop. Read the later chapters about safety and choice, and titrating your experience, and if you can, find a TIM practitioner to support you in your practice.

- **Being present**

The principle of being present is probably the most quintessentially recognisable and characteristic aspect of mindfulness practice. Thich Nhat Hanh eloquently expresses the essence of being present by reminding us that "the present moment is the only moment available to us, and is the doorway to all other moments" (2016, p. 1). Being present is not about just physically turning up, but for your mind and awareness and attention to be focused equally on what is happening, where you are right now. It is very easy to be physically present, whilst our mind and attention is somewhere very different, thinking about someone or something else instead of who and what is immediately in front of us. For example: "while washing the dishes one should only be washing the dishes, which means that while washing the dishes one should be completely aware of the fact that one is washing the dishes" (Hanh, 2016, p. 1). This quotation from Hahn expresses the fact that being present is not about the so called 'remarkable' moments of life, but in the mundane ordinariness of everyday life. It also highlights the importance of awareness. Rather than washing dishes (or walking along a lane, or eating a meal, or riding a bike) with our body engaged in the task, but our attention elsewhere, being present is re-acquiring the skill of joining up our attention with our activity. In this way, we bring our attention to what we see and feel and hear around us as we walk along a lane, we notice what we taste and smell and feel whilst we are eating, we pay attention to those that are with us and how they look and sound and talk. We give up dual, split attention, and give ourselves completely to now, and here. As Hahn expresses, there is a joy in being present like no other; "I like to walk alone on country paths, rice plants and wild grasses on both sides, putting each foot down on the earth in mindfulness, knowing that I walk on the wondrous earth. In such moments, existence is a miraculous and mysterious reality" (Hanh, 2016, p. 2).

- **Having hope**

There is a clear relationship between psychological wellbeing and having a hopeful outlook on life (Libman-Sokołowska and Nasierowski, 2013). For those with a mental health difficulty, hope relates to optimism that there is life beyond their current challenges or diagnosis. When someone has hope, they expect an improvement in their life, and have a greater determination to overcome their illness (Roe, Chopra and Rudnick, 2004). When working with people and sharing mindfulness practices with them, having hope for clients when they are struggling to have hope for themselves is important. As people who practice mindfulness, we know first-hand how valuable and powerful it is, and it is exactly because of that first-hand experiential knowledge that we can have the confidence to trust the process for someone else. People who are new to mindfulness have not yet experienced its benefits and so there is a great need for trust and hope. Also, mindfulness is about bringing awareness to what is. Sometimes 'what is' is exactly what has been avoided in the case of people who have experienced trauma, and so bringing awareness to what is can be very uncomfortable to start with. That is why it is so important to combine self-compassion and practicing non-judgement with awareness building so that it is tolerable.

*   **Self-compassion**

Practicing self-compassion means having an attitude of willingness to experience life rather than trying to force or control your life. For example, rushing can increase feelings of anxiety, whereas taking a gentle attitude of self-compassion can help you feel calmer and kinder to yourself and others. Self-compassion includes noticing what your body and mind are doing without being critical or harsh towards yourself if mistakes happen. You can be gentle with everything in your environment and with your body, your time, and your state of mind. Practicing self-compassion means having an attitude of feeling grounded and friendly, willing to experience life rather than trying to force or control your life. You can be gentle with everything in your environment and with your body, your time, and your state of mind.

The analogy of 'puppy training the mind' has been used as a way of explaining how to take a self-compassionate attitude with ourselves when learning to practice mindfulness. The best way to train a puppy is not to be harsh and punitive, but gentle. The same is the case with our mind, we watch it carefully and as soon as it wanders off we gently bring it back and re-focus on our intended object of attention. Of course, it will wander off again, but we just continue to repeatedly bring it gently back to where we want it to be. We do this over and over again. Eventually the mind, just like the puppy learns to relax and understand where we want it to be. If we get frustrated or self-critical of ourselves when our mind wanders off, and attempt to force or drag it back harshly to where we want it to be, it actually agitates the mind even more, and is ultimately counterproductive.

- **Having patience**

It is the nature of an untrained puppy to wander, just as it is the nature of the untrained mind to wander. We have to develop patience with ourselves when starting a mindfulness practice, repeatedly and gently bringing the mind back to re-focus. Impatience is chronic in Western society, and even as much as we try to be more patient, it is a constant challenge. It is very tempting to rush around to 'get more done', but the saying 'more haste less speed' is very true, and learning patience is a life-long task. Within mindfulness, the term 'practice' still applies whether it is the first mindfulness exercise you have ever done or the millionth. We can never really say we have 'made it', and that we are now a mindfulness expert, there are always more layers and more nuances to work with. In a way, patience could be thought of as an aspect of self-compassion, which is an essential component in TIM. Being patient also relates to being non-judgemental; by definition, if you are feeling impatient you have judged yourself, someone else or the situation as not going fast enough. With regards to practicing mindfulness, you may feel you are not making 'progress' quickly enough. If you can find a way to let go of that self-criticism and self-judgement, and be gentle, compassionate and patient with yourself, things will go much better.

- **Being honest**

Honesty is not usually talked about in mindfulness training, but it plays a big part; it is about being willing and open to see things as they really are not how we imagine or hope they are. Honesty relates to being courageous enough to face the reality of a situation and to accept it for what it is. There are many facets to honesty, and one aspect is to look to having a more realistic rather than distorted or biased perception. For example, if we sit indoors and draw a tree, we tend to have a 'typical' tree in mind that we draw. It is not an actual tree but a representation of all trees in general. However, if we sit in front of a tree to draw that particular tree, then we need to suspend our abstract ideas of what trees in general look like, and honestly try to draw what *this* tree looks like. In a similar way, when practicing TIM, working with the attitude of honesty means to be open to noticing and perceiving things as they really are, not just according to our abstracted notions of how things are. Again, as with many qualities of mindfulness there is a need for self-compassion when becoming more honest about self, the world, and others, and seeing ourselves and others more as they really are, rather than how we imagine they are.

Use anything that you have nearby such as a notebook or a piece of fruit, and place it in front of you. Now draw exactly what you see in front of you. Pay attention to how the thing you are drawing *really* is, and suspend any expectations, judgements or thoughts about how you think that it 'should' look.

- **Being courageous**

Turning towards, acceptance, honesty and letting go, all take a lot of courage. It is only natural to feel fearful of turning towards something that is perceived as painful, or to resist seeing something as it really is, so it takes courage to do so. It is always helpful to let a client know that you appreciate that it is hard to practice mindfulness, acknowledge and validate it as something that is challenging and takes time and courage. This is important because unless this is explicitly said, a client might assume that because it is difficult there is something wrong with them, assuming incorrectly that everyone else can do it except them. A tendency towards a feeling of failure or worry about failing can be quite common with people who have experienced complex trauma, and so sensitivity to the client's perception of failing is valuable to bear in mind. When supporting a person towards an area of change in their life, the balance of validation is an important part of the process. When a client is validated in a way that acknowledges the struggle that they are engaged in, it can make their acceptance of the benefits of change easier. One way to offer validation is to acknowledge explicitly to the client the courage that it takes to engage in a change process, and the fact that it is not easy to do. This is also a way of demonstrating respect for the client, and not inadvertently minimising the challenge that they face.

- **Accepting what is**

Acceptance is not 'giving up' or 'giving in' or agreeing that something is right, it is simply acknowledging what currently 'is'. Accepting what is, is just a starting point, it does not preclude seeking change. Follette, Palm and Pearson (2006) propose that mindfulness can facilitate healing by prompting acceptance of experiences. It could be said that acceptance follows on from honesty. When it becomes possible to look at the circumstances, environment, living conditions, relationships, physical health or anything else around us honestly, without denial or avoidance, then we are closer to the meaning of acceptance. Acceptance requires both honesty and courage. It means to be brave enough to see things not only as they really are, but to acknowledge that this is the starting point that we are working from. For example, someone may be drinking several bottles of wine or a number of cans of beer every day, but deny that they 'need' that alcohol to manage their emotions, or perhaps delude themselves about how much alcohol they are actually consuming each day. An example of acceptance would be to face the reality of the amount they are drinking and perhaps it being a need and not just a want. This would not necessarily mean that the person stays trapped in that cycle, in fact the opposite, by accepting the reality of the situation, the person has a firm footing to move forward from.

The seven skills of TIM

In TIM there are seven skills that are used as the focus of intention and inquiry for each practice exercise. These are described in table 1.5, and are: 1. Curiosity; 2. Observation; 3. Factual description; 4. Non-judgement; 5. Non-resistance; 6. Turning towards; and 7. Letting go. The seven skills that form this part of the TIM doughnut model are the actual skills that are practiced during mindfulness exercises. Whatever the exercise is, whether it is drawing a picture of a cow, eating a grape, or watching a candle flame, the **skill** is the part that is being built for the client as they learn to manage their attention. In effect, the whole practice is made up of three core elements as illustrated in figure 1.4. As a facilitator, your role is to work with your client to choose one thing from each of these three categories that make up the practice.

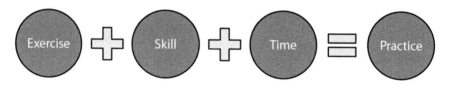

Figure 1.4: TIM Exercise + Skill + Time = Practice

For example, a person might be using the **exercise** of watching a candle flame, with the intention at the outset to practice the first **skill** of being curious. As facilitator, you will suggest and agree an appropriate length of **time** for the client to engage in the exercise, using that particular TIM skill. Table 1.5 shows how to make choices about how to build the components of the exercise, together with the skill being practiced, and its duration. The first example in this table is selecting the exercise of 'watch a candle flame' together with practicing the mindfulness skill of 'curiosity' for the length of time of '30 seconds'. After the practice is complete, the inquiry could take the form of asking a question about what the client noticed about the flame whilst practicing the skill of curiosity. As you can see, this system has been designed to provide a mix-and-match menu of components so that each exercise can be specifically tailored to your client, and so that each exercise can be titrated incrementally in one of these components as the client develops their practice.

Table 1.3: Trauma-Informed Mindfulness (TIM) component building: Exercise + Skill + Time

Practice exercise examples (choose one)	TIM SKILL being practiced (choose one)	Time (choose one)
Watch a candle flame	Curiosity	30 seconds
Examine the texture of tree bark	Observation	One minute
Draw a cow	Factual description	90 seconds
Feel the breeze of a fan	Non-judgement	Two minutes
Eat a sour sweet	Non-resistance	Three minutes
Complete a maze	Turning towards	Four minutes
Listen to the sound of birds	Letting go	Five minutes

In the second example provided in table 1.3, the exercise of 'draw a cow' has been selected, together with practicing the mindfulness skill of 'non-judgement' for the duration of '90 seconds'. This is often a good combination, as many people feel quite critical and judgemental of their drawing skills, and therefore it is a good exercise to choose to practice this skill. The time chosen to practice the skill of non-judgement whilst drawing a cow has been 90 seconds. As you can see, all of these exercises are designed to be very brief and focused. From experience, these shorter timeframes mean that clients have less time to get distracted, and tend to try hard to concentrate on the skills practice for a shorter period of time. It also means that they have a greater chance of succeeding. After the practice is complete, the inquiry could take the form of asking a question about what the client noticed about any judgemental thoughts related to their drawing, and how they avoided judging their artwork negatively. A full list of all the seven skills, together with a brief description of each, is provided in table 1.5.

Table 1.5: Trauma-Informed Mindfulness (TIM) seven skills

	TIM Skills	Description
1.	Curiosity	• Curiosity can be developed by approaching everything in life as if it were for the first time • Sometimes imagining yourself as an alien who has just landed on earth can help • Curiosity is natural in young children but something as adults we need to re-learn
2.	Observation	• Observing things is a skill that takes all of our five senses to achieve • We can observe through sight, sound, taste, touch and smell • Observing means not labelling the experience, just being fully immersed in the sensation of what is being observed
3.	Factual description	• It is easy to describe things according to their 'labels', but describing things factually is about removing any labels • Factual description does not involve saying things are OK or rubbish or nice

		or horrible, it involves using facts rather than evaluations • When describing something 'factually' the practice is simply to state its colour or shape or length, etc.
4.	Non-judgement	• It is easy to use shorthand terms to evaluate things as good or bad, but non-judgement is learning the skill of avoiding this tendency • Practicing the skill of not judging yourself or others is central to mindfulness • Judgement tends to happen at a thought level, so when practicing this skill the learner starts to become more aware of which thoughts are evaluative, critical or judgemental and starts to let go of those associations
5.	Non-resistance	• When we resist something it usually makes it worse, because we are still giving our energy and attention to it • Non-resistance is not about fighting against something, but instead not feeding it • Non-resistance is about re-focusing your attention somewhere else
6.	Turning towards	• Often when things are painful, our instinct is to hide, avoid or turn away, but turning towards means facing what we fear • Turning towards in mindfulness is about developing the skill of acting opposite to that instinct to avoid, and being courageous • When we face what we fear, it loses its power over us

7.	Letting go	• Letting go is the skill of not holding on to thoughts and feelings that are harmful • Rumination is about holding on to thoughts and worries, but this only makes it worse • Letting go frees you from being held in negative thought patterns

In order to explain the value and purpose of the practice of these short TIM exercises and skills it can be helpful to use a metaphor. The metaphor that I use most often is that of going to the gym. The objective of doing weight training for example, might be to have bigger muscles, or the objective of increasing the time spent on the treadmill or the number of lengths completed in the swimming pool might be to increase physical fitness or to lose weight. Using the gym as an analogy, you can explain to your client that without training, your mind is like a 'couch potato', it is lazy and takes the easiest path in its thinking. From what you know about your client, this might be untrained thoughts that drift off to worrying about future events, or untrained thoughts that ruminate on past experiences. In the case of someone who has experienced trauma, there may be unpleasant intrusive thoughts, images or emotions over which the client currently has no control.

Use metaphor to explain the purpose of *TIM* exercises, so that your client really understands that the exercises are just a means to an end, not an end in themselves.

Another metaphor that I often use is that of a piece of grass with a path around it (this works in a cultural context where such things exist). The formal path around the piece of grass can sometimes be a longer route than a shortcut across the grass. What you might notice about places where lots of people have taken the shortcut is that a new muddy pathway is created from all the footsteps that have killed the grass along that stretch. This can be likened to a 'lazy' way of thinking, where we take a shortcut. It takes a little bit more time and intentional effort to train ourselves to go the longer way around the grass via the formal path, just as it takes more time and intentional effort to retrain our thinking along a new pathway. However the benefits are realised over time, as just as the grass is allowed to grow back over the bald patches, our mind becomes more healthy, as new neural connections are strengthened along healthier pathways.

It is important to help the client to see the point of engaging in these exercises, and ultimately what value it will be to them. So, in the case of the weightlifting metaphor, the goal is to gradually increase the weight lifted incrementally. Similarly, with mind training, the goal is also to gradually increase the challenge of the exercise, so that incrementally the client builds more and more attentional control over what their mind does. In effect, with weightlifting, the actual object being lifted does not matter as much as the fact that it is being done regularly, intentionally and incrementally.

Similarly, with TIM training, the same applies, it does not matter so much which exercise is being used, as much as the fact that the skills are being practiced regularly, intentionally and incrementally. The exercises themselves are just a means to an end, in the same way that the weights or running machine or swimming pool are items used to build fitness. Explaining the practice in this way can help people who may otherwise be dismissive of what may seem like 'silly' exercises. The exercise in the end is just the vehicle that is being used; the primary focus of TIM practice is on how well the skills are being practiced. The following section allows space for further elaboration of what each of these skills are, so that both you and your client can be clear about what it is that you are practicing.

• Curiosity

One definition of mindfulness is "paying attention to what's happening in the present moment in the mind, body and external environment, with an attitude of curiosity and kindness" (Mindful Nation, 2015, p. 6). Curiosity is central to all mindfulness practice. In some mindfulness books you might read about the concept of 'beginner's mind', which is a similar concept. It relates to the idea that we look at the world afresh as if it were new to us, as if we did not already 'know' what we think we know, and to allow new experiences to come in. Curiosity is linked with a sense of playfulness and creativity (Phillips, 2014). When we are young, we have an innate curiosity. Think of a child who is fascinated by the details of the shell of a snail on the path, or a caterpillar on a leaf. But as we get older, we tend to engage with the world through ideas and concepts rather than directly through the senses, and some of that insatiable curiosity starts to wane. However, when we begin to rekindle our innate curiosity, we start to ask questions (Peters, 1978), explore and examine things that catch our interest (Reeve and Nix, 1997) and persevere with things that are challenging (Sansone and Smith, 2000).

 Use a fir cone, acorn or pebble as the object of attention. Bring an attitude of gentle curiosity to the object, and just be interested in what you notice.

• Observation

A very important part of mindfulness is to understand and practice taking the position of the 'observer'. Another way of thinking about it might be to think of a butterfly on the wall, watching you and what is going on around you. The butterfly has no opinion about what it sees (as far as we know!), it just observes. Observing without labelling or describing or categorising is actually a bit more difficult than you might imagine when you start these practices. We are so conditioned to judge or label immediately, that just allowing what is to be, just observing it without doing any of those things is something that takes a bit of time to learn. The frame of mind of the observer can start with things outside of our body, in the environment around us: observing sounds, smells, sights. We allow ourselves to just notice, coming to our experience without any preconceived ideas or expectations, imagining ourselves as a blank sheet on to which what we observe can imprint itself.

After practicing the observation of the outside world, we can also observe our body, noticing its movement as we breathe, noticing any sensations without judging them or trying to change them. This is an example of titrating the proximity of practice from external to the body, and the next step would be to titrate our practice of observation to sensations and experiences that occur inside the body. One of the interesting things about the mind is that it can watch itself. It is possible to observe what you are thinking, as well as what you are feeling and sensing. This becomes helpful in terms of 'catching' those thoughts that go unnoticed throughout the day. When they have been experienced and noticed, you then have a choice about what to do with these thoughts, but catching them, noticing them and becoming aware of them is the first step.

- **Factual description**

The skill of Factual description is something that also needs practice, as we tend to use labels most of the time as shortcuts for describing things. This is handy most of the time, if we want someone to pass us a book it is much easier to use its 'name' than explaining that we need the rectangular object with lots of thin white sheets in it with black marks on. However, when we use these shortcuts all the time, we become prone to seeing things as generic categories rather than the specific individual thing in front of us. The author Anthony deMello in his excellent book entitled *Awareness* explains this concept of seeing things as they really are; separate from the labels that we attribute to them. This extract captures the essence of this concept so well.

> The great Krisnamurti said "The day you teach the child the name of the bird, the child will never see that bird again". How true! The first time the child sees that fluffy, alive, moving object, and you say to him, 'sparrow', then tomorrow when the child sees another fluffy, moving object similar to it he says, 'oh sparrows. I've seen sparrows. I'm bored of sparrows'. If you don't look at things through your concepts, you'll never be bored. Every single thing is unique. Every sparrow is unlike every other sparrow despite the similarities … If all you experience is your concept, you're not experiencing reality, because reality is concrete. (deMello, 1990, p. 121)

 Find something in a tool-box or in the kitchen, a utensil or piece of equipment. Now try to describe it without using a 'label' of what it is such as a screwdriver or a blender. Instead focus on describing the size and shape and colour instead.

• Non-judgement

As William Shakespeare said in Hamlet "There is nothing either good or bad but thinking makes it so" (Shakespeare, 1885: Act two, scene two). When we start to become curious and interested, then inevitably old habits of evaluation and judgement will also be present. Typically, we have been trained to label and categorise experiences, circumstances, situations, feelings, etc. as 'good' or 'bad'. However, in TIM practice we learn to let go of these labels, and find a way to let what it is to be what it is, free from our imposed judgements. When a thought, feeling or situation is judged as negative, difficult threatening or painful, it is usually either attacked or avoided. Non-judgement practice through mindfulness is important because it offers a way to 'stay with' previously avoided thoughts and feelings that arise.

The mindfulness exercises in TIM can provide a framework for observation of thoughts, feelings, and memories without acting to avoid or change them. TIM is not about fighting against judgements when we recognise them come up, but gently allowing ourselves to just let go of them, to not continue to engage with them. This does not happen straight away, but over time, we can notice the judgements earlier, and start to disengage with them sooner. Self-compassion and non-judgement go hand in hand and are essential to practice alongside the other skills, so that we stay with the process.

- **Non-resistance**

You have probably heard the saying 'what you resist persists', and it is true. If you try to avoid thinking about a pink elephant riding a bike, then it will be difficult. Similarly, if you get frustrated or critical of yourself when your mind wanders off and you attempt to force or drag it back, it actually agitates the mind even more, which is ultimately counterproductive. TIM is not about fighting against judgements. TIM involves gently allowing ourselves to let go of ideas of good and bad, wanted and unwanted and replacing them with 'what is'. By not resisting, we can face those things and see them as they really are. A common challenge that many people face when they start engaging in mindfulness meditation is that they struggle to 'quieten' the many thoughts that rush to grasp our attention. Instead of resisting these thoughts by trying to forcibly 'make them go away', it is best to relax and be aware of the silence that is also present, thereby just shifting the focus of attention instead (Meditation Oasis, 2019).

Hold a pen or pencil at arm's length away from your body. Then just let go. What resistance if any do you notice in yourself?

- **Turning towards**

Rather than turning away from, resisting or fighting against thoughts or feelings that are judged to be 'negative' or 'unwanted', mindfulness teaches us to turn towards them with a gentle sense of interest and curiosity. By not resisting, we can face those things and see them as they really are. TIM provides a way to turn towards those things that are painful, gradually desensitising them. What happens is that by gently bringing our awareness to thoughts and feelings, it is like bringing the sun on to a frozen area; we do not fight against that frozen area, but over time the mere process of turning our attention towards it melts away some of those areas that we are less happy with.

> we need to be able to turn towards and acknowledge when we are suffering, to 'be' with our pain long enough to respond with care and kindness. (Neff and Germer, 2018, p. 11)

When we practice mindfulness, we learn to gently turn towards even things that we thought previously we wanted to avoid or fight against.

Another example of Turning towards might be in the case of physical pain. If you experience pain, it can be tempting to try to distract oneself, to try to not think about it or take some medication to relieve it. An alternative is to intentionally turn your attention towards the pain with an attitude of curiosity. By noticing the type of pain, its shape and texture and warmth or coolness, we courageously face something that we fear and want to turn away from naturally. The same is true of emotional pain. In TIM, turning towards what we fear to be painful starts to loosen the grip of the fear that goes along with the pain, and can help us to see that we can more readily bear those things that we imagined that we could not.

- **Letting go**

When we start to become curious and interested in what we are thinking, then inevitably habits of evaluation and judgement will also be present. But by practicing TIM in a self-compassionate way we can stop fighting against judgements but gently allow ourselves to let go of them. Rather than resisting what we do not want, TIM is about gently letting go of ideas of good and bad, wanted and unwanted. Helpful metaphors for 'letting go' are:

- o **Clouds:** One metaphor for watching thoughts and letting them go is that your thoughts are like clouds passing across the sky. Notice them as they come into your awareness, and then let them gently drift past
- o **Leaves:** Another metaphor to which you may be able to relate is that we can watch our thoughts as if they are leaves floating down a river. We can stand on the bridge over the river or on the riverbank and simply watch them pass by
- o **Window:** Another way to think about letting go in mindfulness is to imagine your thoughts as the images that you see as you look from a train or car window. The scenery constantly changes, and as you sit quietly and observe, the images pass by

For example, your client may choose to use watching a candle flame as the exercise, with the intention to practice the seventh skill of letting go. In this case, the objective would be to use the flame as a focus of attention to return to every time other thoughts popped into their mind. Each time such a thought pops up, they would be asking themselves to 'let go' of that thought, at least just for the length of time of the practice, and use the flame as a point of focus to return to instead. The inquiry after the practice would be for the facilitator to ask the client how well they got on specifically with practicing the skill of 'letting go' of thoughts as they came up.

Summary
This chapter has provided an introduction to the TIM model. The seven characteristics of Psychological trauma knowledge, Mindfulness knowledge, Personal practice of mindfulness and self-compassion, Prioritisation of client safety and choice, Avoidance of harm, Work with titration and Dynamic stabilisation and integration have been discussed in turn. Additionally, the seven TIM attitudes of being present; Having hope; Having self-compassion; Having patience; Being honest; Being courageous; and Accepting what is, have also been introduced, and their relationship to the TIM characteristics explained. Finally the seven TIM skills of Curiosity, Observation, Factual description, Non-judgement, Non-resistance, Turning towards, and Letting go have also been discussed. The essential features of how TIM differs from group mindfulness programmes has been provided, so that those who wish to adopt TIM as an intervention strategy have a clear rationale and basis for both explaining what it is to clients, and in adopting it as a safe practice for working with traumatised clients. This chapter has been intended to serve as an introductory overview of the model, including the use of titration and matching the intention to the inquiry. This has been provided so that as a reader you have a foundational understanding on which to build your knowledge of these elements in more detail in subsequent chapters.

References
Armstrong, J. G., Putnam, F. W., Carlson, E. B., Libero, D. Z., & Smith, S. R. (1997). Development and validation of a measure of adolescent dissociation: The Adolescent Dissociative Experiences Scale. *The Journal of Nervous and Mental Disease, 185*(8), 491–497.

Bernstem, E. M., & Putnam, F. W. (1986). Development, rehability and validity of a dissociation scale. *Journal of Nervous and Mental Disease, 174,* 727–735.

de Mello, A. (1990). *Awareness: The perils and opportunities of reality.* London, United Kingdom: Collins Fount.

Follette, V., Palm, K. M., & Pearson, A. N. (2006). Mindfulness and trauma: Implications for treatment. *Journal of Rational-Emotive and Cognitive-Behavior Therapy, 24*(1), 45–61.

Hanh, T. N. (2016). *The miracle of mindfulness: An introduction to the practice of meditation.* Boston, MA: Beacon Press.

Libman-Sokołowska, M., & Nasierowski, T. (2013). The importance of hope in coping with schizophrenia. *Psychiatria Polska, 47*(5), 933–946.

Meditation Oasis (2019). *Difficulty meditating.* Retrieved from https://www.meditationoasis.com/how-to-meditate/difficulty-meditating

Mindful Nation, UK (2015). *Report by the Mindfulness All-Party Parliamentary Group (MAPPG).* Retrieved from https://www.themindfulnessinitiative.org/mindful-nation-report

Neff, K., & Germer, C. (2018). *The mindful self-compassion workbook: A proven way to accept yourself, build inner strength, and thrive.* London, United Kingdom: Guilford Press.

Peters, R. A. (1978). Effects of anxiety, curiosity, and perceived instructor threat on student verbal behavior in the college classroom. *Journal of Educational Psychology, 70,* 388–395.

Phillips, R. (2014). Space for curiosity. *Progress in Human Geography, 38*(4), 493–512.

Pine, K. J. (2014). *Self-acceptance could be the key to a happier life, yet it's the happy habit many people practise the least.* University of Hertfordshire, United Kingdom. Retrieved from http://blogs.herts.ac.uk/2014/03/self-acceptance-could-be-key-to-happier.html

Reeve, J., & Nix, G. (1997). Expressing intrinsic motivation through acts of exploration and facial displays of interest. *Motivation and Emotion, 21,* 237–250.

Roe, D., Chopra, M., & Rudnick, A. (2004). Persons with psychosis as active agents interacting with their disorder. *Psychiatric Rehabilitation Journal, 28*(2), 122.

Ross, C. A., Heber, S., Norton, G. R., Anderson, D., Anderson, G., & Barchet, P. (1989). The dissociative disorders interview schedule: A structured interview. *Dissociation*, 2(3), 169–189.

Sansone, C., & Smith, J. L. (2000). Interest and self-regulation: The relation between having to and wanting to. In C. Sansone & J. M. Harackiewicz (Eds.), *Intrinsic and extrinsic motivation* (pp. 341–372). San Diego, CA: Academic Press.

Shakespeare, W. (1885). *Tragedy of Hamlet, Prince of Denmark*. Chicago, IL: S. R. Winchell & Company.

CHAPTER TWO
PSYCHOLOGICAL TRAUMA KNOWLEDGE

Chapter contents
• Stress • Trauma • Small 't' and large 'T' trauma • Type 1 and type 2 trauma • Cumulative trauma • PTSD diagnosis in the *DSM-5* • CPTSD in the *ICD-11* • Vicarious impact and the risks of secondary traumatic stress • Trauma physiology • Polyvagal theory • Summary

This chapter provides a contextual overview of what symptoms may present if someone is suffering from the adverse effects of being exposed to a significant trauma stressor or stressors. The chapter begins with an overview of how mental health diagnoses that fall under the heading of 'trauma and stressor-related disorders' in the *Diagnostic and Statistics Manual DSM-5* (APA, 2013) are classified, and how these relate to comparable diagnostic symptom clusters in the *International Classification of Diseases ICD-11* (WHO, 2018). In addition, comparisons are made regarding the new diagnostic classification of complex post-traumatic stress disorder (CPTSD), with previous renditions of PTSD as specified in the *DSM* and the *ICD*. Latterly, a brief introduction to the physiology of trauma is provided showing how the autonomic nervous system is affected. And finally, there is some information provided regarding the risks of secondary traumatic stress for those working with traumatised clients. In chapter one (table 1.1) the full specification for learning requirements relating to the seven TIM characteristics was provided. Table 2.1 is a duplicate of the section of that table that relates to psychological trauma knowledge, and is provided here as a reminder for pedagogical purposes. This chapter explicates in more detail the descriptive elements that relate specifically to this characteristic.

Table 2.1: Trauma-Informed Mindfulness characteristic 1. 'Psychological trauma knowledge' learning aims.

	TIM characteristic	Description
1.	Psychological trauma knowledge	• To have a foundational knowledge of how trauma affects the brain and how the autonomic nervous system operates to manage homeostasis • To understand the main symptom clusters for someone who is suffering from the lasting impact of having experienced trauma • To understand the risks for staff working with traumatised individuals of developing secondary traumatic stress

Stress

Stress is now a ubiquitous factor of modern life, and many physical and mental health conditions are related to chronic stress. Our bodies are simply not designed to remain in a constant state of stress-response arousal for long periods of time, and in doing so a huge physiological burden is placed on the whole body. When the brain or body perceives something to be a threat, an immediate flood of stress-response hormones rushes through the body in what we often refer to as a 'fight or flight' response. The sympathetic nervous system, the regulatory system in the body that quickly ensures that the body is ready to run away or fight the source of threat, pumps extra resources to the heart, lungs and major muscle groups. We are designed, through the process of homeostasis, which keeps the body in balance, to return to a state of equilibrium once a perceived threat has gone. The parasympathetic nervous system is triggered to release calming hormones to regulate the body back into a balanced state again. This is a beautifully designed system. However, the problem lies in the fact that for many people in modern society anxiety about finances, and work and relationships, etc., means that the brain and body can be in an almost perpetual place of perceiving the world as threatening.

What is interesting is that the body cannot distinguish between an actual threat and a perceived threat. This means that if we just *think* of something as being potentially risky or hazardous (including worries about not meeting deadlines, our children's wellbeing, our family's health, or our job security to name a few), the body reacts in exactly the same way as if there was a real tangible threat such as a wild animal chasing us, or a landslide nearby. Thus, the sympathetic (threat) system in the body rarely gets a chance to switch off, have a rest, and bring us back into a physiological state of balance. Commonly, in struggling against the impact of stress, people have either tried to think differently, to try to think positively, or in some way to block the anxious thoughts out, perhaps by distracting themselves with TV, shopping, over-eating, or drugs or alcohol. However, these approaches tend not to have any lasting impact on the stress-response system, and can even cause more struggle and feelings of defeat. Attempts to block out feelings can also often create other problems such as over-spending, or changes physically if mood altering substances are taken. This can create additional issues relationally or within oneself such as conflict or guilt or depression, that in turn become yet another source of stress. So, in trying to deal with the original source of stress by fighting against it or blocking it out, we can inadvertently actually create even more stress. One of the reasons that TIM is so beneficial in helping us to manage stress is that it does not aim to fight against it, but rather it teaches us to learn to sit with discomfort, or to train ourselves to let go of troubling thoughts.

Trauma

The differentiation between extreme stress and a trauma response is difficult to delineate, as it is conceptualised as a continuum. It is also subjective, depending on how the person in the situation appraises it. Furthermore, when seeking to provide a clear definition of trauma, there are some complexities and differences of opinion, depending upon one's epistemic and theoretical perspective. For example, epistemically, from a realist (positivist) perspective, a trauma is a 'thing' that is measurable and experienced in a similar way by different people in different cultures. However, if you come from a social constructionist perspective, a 'trauma' is something that is historically and culturally co-constructed by people who agree on its meaning. This opening caveat is important to bear in mind, as the rest of this chapter necessarily uses more realist language for pedagogical reasons, in seeking to describe the diagnostic definitions of how to identify post-traumatic symptoms, and how to label them in different categories. In 1976, Erikson defined trauma as "a blow to the psyche that breaks through one's defenses so suddenly and with such brutal force, that one cannot react to it effectively" (p. 156). Confusingly, sometimes people use the same word 'trauma' to refer both to the triggering event, and to the physical or psychological impact of that event on the body and mind. In terms of the external triggering event, one could argue that whether it is 'traumatic' or not could be decided either objectively or subjectively. In defining an external event objectively, this is accomplished in terms relating to the variables of that event itself;

such as whether the event was life threatening. Alternatively, the traumatic event can be defined more subjectively, in terms of the perception that an individual has of the event, rather than any intrinsic characteristics of the event itself. Thus, it is a matter of subjective appraisal as to whether or not it is considered to be 'traumatic'. Inevitably however, these two components are not as easily distinguishable as it might appear in theory.

To start with the subjective perspective: an interesting fact about psychological trauma, is that different people can experience the same event, but react in different ways, with some going on to develop PTSD or sub-threshold post-trauma symptoms, whilst others do not. One of the key general differences in how different people respond to the same event relates to their individual *perception* of it. A definition of trauma that takes this subjective element into account is "an individual's perception of an event as threatening to oneself or others" (Miller-Karas, 2015, p. 2). Indeed, this vital component of how an individual perceives the event that they have experienced or witnessed as threatening is central to many primary treatment options. For example, specialised post-trauma cognitive interventions are based on working with the cognitive appraisals that the client has made of the traumatic event and its consequences (Ehlers and Clark, 2000).

When considering 'trauma' from external objective perspective, when PTSD was first presented as a diagnosable mental health condition in the *DSM-III*, the traumatic experience that triggered the onset of the disorder was described as something "outside the range of usual human experience" (American Psychiatric Association, 1980, n.p.). However, in our modern world of wars, terrorist attacks, natural disasters and political upheaval, plus the widespread reporting of such events that are thousands of miles away, perhaps what might now be described as within the bounds of *usual human experience* needs to be reconsidered (Kiyimba, 2017). Additionally, it could easily be argued that what is 'usual' in one person's experience is not at all 'usual' in another's. Nevertheless, there have been a number of attempts to categorise external events as traumatic. One of the ways of categorising these events is to differentiate between so called 'small t' and 'large T' traumas.

Small 't' and large 'T' trauma

One way to think about traumatic events from the objective perspective was proposed by Francine Shapiro, the initiator of the trauma processing therapy, eye movement desensitisation and reprocessing (EMDR). She made a differentiation between what she referred to as *'large-T'* traumas and those that might be better labelled as *'small-t'* traumas (Shapiro, 1987). Large-T traumas according to Shapiro are those that relate to 'big' events such as wars, natural disasters, sexual assault, or terrorist acts; whereas small-t traumas could include routine surgery, minor accidents, dental procedures or a fall (Miller-Karas, 2015). Clinicians recognise that small-t traumas, especially if there has been an accumulation, or if the individual attributes particular meaning to them, could result in post-traumatic stress reactions. This is important, as a 'small-t' trauma is labelled as such, not on the basis that the person experienced it as a minor event, but because certain categories of life events are objectively labelled as such. The individual themselves may actually have experienced the event as large-T. This leads us to reconsider the fact that some definitions of psychological trauma focus more on the subjective meaning or perception of the event held by an individual, rather than purely its objective characteristics. However, there are also other ways that have been devised to objectively define external events as 'traumatic', including whether they are 'type 1' or 'type 2'.

Type 1 and type 2 trauma
Some researchers interested in the neurodevelopmental impacts of trauma have made a distinction between type 1 and type 2 traumas (Terr, 1991). Type 1 trauma refers to acute trauma, such as exposure to one single overwhelming event. Type 2 trauma is also referred to as complex trauma, and describes extended periods of exposure to traumatic situations. The two are differentiated by researchers in the field, who assert a qualitative distinction between acute trauma and complex interpersonal trauma (Kinniburgh et al., 2005). Complex trauma is also known as developmental trauma, and has been defined as having begun early in life and comprising of "multiple, chronic and prolonged, developmentally adverse traumatic events, most often of an interpersonal nature" (van der Kolk, 2005, p. 402). According to Judith Herman (1992), complex PTSD is the product of an individual's exposure to prolonged and/or repeated interpersonal trauma, that often occurs in situations and environments where the individual is unable to escape due to family, social, physical, psychological or developmental constraints. The traumatic stressors related to this situation may be domestic violence, sexual or physical abuse, child soldiering, sex trafficking, torture, and exposure to other forms of violence (Cloitre et al., 2012). Separating out type 1 and type 2 traumas not only acknowledges the significant differences in the nature of the trauma or series of traumas experienced, but also their ongoing impact. In the case of complex interpersonal trauma, it has been argued that there remains longevity of pervasive difficulties for the affected individual in relation to their capacity to effectively manage their emotions and impulses (Bath, 2008). An explanation for this is that where complex interpersonal trauma occurs from an early age, and is frequently encountered, the child's brain is redirected from focusing on activities and interests that would promote growth and development, towards attentional processes that are adaptive

to maintaining personal safety (Bath, 2008). This can have significant implications for adults caring for traumatised children in schools and care settings, as the default position of the child has become one that regards adults as a potential source of threat and harm, rather than comfort and support.

Cumulative trauma

The notion of cumulative trauma or C-trauma is another way of conceptualising the differences in the kinds of traumatic experiences that people suffer worldwide. It is a term that has been used to speak about the chronic experiences of living with racism, homophobia or poverty as well as the continuing impact of colonialism in some parts of the world (Miller-Karas, 2015). In relation to chronic stress from cumulative exposure to these kinds of traumas, some research has indicated that the telomeres (protective caps at the ends of DNA chromosomes) can actually be adversely affected over time. Each time a cell divides, it first has to double its chromosomes so that each of the new cells produced by splitting the first cell in half has a full set of genetic chromosomes. Telomeres shorten each time a chromosome reproduces, and eventually the cell is no longer able to divide and produce new chromosomes. It has been long believed in the scientific community that it is this slowing down and eventual inability of the chromosomes to divide due to telomeres becoming too short, that is the explanation for human aging (American Federation for Aging Research, 2011). Interestingly, research has also found that premature shortening of leukocyte telomeres has been found to occur more in certain populations. For example, in a very interesting study in the United States, a relationship was found between telomere shortening and high levels of racial discrimination amongst African Americans (Lee, Kim and Neblett Jr., 2017). This biological study demonstrates the significant impact of the cumulative trauma (C-trauma) of racial discrimination on

DNA structure, with the ultimate impact of shortening lifespan. Other research has shown that mothers caring for chronically ill children who *perceived* that experience to be stressful have shorter telomere length the longer that they had been involved in caregiving (Epel et al., 2004). This growing body of research into the relationship between telomere length, stress and aging suggests that physiological resilience is influenced both by exposure to stressful situations and differences in the ways in which an individual responds to them (Hawkley et al., 2005). Thus, although there is strong evidence for certain kinds of repeated external events to be legitimately categorised as traumatic, it is not possible to completely separate the events from the subjective internal sense-making practices of the individual experiencing those events, as this process also contributes to the overall impact on their psychological functioning. Obviously, the experiencing of large-T, small-t and C-traumas is not mutually exclusive, and for some, the compounded impact of a combination of these different experiences can be the trigger for a major stress reaction (Miller-Karas, 2015). More recently the term 'polytrauma' has also been adopted by some researchers, to differentiate between clients who have experienced multiple traumas from those who have experienced single incident traumas (Falkenberg et al., 2017).

An accumulation of what might be referred to as 'small- t' traumas can be extremely damaging and impactful. Also take note that the ways in which your client makes sense of their experiences may be different to the way other people (including yourself) might make sense of them, and this will also affect how 'traumatised' they are by their experiences.

PTSD classification in the *DSM-5*
Epidemiological studies suggest that there has been such a considerable increase in the number of people suffering from PTSD across the world, that it should be considered to be a major health concern (Brunello et al., 2001). The criteria for post-traumatic stress disorder (PTSD) have changed considerably with the newest edition of the American Psychiatric Association's (APA) *Diagnostic and Statistical Manual of Mental Disorders* (*DSM-5*). In the transition from the *DSM-IV* to *DSM-5* a number of changes were made to how PTSD and other similar disorders were conceptualised and categorised. The primary change was in the overall meta-structure of where within the *DSM* organisation they were placed. As figure 2.1 shows, a whole new category called 'Trauma and Stressor-Related Disorders' was created in the *DSM-5*, and PTSD and other similar disorders were moved into it from their previous home in the 'Anxiety Disorders' section.

- Neurodevelopmental Disorders
- Schizophrenia Spectrum and Other Psychotic Disorders
- Bipolar and Related Disorders
- Depressive Disorders
- Anxiety Disorders
- Obsessive-Compulsive, Stereotypic and Related Disorders
- Trauma and Stressor-Related Disorders
- Dissociative Disorders
- Somatic Symptom Disorders

Figure 2.1: The change in meta-categorisation of trauma-related disorders from the *DSM-IV* to the *DSM-5*

A further change with the advent of the *DSM-5* was an increased number of symptoms listed in the diagnostic criteria, together with a change in the way they have been organised and ordered (Pai, Suris and North, 2017). According to the *DSM-5* there are five main diagnostic criteria for a diagnosis of PTSD to be made, listed A to

E: 'A' referring to the triggering traumatic event and B to E describing aspects of symptom presentation. In addition, a further three diagnostic criteria relate to the severity, longevity and impact of symptoms B to E. All eight are listed in Table 2.2, and criteria A to E are subsequently discussed in further detail, as symptoms F to H are relatively self-explanatory.

Table 2.2: The diagnostic criteria for PTSD in the *DSM-5*

Criterion	Description
One unique criterion that is not symptom specific	
Criterion A:	A traumatic event
Four primary criteria relating to symptoms B–E	
Criterion B:	Intrusion or re-experiencing the traumatic event
Criterion C:	Avoidant symptoms
Criterion D:	Negative alterations in mood or cognitions
Criterion E:	Increased arousal symptoms
Three additional criteria that relate to the severity, longevity and impact of symptoms B–E	
Criterion F:	Symptoms have to have lasted at least a month
Criterion G:	Symptoms seriously affect the person's ability to function
Criterion H:	Symptoms not due to substance use, medical illness or anything except the event

- *Criterion A: Traumatic event* – to fulfil this criterion, a person must have been exposed to either threatened or actual death, serious injury or sexual violence. Exposure in this case could be direct, witnessed or indirect. Indirect exposure refers to situations whereby the individual may have heard about the accidental or violent traumatic experience of a relative or close friend. Importantly, the caveat to this criterion is that repeated or extreme indirect exposure to a specified traumatic event by professionals would not qualify. Additionally, exposure to a traumatic event by non-professionals where the trauma was indirectly experienced through the media would also not qualify as a criterion A event.

- *Criterion B: Intrusion or re-experiencing a traumatic event* – These symptoms relate to the various ways in which an individual may re-experience the criterion A event. The ways this might present could be: intrusive memories or thoughts, nightmares, flashbacks (re-experiencing the event and associated physical sensations, images, sounds, smells, thoughts and feelings as if the event were happening again in the present moment), and physical or psychological reactivity to reminders of the traumatic event, such as an anniversary, or a 'trigger' image, sound, smell or thought.

- *Criterion C: Avoidant symptoms* – Avoidant symptoms describe ways that an individual might try to avoid a memory of the event (and usually the associated intrusive symptoms that accompany it), and for diagnosis must include either avoiding thoughts or feelings connected to the criterion A event, or avoiding situations or people associated with or connected to the criterion A event.

- *Criterion D: Negative alterations in mood or cognitions* – This criterion is new in the *DSM-5*, but relates to many of the symptoms that clinicians and individuals experiencing PTSD have observed in practice. In summary, this criterion relates to an individual's decline in mood or thought patterns, which can include: memory difficulties exclusive to the event; negative thoughts or beliefs about one's self or the world; a distorted sense of blame for one's self or others related to the event; feeling 'stuck' in experiences of severe emotions related to the trauma such as horror, shame or grief; a severe reduction of interest in activities previously enjoyed before the traumatic event; and feeling disconnected, detached or isolated from others.

- *Criterion E: Increased arousal* – This criterion relates to a wariness and alertness to watching for potential further threats that may present. The symptoms can include: difficulty with concentration; irritability or anger; difficulty falling or staying asleep; hyper-vigilance; exaggerated or over-sensitive startle reflex.

Two of the other changes to the diagnostic criteria from the *DSM-IV* to the *DSM-5* were the tightening and explication of how trauma and exposure to trauma were defined, as well as the removal of the previous more subjective aspect of the definition of trauma (Pai, Suris and North, 2017). Additionally, there is now no longer a requirement in the *DSM-5* as there was in the *DSM-IV*, that someone had to have an intense emotional response at the time of the criterion A event. Despite these edits to the *DSM-5* it remains one of the most complex diagnoses in the *DSM*, and it has been calculated that there are 636,120 different ways that the various symptoms could be combined together and still qualify for a PTSD diagnosis (Galatzer-Levy and Bryant, 2013). Arguably, because of this broad scope, and perhaps also because there are such high levels of comorbidity with other conditions, research shows that PTSD is still often not recognised in patients either after a major disaster (Brewin et al., 2010) or in general practice (Ehlers, Gene-Cos and Perrin, 2009; Liebschutz et al., 2007).

When thinking about how the notion of trauma is historically and culturally located, and the fact that the *DSM* and the *ICD* are constantly open to change and revision, it is important to maintain a critical perspective when considering what appear to be very fixed and definitive classifications of 'disorders'. For example, for those clients who are still within the first month after experiencing a traumatic event, a diagnosis of acute stress disorder may be given within the *DSM-5*. This diagnosis requires a client to present with symptoms from each of the categories B–E (intrusion, avoidance, negative mood and arousal). However, the revisions to the *ICD-11* no longer consider acute stress (defined as 'a brief experience of intense psychological distress following exposure to a traumatic event') to require classification as a mental health disorder. It has instead been moved elsewhere and categorised as a 'factor influencing health' under a section by that name. The reason for this declassification has purportedly been an attempt to de-pathologise shorter periods of post-traumatic distress. Interestingly, the implications of these changes are that a person might still be considered to have a clinically diagnosable (and therefore in effect *abnormal*) condition according to the *DSM-5*, if they have a short period of emotional upset after experiencing a traumatic event. However, this period of distress within the first month after experiencing a traumatic event would not be seen as abnormal, or warranting a diagnostic category according to the *ICD-11*.

It is recognised that the *DSM* is extremely influential and is widely used by clinicians and researchers alike as a scientific tool for the identification and classification of symptom presentations. However, it is wise to remember that there are a multitude of factors and influences that are active in determining which personal characteristics, behaviours, thoughts, emotions or other activities are deemed to be *abnormal*. As Pilgrim (2007) advises, it is important to remember that the *DSM* is also a political document that is continuously revised in light of research evidence; what is constructed as 'abnormal' or 'disordered' depends both on current trends in culture, and social thinking (Scheff, 1970). Any diagnosable condition's status as a 'disorder' is thus always potentially revisable (Brorstrom, 2009) and is dependent on a number of factors. Indeed some classifications of human activity that have previously been pathologised, may at some point even be taken out of existence, as notions of normality and abnormality sway in the constant flux of multiple influences. A frequently reported example of this kind of radical change was the revoking of homosexuality as a diagnostic label of abnormality, as heteronormative assumptions were challenged and 'pathology' reconsidered in the light of changes in moral, social and political order. Another condition that has been historically conceptualised as a medical disorder, but which has been under dispute for many decades is the diagnosis of schizophrenia (Scheff, 1970; Dillon, Johnstone and Longden, 2014). Scheff argued that schizophrenia is not so much a medical reality but an ideology that itself needs to be recognised as being embedded within the particular Western historical context and culture (Brorstrom, 2009).

Bearing in mind these cautionary remarks and indeed taking heed of the fact that diagnoses do change over time in response to social and clinical influence, there are other situations where diagnostic categories may also be *added* to medical reference manuals such as the *DSM* and the *ICD*. One example is that until the advent of the *ICD-11* there was no diagnosis of attention-deficit hyperactivity disorder (ADHD), but this has recently been added. In relation to trauma specifically, a topic of much interest, argument and speculation has been the possibility of developing a classificatory category that captures the complexity of trauma not covered by the PTSD diagnosis. In May 2019 the *ICD-11* was presented to the World Health Assembly, for adoption by Member States with effect from 1 January 2022. This includes the completely new category of Complex PTSD, which has attracted much attention and will be discussed in more detail shortly. First, a summary of the key similarities and differences between the *DSM-5* diagnostic criteria for PTSD and the *ICD-11* criteria will be briefly presented and discussed.

Comparing PTSD diagnosis in the *DSM-5* and the *ICD-11*
In the *DSM-5* as described earlier, PTSD was moved out of the meta-category of 'Anxiety Disorders' (in *DSM-IV*) and into its own new meta-category of 'Trauma and Stressor-Related Disorders'. In the *ICD-11*, both PTSD and Complex PTSD (CPTSD) have been placed under a meta-category of 'Disorders Specifically Associated with Stress'. In Table 2.3 a comparison of the symptom checklist has been provided between PTSD in the *ICD-11* and PTSD in the *DSM-5*. There are key differences in the implications of the way that the criterion A event has been specified in each of the manuals. For example, the slightly more general descriptor of a traumatic event in the *ICD-11* allows a broader range of traumatic situations to come within its scope, such experiencing a psychotic episode (Fornells-Ambrojo, Gracie, Brewin and Hardy, 2016), and being a patient in intensive care (Wade et al., 2012). Also, in the *ICD-11* there is no defined time scale for onset of PTSD, thus the criterion A traumatic event does not need to cause immediate distress (Brewin et al., 2009), and symptom onset that occurs more than six months post-trauma could still be attributable to the event (Andrews, Brewin, Philpott, and Stewart, 2007), despite there being no additional category of 'delayed onset'.

Apart from the difference in wording to define a criterion A traumatic event, and the implications that has for the range of people who may fall within its scope, what is immediately apparent is that there are far fewer essential criteria in the *ICD-11* than the *DSM-5*. In effect there are just three categories: re-experiencing, avoidance of reminders of the traumatic event, and hyper-vigilance. Of these, only six symptoms in total from these three categories are needed to fulfil the requirements for a PTSD diagnosis. Unlike the 636,120 possible combinations of symptoms possible for a *DSM-5* PTSD diagnosis (Galatzer-Levy and Bryant, 2013), the total possible symptom combinations in the *ICD-11* are only 27. The working group of experts who developed the PTSD guidelines for the *ICD-11* also chose to remove more ubiquitous specifiers, such as difficulty with concentration, irritability, loss of interest and sleep problems, due to their lack of uniqueness to this particular condition. In other words, "by using a narrower and briefer *ICD-11* set of symptoms, *ICD-11* aims to better differentiate PTSD from often comorbid conditions" (Stein et al., 2014, p. 495). Table 2.3 provides a comparative overview of the key differences in diagnostic criteria for PTSD between the *ICD-11* and the *DSM-5*.

Table 2.3: The key differences in diagnostic criteria for PTSD between the *ICD-11* and the *DSM-5*

	ICD-11 criteria	*DSM-5* criteria
A	Exposure to a stressful event or situation of exceptionally threatening or horrific nature likely to cause pervasive distress in almost anyone	Exposure to a traumatic event where a person has experienced direct or indirect exposure to either threatened or actual death, serious injury or sexual violence
B	Persistent re-experiencing that involves not only remembering the traumatic episode, but also experiencing it as occurring again presently (nightmares or intrusive memories/flashbacks: one of these two symptoms required for diagnosis)	Intrusion or re-experiencing a traumatic event via intrusive memories, thoughts, nightmares, flashbacks, and physical or psychological reactivity to reminders of the traumatic event (at least one of these symptoms required for diagnosis)

C	Avoidance of traumatic reminders (internal reminders such as thoughts or external reminders such as places or people: one out of these two symptoms required for diagnosis)	Avoidance of either thoughts or feelings connected to the traumatic event, or avoiding situations, places, people, activities, objects, or conversations associated with or connected to the traumatic event (at least one of these symptoms required for diagnosis)
D		Negative alterations in mood or cognitions including memory difficulties exclusive to the event, persistent negative evaluations about self, others or the world, significant self-blame or blame of others, pervasive negative emotional state such as fear, anger or shame, loss of previously enjoyed activities, feeling detached or unable to experience positive emotions (at least two of these symptoms required for diagnosis)
E	Persistent hyper-arousal or heightened perception of current threat (hyper-vigilance or exaggerated startle response: one out of these two symptoms required for diagnosis)	Increased arousal, including lack of concentration, irritability or anger, difficulty falling or staying asleep, hyper-vigilance, exaggerated startle reflex, impulsivity or self-destructive behaviour (at least two of these symptoms required for diagnosis)

F	Symptoms may persist for several weeks (no onset period specified)	Duration of at least one month
G	Impairment in at least one area of functioning that causes "significant impairment in personal, family, social, educational, occupational or other important areas of functioning"	Clinically significant distress/ impairment in a number of different areas of life
H		Symptoms are not better explained by another medical condition or by substance misuse

The aim of the World Health Organisation (WHO) in trying to focus on the symptoms of PTSD that distinguish it clearly from other disorders, was to try to make PTSD more easily recognisable and treated worldwide. A further rationale for the PTSD diagnosis revisions between the *ICD-10* and *ICD-11* were to "emphasize that the construct of PTSD should have both global applicability and clinical utility" (Stein et al., 2014, p. 495). Indeed, this consideration does seem to be pragmatically oriented, and does seem to take into account cultural variability.

CPTSD in the *ICD-11*
When turning attention to the newest diagnostic criteria of Complex PTSD (CPTSD), the difference with the *DSM-5* is more notable, as the *DSM-5* does not include within it a diagnosis of complex PTSD. Arguably, a wider scope of PTSD presentations can be encompassed within the much wider range of core PTSD symptoms in the *DSM-5*, particularly in criterion D, negative alterations in mood or cognitions. Additionally, the *DSM-5* has the

potential for using a subtype category of PTSD called PTSD with dissociation, which further increases its range. However, regarding the diagnostic criteria for CPTSD, which only exist in the *ICD-11*, it is still a requirement that the criterion A and additional three core categories of symptoms are present *plus* three extra ones that reflect 'disturbances in self-organisation' (DSO). These three additional criteria are:

1. **Affect dysregulation**: severe and pervasive problems in emotion regulation
2. **Negative self-concept**: persistent negative self-beliefs together with a pervasive feeling of guilt, shame or failure related to the traumatic event
3. **Disturbances in relationships**: persistent problems with feeling close to others and maintaining relationships

These disturbances in self-organisation are proposed to be typically, but not exclusively associated with sustained, repeated or multiple forms of traumatic exposure (e.g. genocide campaigns, childhood sexual abuse, child soldiering, severe domestic violence, torture or slavery), and reflect a loss of psychological, emotional and social resources under conditions of prolonged adversity (Cloitre, Garvert, Brewin, Bryant and Maercker, 2013). The research that has been conducted to assess whether the differentiation between PTSD and CPTSD is clinically justifiable has so far indicated support for the distinction (Brewin et al., 2017). Figure 2.2 shows visually how these symptom clusters relate to one another within the *ICD-11* CPTSD categorisation.

Vicarious impact and the risks of secondary traumatic stress
Secondary traumatic stress (STS) is a condition that occurs when a person is vicariously, or indirectly, exposed to a traumatic event through their interactions with people who have themselves been directly impacted by a traumatic event (Cieslak et al., 2014). Those who experience vicarious or 'secondary' trauma indirectly can also

Psychological trauma knowledge

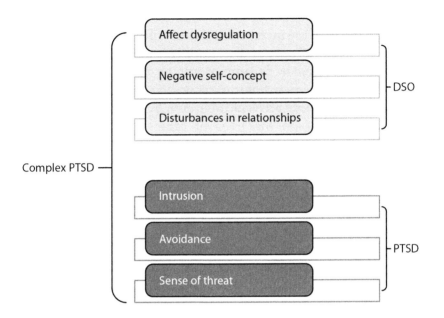

Figure 2.2: CPTSD symptom clusters within the *ICD-11*

experience very similar symptoms to the person experiencing PTSD, including exhaustion, guilt, fear, hyper-vigilance and avoidance (Craig and Sprang, 2010). In addition, those vicariously experiencing the trauma of another can also find that they have changes in their belief systems about the world and other people, and even their own capabilities and safety, which in addition to the symptoms already listed can have the ripple effect of emotional numbing and a lack of self-care (Sabin-Farrell and Turpin, 2003). Those thought to be most at risk of this vicarious impact are often those in professions which regularly expose them to being in close contact with people who have experienced trauma, such as therapists. Secondary traumatisation has also been found to be common in medical settings such as hospitals, particularly in emergency departments, heart units and children's wards (Duffy,

Avalos and Dowling, 2015). The reason for this is thought to be largely the result of the increased amount of time that staff in these professions are exposed to the traumatic experiences of their patients. Therefore, it is important to be aware that the ramifications of the impact of trauma on one individual can ripple out, not only into more areas of their own lives, but can also have a vicarious impact on the lives of others. For those readers involved in supporting clients through the healing process from the traumatic experiences they have been exposed to, care ought to be taken of one's own wellbeing with this in mind.

Trauma physiology

The primary system in the body that relates to how people are affected by traumatic experiences is the autonomic nervous system (ANS), which is a subdivision of the peripheral nervous system (PNS). The role of the ANS is to regulate the processes within the body that are unconscious. The ANS is divided into two regulatory systems: the sympathetic nervous system which controls responses related to *stimulation*, or the fight/flight response; and the parasympathetic nervous system which controls responses related to system *relaxation*, or the rest/digest response.

• The limbic system

Descriptions of the brain often differentiate between the fore (front), mid and hind (rear) parts. The hind brain is connected to the brain stem and is sometimes colloquially named the 'reptilian' brain to describe its function as primarily related to instinctive and automatic functions such as regulating breathing and digestion. The mid brain is sometimes referred to as the 'mammalian' brain and is the part that is largely responsible for processes related to emotional responses. The fore brain is also known as the 'neo-mammalian' brain, and is where executive functioning tasks such as reasoning and thinking and planning occur. The limbic system is located in the mid brain and is the part most closely concerned with the impact of psychological trauma. The two key structures that are important to understand are the hippocampus and the amygdala.

The hippocampus is not just one structure but a pair, one in each of the left and right brain hemispheres, and is named after its shape which resembles a seahorse. In simple terms this can be thought of as the memory storage area or long-term memory 'filing cabinet' of the brain. The hippocampus plays an important role in spatial awareness and orientation as well as connecting memories with sensory experiences. It is also one of the places where new cells are made through the process of neurogenesis, a form of brain plasticity, so plays an important role in learning new things.

The amygdala gains its name from its shape which is like an almond. Like the hippocampus it is also a pair of structures, and these are located on the left and right hemispheres of the brain close to the hippocampus. The pair of amygdalae perform an important function in relation to the ways in which people experience emotion. One of these functions is to attach emotional content to memories, and in doing so it plays a very important role in determining how robustly memories are made and consolidated. In particular, it is significant in determining the way that memories that have an emotional connection with fear are laid down.

In simple terms, the amygdala provides direction to the brain's emotional response system, and records emotionally-charged experiences. It is able to record the emotional feeling of a memory, but not the specific details or facts that connect with the memory. In contrast, the hippocampus tends to record the specific facts, and the timeframe or timeline of events but not the emotional charge connected with those facts or events. During a traumatic experience however, the very high levels of stress hormones released during a fight/flight response inhibit the functioning of the hippocampus so that an accurate timeframe of events is not properly recorded (Rothschild, 2010). Sometimes this can be described as 'going offline' or 'short-circuited' or that a 'fuse has blown'. The result is that the event may be recalled in a mixed up order or with parts missing, or without an 'end date/time' encoded. This might mean that the hippocampus does not have a clear record that the traumatic event is now over. Usually the hippocampus needs some help to reorganise its jumbled memory pieces so that it can rest knowing that there is a proper 'end' date stamp in the past, which is clearly differentiated from the present time.

• **The vagus nerve**
There are several cranial nerve fibres that operate specifically within the parasympathetic nervous system, including the tenth cranial nerve (CN X), which is the longest nerve in the ANS and is called the vagus nerve. The vagus nerve is in two parts that both travel from the medulla in the brain stem all the way down to the colon. It functions to influence the operation of the digestive tract, the lungs and heart during parasympathetic nervous system activation. Due to its connection to a number of major organs, the vagal nerve can influence many bodily responses including gastrointestinal peristalsis, the gag reflex, heart rate, sweating, and some aspects of speech and hearing. A very helpful and important development in our understanding of the autonomic nervous system is the proposition that the parasympathetic nervous system may have two 'branches'. The work in this area has been primarily spearheaded by Steven Porges and is known as the 'polyvagal theory'. In essence, there is now considerable evidence to suggest that the vagus nerve, which is the primary regulatory neurological component in activating the parasympathetic nervous system, is not unitary but has two branches; the dorsal and ventral. For clarity Porges published a paper in 2007 clearly outlining what the polyvagal theory is, and this is summarised in table 2.4.

Table 2.4: The polyvagal theory (summarised from Porges, 2007)

	Original theory	Subsequent additions
1.	The vagal system is non-unitary	Identification of the evolutionary development of heart regulation through neural networks
2.	There are two vagal motor systems	Development of the distinctions between the vagal pathways originating in either the nucleus ambiguous or the dorsal motor nucleus
3.	The idea that vagal tone is a single system has limited value	The recognition and understanding of the evolutionary functions of the three neural circuits regulating the heart
4.	The functional effect on the heart of vagal conduits can be monitored	Appliance of the 'Jackson's principle of dissolution' (that more recently evolved neural circuits in the brain inhibit 'older' circuits) an explanation for the way that the neural response hierarchy is sequenced
5.	The degree of neurogenetic (genetically influenced) bradycardia (slow heart rate) is influenced by the vagus nerve	The proposition of the term 'neuroception' to explain the neural processes involved in the evaluation of risk and the regulation of vagal activity, using higher brain structures
6.	There is a common cardiopulmonary oscillator	The neuroanatomical and neurophysiological link between the vagal regulation of the heart and the neural regulation of the striated muscles of the face and head

7.	Autonomic nervous system function is related to primary emotion	Identification and presentation of the important role that physiological state has on reactivity to environmental stimuli, via afferent feedback to brain structures
8.		The use of the term polyvagal to emphasise the variety of attributes of the vagus nerve including 'bringing to' and 'taking away' functions

The introduction of polyvagal theory has had an impact on those working with clients who have experienced psychological trauma, as it adds another dimension to our understanding of what happens to people neurologically. In particular, the separation between the functions of the dorsal and vagal nerves operating the parasympathetic nervous system have allowed a better understanding of how practitioners might better engage the PNS for clients whose ANS is stuck in 'fight/flight' mode. The dorsal vagus is considered to be the mechanism by which the freeze response (shut-down or collapse) operates. The ventral vagus is referred to by Porges as the 'face-heart connection'. In other words, the ventral vagal network is able to take account of the tone of voice and facial expression of others as a way to facilitate activation of the 'rest recover' PNS. This happens through a mechanism called 'neuroception', which refers to the way that people tend to scan their environment for cues that indicate whether they are safe. In particular, one of the aspects of our environment that we frequently 'scan' for signs of danger is other people. We observe other people's facial expressions and tone of voice as cues to inform us about whether they are a threat or a friend. The process of neuroception operates at an unconscious level, and very quickly either our ANS (fight/flight) will be activated or our PNS (rest recover). Because of this responsiveness to others, it is also known as the 'social engagement' part of the vagal nerve system. Therefore, what has been known anecdotally for some time, that pleasant social interaction can be soothing and calming, now has a neurobiological explanation through the polyvagal theory.

In actual practice, knowledge of polyvagal theory is useful for those working with clients who have experienced trauma, and for whom activation of the ANS is problematically in a constant state of arousal. In the first instance it provides a clear psycho-educational framework to offer clients who have experienced psychological trauma, so that they can have a 'no-blame' understanding of their reactions, by appreciating the adaptive survival function of those reactions. In addition, polyvagal theory can explain how at times our neuroception of the environment can be mistaken, and threats are perceived where there is no actual or real danger. Knowledge of the value of relational interaction as mechanisms for PNS activation is a valuable confirmation of how important social connections are in recovery from trauma. It offers us a secure neuro-theoretical foundation for prioritising the importance of finding relational safety in a therapeutic situation, and the importance of this as a vital element in promoting healing.

Summary
This chapter has introduced the differences between stress and trauma and has outlined, from a medical perspective, how PTSD and complex PTSD are diagnosed in both the *ICD-11* and the *DSM-5*. This has provided a context for understanding the behavioural symptom presentations for those who are suffering from the ongoing impact of the traumatic experiences that they have encountered. Knowledge of the behavioural presentation of trauma is important as PTSD itself is known to be under-diagnosed, and therefore these behaviours may otherwise be mis-

interpreted as personality defects or social deviance. In situations where behavioural symptomology is not understood as having trauma aetiology, inappropriate behavioural management strategies including punishment, restraint and sanctions may be being used in place of trauma-informed interventions. The chapter also highlights the necessity of reflective self-awareness and deliberate self-care for those working with people who have been affected by traumatic experiences, through highlighting some of the issues of vicarious impact and the possibility for secondary traumatic stress. The chapter ends with a brief summary of the basic aspects of trauma physiology as it is currently understood from a medical perspective, focusing in particular on the practical implications of polyvagal theory in our work with people who have experienced psychological trauma. Being able to share this knowledge with clients can serve as a valuable psycho-education component, and help to minimise some of the self-blame that clients feel about struggling with their symptoms. By demonstrating how the nervous system is affected by trauma, and being able to validate for a client that the symptoms that they are experiencing are a normal physiological response to extreme states of stress or abuse, the client can be in a better position to develop self-compassion and to have hope for their recovery.

References

American Federation for Aging Research (AFAR) (2011). *Theories of aging: An introduction to aging science*. infoaging guides. New York, NY: American Federation for Aging Research.

American Psychiatric Association (APA) (1980). *Diagnostic and statistical manual of mental disorders, Third edition (DSM-III)*. Washington, DC: American Psychiatric Association.

American Psychiatric Association (APA) (2013). *Diagnostic and statistical manual of mental disorders, Fifth edition (DSM-5)*. Washington, DC: American Psychiatric Association.

Psychological trauma knowledge

Andrews, B., Brewin, C. R., Philpott, R., & Stewart, L. (2007). Delayed-onset posttraumatic stress disorder: A systematic review of the evidence. *American Journal of Psychiatry, 164*(9), 1319–1326.

Bath, H. (2008). The three pillars of trauma-informed care. *Reclaiming children and youth, 17*(3), 17–21.

Brewin, C. R., Cloitre, M., Hyland, P., Shevlin, M., Maercker, A., Bryant, R. A., Humayun, A., Jones, L. M., Kagee, A., Rousseau, C., & Somasundaram, D. (2017). A review of current evidence regarding the ICD-11 proposals for diagnosing PTSD and complex PTSD. *Clinical Psychology Review, 58*, 1–15.

Brewin, C. R., Fuchkan, N., Huntley, Z., Robertson, M., Thompson, M., Scragg, P., d'Ardenne, P., & Ehlers, A. (2010). Outreach and screening following the 2005 London bombings: usage and outcomes. *Psychological Medicine, 40*(12), 2049–2057.

Brewin, C. R., Lanius, R. A., Novac, A., Schnyder, U., & Galea, S. (2009). Reformulating PTSD for DSM-V: Life after criterion A. *Journal of Traumatic Stress, 22*(5), 366–373.

Brorstrom, L. (2009). *Portfolio of academic, therapeutic practice and research work including an investigation of trauma therapy in a landscape of suffering: Towards a grounded theory* (Doctoral dissertation). University of Surrey, United Kingdom.

Brunello, N., Davidson, J., Deahl, M., Kassler, R. C., Mendlewicz, J., Racagni, G., Shalev, A. Y., & Zohar, J. (2001). Post-traumatic stress disorder: Diagnosis and epidemiology, comorbidity and social consequences, biology and treatment. *Neuropsychobiology, 43*(3), 150–162.

Cieslak, R., Shoji, K., Douglas, A., Melville, E., Luszczynska, A., & Benight, C. C. (2014). A meta-analysis of the relationship between job burnout and secondary traumatic stress among workers with indirect exposure to trauma. *Psychological Services, 11*(1), 75.

Cloitre, M., Courtois, C. A., Ford, J. D., Green, B. L., Alexander, P., Briere, J., & van der Hart, O. (2012). *The ISTSS expert consensus treatment guidelines for complex PTSD in adults.* Retrieved from https://www.istss.org/ISTSS_Main/media/Documents/ISTSS-Expert-Concesnsus-Guidelines-for-Complex-PTSD-Updated-060315.pdf

Cloitre, M., Garvert, D. W., Brewin, C. R., Bryant, R. A., & Maercker, A. (2013). Evidence for proposed ICD-11 PTSD and complex PTSD: A latent profile analysis. *European Journal of Psychotraumatology*, 4(1), 20706.

Craig, C. D., & Sprang, G. (2010). Compassion satisfaction, compassion fatigue, and burnout in a national sample of trauma treatment therapists. *Anxiety, Stress, & Coping*, 23(3), 319–339.

Dillon, J., Johnstone, L., & Longden, E. (2014). Trauma, dissociation, attachment and neuroscience: A new paradigm for understanding severe mental distress. In E. Speed, J. Moncrieff, & M. Rapley (Eds.), *De-medicalizing misery II: Society, politics and the mental health industry* (pp. 226–234). London, United Kingdom: Palgrave Macmillan.

Duffy, E., Avalos, G., & Dowling, M. (2015). Secondary traumatic stress among emergency nurses: A cross-sectional study. *International Emergency Nursing*, 23(2), 53–58.

Ehlers, A., & Clark, D. M. (2000). A cognitive model of posttraumatic stress disorder. *Behaviour Research and Therapy*, 38, 319–345.

Ehlers, A., Gene-Cos, N., & Perrin, S. (2009). Low recognition of post-traumatic stress disorder in primary care. *London Journal of Primary Care*, 2(1), 36–42.

Epel, E. S., Blackburn, E. H., Lin, J., Dhabhar, F. S., Adler, N. E., Morrow, J. D., & Cawthon, R. M. (2004). Accelerated telomere shortening in response to life stress. *Proceedings of the National Academy of Sciences*, 101(49), 17312–17315.

Erikson, K. T. (1976). *Everything in its path*. New York, NY: Simon and Schuster.

Falkenberg, L., Zeckey, C., Mommsen, P., Winkelmann, M., Zelle, B. A., Panzica, M., Pape, C., Krettek, C., & Probst, C. (2017). Long-term outcome in 324 polytrauma patients: What factors are associated with posttraumatic stress disorder and depressive disorder symptoms? *European Journal of Medical Research*, 22(1), 44.

Fornells-Ambrojo, M., Gracie, A., Brewin, C. R., Hardy, A. (2016). Narrowing the focus on the assessment of psychosis-related PTSD: A methodologically orientated systematic review. *European Journal of Psychotraumatology*, 7:32095. doi: 10.3402/ejpt.v7.32095.

Galatzer-Levy, I. R., Bryant, R. A. (2013). 636,120 ways to have posttraumatic stress disorder. *Perspectives on Psychological Science, 8*(6), 651–662.

Hawkley, L. C., Berntson, G. G., Engeland, C. G., Marucha, P. T., Masi, C. M., & Cacioppo, J. T. (2005). Stress, aging, and resilience: Can accrued wear and tear be slowed? *Canadian Psychology, 46*(3), 115.

Herman, J. L. (1992). Complex PTSD: A syndrome in survivors of prolonged and repeated trauma. *Journal of Traumatic Stress, 5*(3), 377–391.

Kinniburgh, K., Blaustein, M., Spinazzola, J., & van der Kolk, B. (2005). Attachment, self-regulation and competency: A comprehensive intervention framework for children with complex trauma. *Psychiatric Annals, 35*(5), 424–430.

Kiyimba, N. (2017). Trauma and spiritual growth. In P. M. Gubi (Ed.), *What counsellors and spiritual directors can learn from each other: Ethical practice training and supervision* (pp. 138–156). London, United Kingdom: Jessica Kingsley Publishers.

Lee, D. B., Kim, E. S., & Neblett Jr., E. W. (2017). The link between discrimination and telomere length in African American adults. *Health Psychology, 36*(5), 458.

Liebschutz, J., Saitz, R., Brower, V., Keane, T. M., Lloyd-Travaglini, C., Averbuch, T., & Samet, J. H. (2007). PTSD in urban primary care: High prevalence and low physician recognition. *Journal of General Internal Medicine, 22*(6), 719–726.

Miller-Karas, E. (2015). Resilience and trauma defined. In E. Miller-Karas (Ed.), *Building resilience to trauma: The trauma and community resilience models* (pp. 1–9). New York, NY: Routledge.

Pai, A., Suris, A., & North, C. (2017). Posttraumatic stress disorder in the DSM-5: Controversy, change, and conceptual considerations. *Behavioral Sciences, 7*(1), 7.

Pilgrim, D. (2007). The survival of psychiatric diagnosis. *Social Science and Medicine, 65*(3), 536–547.

Porges, S. W. (2007). The polyvagal perspective. *Biological Psychology, 74*(2), 116–143.

Rothschild, B. (2010). *Eight keys to safe trauma recovery. Take-charge strategies to empower your healing.* New York, NY: W. W. Norton & Company Inc.

Sabin-Farrell, R., & Turpin, G. (2003). Vicarious traumatization: implications for the mental health of health workers? *Clinical Psychology Review, 23*(3), 449–480.

Scheff, T. J. (1970). Schizophrenia as ideology. *Schizophrenia Bulletin, 1*(2), 15.

Shapiro, F. (1989). Eye movement desensitization: A new treatment for post-traumatic stress disorder. *Journal of Behavior Therapy and Experimental Psychiatry, 20*(3), 211–217.

Stein, D. J., McLaughlin, K. A., Koenen, K. C., Atwoli, L., Friedman, M. J., Hill, E. D., Maercker, A., Petukhova, M., Shahly, V., van Ommeren, M., & Alonso, J. (2014). DSM-5 and ICD-11 definitions of posttraumatic stress disorder: Investigating "narrow" and "broad" approaches. *Depression and Anxiety, 31*(6), 494–505.

Terr, L. C. (1991). Childhood traumas: An outline and overview. *American Journal of Psychiatry, 1*(48), 10–20.

van der Kolk, B. (2005). Developmental trauma disorder: Towards a rational diagnosis for children with complex trauma histories. *Psychiatric Annals, 33*(5), 401–408.

Wade, D. M., Howell, D. C., Weinman, J. A., Hardy, R. J., Mythen, M. G., Brewin, C. R., Borja-Boluda, S., Matejowsky, C. F., & Raine, R. A. (2012). Investigating risk factors for psychological morbidity three months after intensive care: A prospective cohort study. *Critical Care, 16*(5), R192.

World Health Organization (WHO) (2018). International Classification of Diseases, 11th Revision (ICD-11) Retrieved from https://www.who.int/classifications/icd/en/

CHAPTER THREE
MINDFULNESS KNOWLEDGE

Chapter contents
• The origins of mindfulness • Mindfulness in the West • Mindfulness and 'third wave' therapies • Compassionate mindfulness for trauma • Summary

This chapter will provide an overview of the foundations of mindfulness and will briefly explain the principles of mindfulness. This chapter will also consider the ways in which mindfulness has been incorporated into a number of psychological therapies such as mindfulness-based stress reduction (MBSR) and mindfulness-based cognitive therapy (MBCT) for treating depression and anxiety. Other 'third wave' therapies that include mindfulness as a key component are mindful self-compassion (MSC), dialectical behaviour therapy (DBT) and acceptance and commitment therapy (ACT). This chapter will introduce the principles of each of these interventions, and will explain how mindfulness is practiced slightly differently within each of them. Finally this chapter ends with a brief summary of the importance of adapting existing mindfulness approaches to help people who have been affected by psychological trauma in order to help them to engage safely and effectively with the practices. It is argued that in designing a trauma-informed approach to mindfulness practice, self-compassion must also be woven into its infrastructure to support integration of mindfulness, especially for people with shame-based or shame-inducing trauma experiences. In chapter one (table 1.1) the full specification for learning requirements relating to the seven TIM characteristics was provided. Table 3.1 is a duplicate of the section of that table that relates to mindfulness knowledge, and is provided here as a reminder for pedagogical purposes. This chapter explicates in more detail the descriptive elements that relate specifically to this characteristic.

Table 3.1: Trauma-Informed Mindfulness characteristic 2. 'Mindfulness knowledge' learning aims

TIM characteristic	Description
2. Mindfulness knowledge	• To have a foundational knowledge of the history of mindfulness and how it has been adapted for Western use in third wave psychological therapies • To understand the aims of mindfulness practice and how mindfulness can achieve those goals • To learn and use a number of different mindfulness practice exercises

The origins of mindfulness

Mindfulness, although also found as a component of Taoist thought, is best known as a form of Buddhist meditation that seeks to develop one's self-awareness gradually and gently. The 'four noble truths' of Buddhism are that, i) suffering is part of life, ii) suffering originates from desire, iii) suffering can be stopped by changing your view and that iv) there is a way that prevents suffering. Mindfulness or rather 'right mindfulness' is one of the eight components of this philosophy:

- Right view: see things as they really are
- Right intention: moment to moment wisdom
- Right speech: truthful, kind
- Right action: living ethically
- Right livelihood: e.g. avoid killing
- Right effort: cultivating wholesome states

- **Right mindfulness: full attention to now**
- Right concentration: one-point awareness

In Buddhist teaching, the purpose and goal of mindfulness meditation is nothing short of personal transformation, as emotional 'irritants' such as greed, jealousy and hatred gradually give way to flexibility, compassion and tolerance. The way that this is achieved is through becoming more sensitised to and aware of one's thoughts, attitudes, reactions and behaviours. In Buddhist meditation, there are two main approaches, *vipassana* and *samatha*. A simple translation of vipassana might be 'insight', or in other words, looking deeply, clear awareness and understanding. Samatha relates to 'tranquillity' or 'concentration', and refers to the mind being at rest on one object without wandering (Gunaratana, 2002). Another way of describing Samatha (or Shamatha) is 'stopping', and is something that the Buddhist teacher Thich Nhat Hanh says is essential for mindfulness practice, because "if we cannot stop, we cannot have insight" (2008, p. 3). Most often the breath is used as a point of focus whilst the practitioner learns to observe both their internal state and external experience compassionately and patiently. As such it is fundamentally an activity that can only be fully appreciated or understood through the experience of it. Thich Nhat Hanh (1998) explains the Buddha's teaching about how to calm the body and mind through five stages:

1. **Recognition:** This means that we become aware and able to notice what we are experiencing. For example, if we notice we feel angry, recognition is to say 'I know I have anger in me'.
2. **Acceptance:** Instead of denying what we recognise in ourselves, we accept that it is present. For example, acceptance is to say 'I accept that I have anger in me'.
3. **Embracing:** The next step in the process of mindfulness is to embrace the emotion that we have recognised and accepted, as if we were tenderly holding and embracing a loved one.

4. **Looking deeply:** The act of gentle embrace serves to calm that part that is distressed by what has been recognised. At this point we can begin to look more deeply to understand where the emotion came from.
5. **Insight:** The benefit of a compassionate act of looking deeply for the cause of the hurt is to understand what brought it about. Perhaps we will recognise a trigger or something that had previously been unseen. At this point, there may be opportunity to use the insight to make changes.

The context for mindfulness as a meditation practice is that traditionally it has been a component or technique that forms part of a spiritual journey. In this sense, 'spirituality' is understood not in a formal religious way, but in its widest and most inclusive perspective, as those who are 'seeking' a more peaceful, happy and rewarding life. As mindfulness teacher Larry Yang explains:

> We are all seekers even if we do not espouse any religious faith at all. We all search for meaningful experiences, satisfying objects, compatible people, useful knowledge, fulfilling activities, wellbeing and more. Seeking is part of our humanity. When we seek, enquire and explore, we open up to our own life and to the world. This openness is a tender place for both our minds and hearts. From this tender place we look for the things that we hope will create more happiness and contentment for ourselves. (Yang and Willis, 2017, p. 7)

Coming from the perspective of developing a greater sense of awareness, spirituality means 'waking up' from the sleepwalking state that we are born into, and may live our whole lives in. Far from being a woolly, navel gazing hobby, as de Mello explains, this kind of spirituality is "the most practical thing in the whole world" (de Mello, 1990, p. 11). But what is there a need to 'wake up' from? In the Buddhist tradition the notion of 'suffering' or *dukkha* relates to a deep feeling of dissatisfaction, and is something that is considered to be an essential and inescapable part of life. However, in the *Dhammapada* it is stated that along with virtue and wise actions, a disciplined mind is the pathway to happiness (Fronsdal,

2006). Sometimes in Buddhism, the term 'monkey mind' is used to describe the kind of frenetic activity in which the untrained mind may be engaged. It is the discipline of the mind through steady and deliberate mindful attention to a chosen focal point that is the mechanism for attaining this kind of wakeful awareness to the reality of life, to the "loveliness and the beauty of this thing that we call human existence" (de Mello, 1990, p. 5).

Mindfulness in the West

Although mindfulness was originally part of a traditional Buddhist spiritual practice, it has now been widely accepted in an adapted form in the West as a valuable part of therapeutic work. Jon Kabat-Zinn is the person who first introduced mindfulness into mainstream Western society in an attempt to "relieve suffering and catalyse greater compassion" (Kabat-Zinn, 2011, p. 285). He established the Centre for Mindfulness at the University of Massachusetts Medical School in 1979 treating chronic health problems, and went on to devise the programme Mindfulness-Based Stress Reduction (MBSR). In bringing mindfulness into greater visibility, Kabat-Zinn's intention was to make it accessible to anyone overwhelmed with suffering who was also willing to put in the work to practice the exercises of mindfulness daily. His simple and widely accepted definition of mindfulness is, "paying attention in a particular way: on purpose, in the present moment, and non-judgementally" (Kabat-Zinn, 1994, p. 4).

Mindfulness teaches us that we can learn to adjust the way that we respond to the events of life that cause stress by changing the focus of our attention, and the way we use our minds to respond to those events. Engaging in regular mindfulness practice trains us to become more able to notice when we are caught up in thinking about things in an unhelpful way, such as ruminating on the past or anxiously worrying about the future, and simply return our attention to the present moment. By bringing our attention back to the present in this way, we learn to be more aware, to have greater clarity, and to become more accepting of our present reality (Kabat-Zinn, 1994). As we will see later in this chapter, mindfulness has been adapted in various different ways, as it has been introduced into the mainstream as a valid psychological intervention. However there are usually a number of core components that the different practices have in common. According to Germer, Siegel and Fulton (2016), the key components of modern mindfulness practice as used in psychotherapy are: non-conceptual, present-centred, non-judgemental, intentional, participant observation, nonverbal, exploratory and liberating.

Mindfulness in both Eastern traditions and Western applications hold the same basic tenet that it is of physical, emotional and mental benefit to consciously train the mind to be subject to the will and intent of the individual rather than allow the reckless and uncultivated mind to be in control.

Essentially, one of the most valuable aspects of mindfulness in therapeutic work is its capacity to provide a structured way to learn how to step back from and observe inner processes such as thoughts, attitudes and feelings. This kind of self-reflection and knowledge is the starting point for making any changes that may be desired. Through practice, "mindfulness is associated with heightened self-knowledge, a key element of self-regulation" (Brown and Ryan, 2003, p. 822). There is also a growing body of research literature that strongly supports the claims that mindfulness is significantly beneficial in reducing cortisol, which is one of the key hormones secreted during the body's stress response (see for example Carlson, Speca, Patel and Goodey, 2004; Matousek, Dobkin and Pruessner, 2010), especially for those who use mindfulness more frequently (Brand, Holsboer-Trachsler, Naranjo and Schmidt, 2012). Additionally, qualitative reports from participants engaging in a structured mindfulness practice show improvements in perceptions of stress, feelings of burnout, physical and mental health, and better sleep (see for example Christopher et al., 2016). In essence, the benefits of mindfulness are that it helps us to change our relationship with our thoughts, emotions and our bodies. Instead of being so enmeshed with our thoughts that we just accept them as true, mindfulness teaches us to take a step back and just observe them neutrally.

Mindfulness also helps us to tune in to what is going on in our physical body, becoming more aware of its signs and signals, and listening to it instead of disconnecting or overriding its messages. Mindfulness helps us to gain greater awareness of our emotions, noticing the physical sensations and thoughts that might accompany them, and learning to label them descriptively rather than judgementally in terms of 'good' or 'bad'. Mindfulness also helps us to pay attention to things around us in our environment in a more present and accepting way, allowing ourselves to experience fully where we are at any one time. For most people, embracing a mindful way of life requires a shift from a fast-paced, on-to-the-next-thing, anxious-about-the future, habitual way of being, to a more reflective and considered engagement with the world. It definitely takes practice for all of us, as we work on re-wiring our brains and re-training our bodies.

Mindful theory proposes that our lives are a series of current moments that continue to unfold, and that whether we are thinking about the past or the future, we are doing it *now*. Therefore, if we can learn to focus more constructively and consciously on the present moment, this can alleviate the suffering that we can bring upon ourselves by conveying past or future-related anxious, struggling or painful thoughts into our current now. Additionally, we can cause ourselves suffering by allowing our minds to dwell on critical or judgemental thoughts, especially when they are self-directed. Mindfulness teaches the art of systematically noticing and letting go of these kinds of thoughts, acknowledging that we are not what our thoughts tell us that we are; the thoughts are just thoughts and we can choose to hold on to them, or let them go. Not only do we perpetuate suffering from past painful experiences by reliving them over and over in our current unfolding present moments, but we are also in danger of not being fully present for what we are experiencing right now. As Kabat-Zinn encourages us, "we may not only miss what is most valuable in our lives but also fail to realize the richness and the depth of our possibilities for growth and transformation" (1994, p. 4). In other words, instead of believing the critical or judgemental thoughts that we might have about ourselves, we can learn to separate ourselves from our thoughts and observe them in a more detached way. This allows us to not be so caught up with our thoughts, but to find a way to let go of them, at least for the time being.

In terms of seeking to understand what is happening in the brain at a neural level during the practice of mindfulness, there has been an increasing interest in research that involves neuroimaging. The literature indicates that mindfulness affects the medial cortex, amygdala and hippocampus (Marchand, 2014), which in turn influences cognitive patterns, emotion regulation and attention (Marchand, 2012). An example of research in this area is an fMRI (functional MRI) study that investigated how mindfulness affected neural responses to emotional stimuli (Taylor et al., 2011). In this study, both new and experienced mindfulness practitioners were connected to the fMRI scanner at the same time as being asked to view pictures classified as neutral, positive or negative. The experiment was conducted when participants were in either a mindful state or a non-mindful state, and the results compared. The findings indicated that those participants who were more experienced and had a more established mindfulness practice had less emotional reactivity to the stimuli, due to their ability to tolerate their emotional responses better, and also their enhanced awareness of the present moment (ibid.). Another study, again using an fMRI scan, assessed both non-meditators and meditators to assess their performance during a task on the Stroop test. The Stroop test is a well-known test involving words and colours, such as the word 'yellow' being written in a blue colour. The respondent has to say what the word says without being distracted by the colour in which it is written. This test requires quite a bit of concentration and attentional control. The researchers involved in this study concluded that meditation caused the participants to be more accurate in their statements, which indicates that the result of meditation is a greater ability to control impulses and to sustain concentration and attention (Kozasa et al., 2012).

In addition to research focused on the benefits of mindfulness for populations within mental health services, there is also a wealth of literature that indicates its value and benefits for other populations. For example, a qualitative review of 67 workplace mindfulness intervention studies for employees found that the most common reason for introducing a mindfulness programme was to help with staff stress-reduction (more than 80%) (Eby et al., 2019). This is an indication of how widespread the introduction and implementation of mindfulness-based interventions has become.

Mindfulness and 'third wave' therapies
There are a growing number of therapies now that are being introduced into Western psychological therapy work that have their origins in the practice of mindfulness. This is also known as the 'Third Wave'. So if you read anywhere about third wave therapies, it usually means that it is a therapeutic approach that has found benefit in including elements of mindfulness within its practice.

- *Mindfulness-Based Stress Reduction (MBSR)*

MBSR was one of the first secular uses of Mindfulness in the West. Originally it was called the Stress Reduction and Relaxation Program (SR-RP) (Kabat-Zinn, 1982, 1990), and was created for a wide range of people with chronic pain and stress-related disorders. Usually it has been taught as an eight-week group programme, with participants attending for a weekly two-hour session for the duration of the course. There is also usually an additional whole day retreat in many cases at the end of the course (sometimes in silence). The following schedule is a typical example of what might be covered in an eight-week mindfulness-based stress reduction course (although it should be noted that there can be some variation in this programme depending on the instructor, the setting and the participant group):

> Week 1 – Simple awareness: Introduction to the body scan
> Week 2 – Attention and the brain: Introduction to sitting meditation
> Week 3 – Dealing with thoughts: Introduction to yoga
> Week 4 – Stress: Responding vs reacting: The one-minute breathing space
> Week 5 – Dealing with difficult emotions: RAIN (Recognise, Accept, Investigate, Non-identify)
> Week 6 – Mindfulness and communication: Mountain meditation
> Week 7 – Mindfulness and compassion: Loving-kindness meditation
> Week 8 – Conclusion: Developing a practice of your own

Importantly, not only are the participants in MBSR courses expected to practice on their own in between the group sessions, but teachers themselves are required to make mindfulness part of their own daily routines or rituals. Kabat-Zinn is very clear in stating "the quality of MBSR as an intervention is only as good as the MBSR instructor" (2011, p. 281). The regular practice of mindfulness is encouraged for trainers, therapists and teachers as much as for the clients or students they may be working with. It is very much a lifestyle approach, a way of being with oneself, with the world and with others. With the increase of interest in using mindfulness to work with common mental health problems, there has also been a surge in the number of research articles that have been published which demonstrate its efficacy. For example, a meta-analysis of 64 studies that had used MBSR was conducted in 2004. This demonstrated that it was a useful approach in helping a wide range of people with both clinical and non-clinical problems to deal with their difficulties (Grossman et al., 2004). Another study in 2009 which focused specifically on what advantages MBSR may have for healthy people, not just people with mental health difficulties, found that MBSR reduced ruminative thinking and trait anxiety. It also demonstrated that engaging in a course of MBSR increased empathy and self-compassion in its participants (Chiesa and Serretti, 2009).

- *Mindfulness-Based Cognitive Therapy (MBCT)*
The MBCT programme was designed to help people specifically who suffer from depression (Teasdale, Segal and Williams, 1995; Segal, Williams and Teasdale, 2013; Teasdale and Williams, 2013) and is based on Jon Kabat-Zinn's Mindfulness-Based Stress Reduction (MBSR) programme. In 2002 the book Mindfulness-Based Cognitive Therapy (MBCT) for recurrent depression was published (Zindel, Segal, Williams and Teasdale, 2002). The central proposition of this approach is that learning to control attention through mindfulness meditation can help prevent relapses of depressive episodes. The information-processing theory that underlies this hypothesis is that when people experience major depressive episodes, they become more vulnerable to recurrences of new episodes. MBCT incorporates some of the components of cognitive therapy including teaching people that 'thoughts are not facts' and 'I am not my thoughts'.

93

These statements are designed to help people to develop a decentred or detached perspective on their thoughts. The process is to teach people to observe their feelings and thoughts in a non-judgemental way, considering them to be just mental events that tend to come and go, rather than being necessarily accurate reflections of reality (Baer, 2003).

Like the MBSR course, MBCT is a manualised intervention (Segal, Teasdale, Williams and Gemar, 2002) usually taught to groups over eight weekly classes, plus an all-day session that is introduced around week six. Participants are usually also encouraged to practice during the week between sessions and may be given audio files of guided meditations to use at home. The results of numerous research trials indicate that MBCT has been found to be effective in treating patients with several previous episodes of depression. For example, a recent systematic review of 23 MBCT articles relating to its use in treating major depressive disorder indicated that MBCT is effective in creating changes in levels of rumination, worry, compassion and meta-awareness (van der Velden, et al., 2015). Following the building of a considerable evidence base relating to its efficacy, in the UK the National Institute for Health and Clinical Excellence (NICE) has listed MBCT as a recommended treatment for preventing relapse in depression (NICE, 2004; 2009).

- *Mindful Self-Compassion (MSC)*
Compassion is the experience of sensitivity to suffering, together with a desire to alleviate that suffering (Goetz, Keltner and Simon-Thomas, 2010). Learning self-compassion is a process of developing the kind of compassion one may have for others for oneself. To have compassion for others means to first notice that they are suffering, and secondly to feel moved emotionally, to feel sympathy and concern. This creates warmth, a feeling of care, and a desire to help the suffering person in some way. Having compassion also means to offer understanding and kindness to

94

others when they fail or make mistakes, rather than judging them harshly, and is a means to appreciate that suffering, failure, and imperfection is part of the shared human experience. Self-compassion involves having this same attitude towards yourself if you make a mistake or notice something about yourself that you do not like, or when something you are experiencing feels difficult or painful. In Western culture people often tend to confuse self-compassion with self-indulgence or self-pity, which unfortunately can lead to people relating to themselves harshly.

In MSC, or as it is sometimes called Mindfulness Based Compassion (MBC), people are taught that rather than criticising themselves, judging, condemning, ignoring or 'putting up with' the pain, self-compassion is a process of kindly allowing yourself to acknowledge that what you are experiencing is really difficult and asking how you might care for or comfort yourself at that moment. As a result of practicing self-compassion a person may try to make changes to their lifestyle that allows them to be more healthy and happy. These changes, from a compassion-focused perspective are motivated by self-care rather than as an aggressive effort towards self-improvement motivated by not feeling good enough in some way. Self-compassion recognises that as a human being there are difficulties and challenges and painful things that happen in life, and that it is inevitable that situations will arise that cause frustration, that losses will occur, that you will make mistakes and fall short of your ideals. However, this humanity is common to us all, and the more that you gently and compassionately accept this reality in your own life instead of fighting against it, the more you will be able to be kind to yourself. Dr Kristen Neff talks about self-compassion as being kind to ourselves in the way that we would be to a good friend, and explains that it contains the three elements of self-kindness, common humanity and mindfulness (Neff and Germer, 2018):

1. Self-kindness: Understanding not punishment
2. Sense of common humanity: Everybody goes through this
3. Mindfulness: Being aware in the moment in a balanced and clear way

MSC courses have been developed to teach people how to develop this warm-hearted approach to self-care, particularly at times of difficulty, struggle, pain or loss. The development of self-compassion provides emotional strength and resilience that can also help encourage those who engage in MSC courses to be gentle and self-forgiving, taking greater self-care by befriending the self, and ultimately being able to live more authentically. Research indicates that self-compassion is associated with emotional wellbeing, lower levels of anxiety and depression, healthy habits such as diet and exercise, and more satisfying personal relationships. A typical MSC course is likely to include aspects such as these listed below (Neff and Dahm, 2015):

- How to practice mindfulness and self-compassion in daily life
- The science of self-compassion
- How to handle difficult emotions with greater ease
- Learning to motivate yourself with kindness rather than criticism
- How to transform challenging relationships
- Developing tools for managing compassion fatigue
- The art of savouring and self-appreciation
- How to teach self-compassion practices to others

The self-compassion exercises taught in MBC courses are designed to help people bring a self-compassion attitude to themselves in the actual situations in which they are currently struggling. One example is the 'self-compassion break'. This involves bringing to mind a current life struggle, and then experimenting to find a soothing physical expression of compassion, which might be putting one hand over your heart or wrapping your arms around yourself. Then a simple phrase is repeated to yourself that conveys self-compassion: *This is a moment of suffering, suffering is part of life, may I be kind to myself in this moment, may I give myself the compassion I need.'* This is a great technique as it is simple and effective. Although there is little empirical research as yet about the efficacy of MSC programmes, one study by Neff and Germer (2012) demonstrated that participants' self-compassion levels were raised by 43%, and that these gains were still maintained a year later. Another excellent aspect of MSC is the practice of 'savouring'. This involves a particular kind of mindfulness that involves "processes through which people actively derive pleasure and fulfilment in relation to positive experience" (Bryant and Veroff, 2007, p. 2). In other words, where mindfulness involves being in the present moment with a sense of awareness of one's experiences, savouring includes the addition of prolonging the positive aspects of those experiences (Beaumont, 2011). Bryant and Veroff (2007) argued that mindfulness is related to savouring and that people who are dispositionally mindful are more likely to employ mindful attention skills when experiencing positive emotions. As a result of this natural tendency to be more mindfully aware and present pleasant positive experiences, these people tend to score highly on savouring self-report measures (Bryant and Veroff, 2007). Together, mindfulness and savouring are compatible forms of selective attentional focusing that are also argued to increase capacity for greater emotional maturity (Beaumont, 2011).

- *Dialectical Behaviour Therapy (DBT)*

DBT is a type of cognitive-behavioural psychotherapy developed by psychologist Marsha Linehan initially for the treatment of clients with Borderline Personality Disorder (Linehan, 1993, 2018; Linehan et al., 1991). However, since its development in the 1980s its uses have expanded, and it is now used for the treatment of other mental health difficulties, especially where there is emotional distress and/or dysregulation. The theory behind this approach is that some people are more prone to react to situations in an extreme or intense way, especially those situations that arouse emotional responses. This can be particularly problematic in interpersonal relationships with friends, family and work colleagues, as well as strangers in everyday encounters during ordinary life. The goal of DBT is to help clients to create 'a life worth living'. DBT theory suggests that some people's arousal levels in certain situations can increase a lot more quickly than the average person's, and when this happens, they also elevate their arousal to a high level of emotional stimulation, and take a significant amount of time to return to baseline arousal levels. Sometimes this is described as having a very 'thin skin' emotionally and being acutely sensitive to situations that others may not find as reactive. DBT was created as a therapeutic approach to help clients to manage these sudden, intense surges of emotion, and is designed to be primarily skills-based, in order to teach ways to manage these responses. There are three core characteristics of DBT: support, collaboration and cognitive-based. Each of these are described in more detail:

- **Support:** The philosophy of DBT is to encourage clients to identify their strengths so that they can build on them and feel better about themselves and their life
- **Collaboration:** In DBT clients are encouraged to work out problems in their relationships with their therapist, to complete homework assignments, to role-play new ways of interacting with others, and to practice mindfulness and self-soothing skills.
- **Cognitive-based:** DBT also aims to help clients identify thoughts, beliefs and assumptions that they hold that make life more difficult, such as 'I have to be perfect at everything' or 'if I get angry, I'm a terrible person'. It then offers ways to think differently and more self-compassionately in order to make life more bearable

A full DBT programme consists of three core components, which are listed in table 3.2.

Table 3.2: Description of the three core components of a full DBT programme

	Type of intervention/ support	Description
1.	Individual	One-to-one weekly therapy sessions that are aimed at reviewing particularly life-threatening or difficult situations by analysing the components (emotions, thoughts, actions, urges etc.) that lead up to a particular response. In doing so, more helpful alternative ways of responding can be identified
2.	Group	Weekly skills-based training groups where the four key areas of skills training are covered. In the skills groups these relate to the four taught modules, usually over six weeks each, which are: • Mindfulness • Emotion Regulation • Distress Tolerance • Interpersonal Effectiveness
3.	Telephone support	A behaviourally responsive telephone helpline. What is meant by this is that clients have access to a telephone service staffed by one of the therapists in the DBT team. This service operates during the week between sessions and is designed to be used by clients when they experience strong emotional distress and/or urges to self-harm. By telephoning a therapist clients are able to access coaching in how to apply the skills that they have learned in the group setting to the particular situation that they are in at that moment. Behaviourally, support is thus provided during the struggle prior to engaging in a self-harming behaviour (reinforcing help-seeking behaviour), rather than being offered afterwards

The 'dialectic' aspect of DBT refers to the balance that is maintained between two apparently opposite poles, such as good and bad, or kind and selfish. The motto in DBT is that it is not 'either or' but 'both and'. In essence, DBT strives for a balance between acceptance and validation of what currently 'is', whilst at the same time looking for and working towards positive change. In this way it manages to integrate what may otherwise appear to be rather contradictory philosophies ('you are loved the way you are', and also 'you must strive to change'). The way that Marsha Linehan discusses this dialectic is to think of it as practicing and learning to live the Serenity Prayer: accepting the things we cannot change, finding the courage to change what we can, and using our therapists as guides to help us distinguish between the two (Dimeff and Linehan, 2008). In order to achieve this, one of the core principles in DBT is to practice mindfulness. However, in DBT the way that mindfulness is conceptualised and taught in a particular way. The premise of the teaching is that we have 'three minds' – these are emotional mind, rational mind, and wise mind, which are described in more detail in table 3.3, and illustrated in figure 3.1.

Table 3.3: Description of the three states of mind in DBT

State of mind	Description
Emotional Mind	This state is made up of raw emotions or feelings and emotion-driven thoughts. Emotion-driven thoughts are those that occur when in an emotional state
Rational Mind or Reasonable Mind	This state is one of thinking rationally and logically, and seeing reality as it is. Unlike emotional mind where perspective is distorted by the current emotion, rational mind is very pragmatic and unaffected

Wise Mind	In wise mind there is a focus on problem solving. It is based on the input of both emotional mind and rational mind. Wise mind is action-oriented and is the state of mind that aims to be achieved in DBT

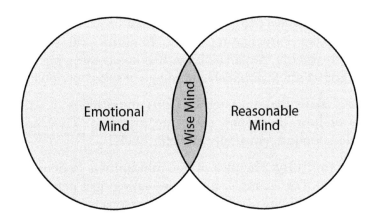

Figure 3.1: The three states of mind in DBT.

The aim of working through a DBT programme is to learn to identify when you are either in emotional mind or reasonable mind, and to find ways to moderate these extremes so as to function more frequently from a place of 'wise mind'. Wise mind incorporates the best aspects of both emotional mind and reasonable mind to make decisions. In the mindfulness skills module, mindfulness is taught using three 'what' skills and three 'how' skills.[iii] The 'what' skills refer to ways of practicing thinking or taking control of your mind; observe, describe and participate:

[iii] It is noted that in more recent adaptations of DBT this distinction is presented slightly differently.

- **Observe:** Observing is the skill of sensing or experiencing something without describing or labelling the experience. It is about just noticing or attending to something
- **Describe:** Describing is the skill of using words to represent what has been observed and labelling it. However, mindful describing involves using words to talk about the 'facts' rather than using labels that may be evaluative
- **Participate:** Participating is the mindful skill of entering wholeheartedly into an activity. It is about throwing yourself into something completely, letting go of self-consciousness

The 'how' skills that are taught in DBT mindfulness refer to the process of how the 'what' skills are practiced. They are one-mindfully, non-judgementally and effectively:

- **One-mindfully:** The idea of one-mindfully is to do one thing at a time. For example, if you are eating, just eat; if you are talking to a friend, just do that. The reasons for this are so that you can give your full attention to what you are doing and also to be completely present
- **Non-judgementally:** taking a non-judgemental stance when practicing mindfulness means not to evaluate anything as good or bad but to accept that it 'just is what it is'
- **Effectively:** This means that you don't 'cut off your nose to spite your face'. In other words not being drawn into or distracted and upset by thinking about how things 'should' or 'ought' to be, but being able to accept things as they are in order to take action in an effective way that will have the best chance of achieving your goals

The following example in table 3.4 shows how these DBT skills might be put into practice. By starting with increasing awareness, the client is taught to notice what he or she is experiencing by just 'observing' (what skill). Next, this is followed by learning to describe what is being observed using neutral factual descriptive

Mindfulness knowledge

Table 3.4: An example of how to implement the DBT 'how' skill of taking a non-judgemental stance

DBT skill used	Action	Description
DBT mindfulness 'what' skills	Observe	I notice that I am feeling sad
	Observe and Describe	I notice that the corners of my mouth are turned down, my jaw muscles are tense, and my eyelids seem heavy. I notice that I am tired and feel like I could cry. I notice that there is an uncomfortable feeling in the pit of my stomach
	Judgement	Sadness is a bad emotion. When I am sad that means that I am bad. Therefore something must be wrong with me because I feel sad
DBT mindfulness 'how' skill	Non-judgemental stance	Sadness is an emotion. It is not good or bad. The fact that I exhibit the symptoms I associate with sadness does not make me a bad person, nor is experiencing the emotion a good or a bad thing. It simply is. Right now, I am experiencing sadness, that is all. It is OK to feel sad
	Possible results	When I judge the sadness, I am more likely to react negatively to it by engaging in destructive behaviour. When I do not judge the sadness, I am more likely to experience the emotion until it dissipates

words, rather than evaluation-laden terms. In the example provided, this awareness and description is followed initially by a judgement about it being wrong to experience the feeling of sadness. This is a very typical reaction for the kinds of clients that

DBT was designed to help, and so learning the 'how' skill of mindful non-judgement is both challenging and rewarding. The example shows how a cognitive reframing of the initial judgement can be used to learn that self-judgement is the characteristically harmful element in this chain of events, rather than the emotion itself. By learning kindness and self-compassion rather than self-criticism and judgement, the client can start to tolerate the difficult emotions and allow them to pass in their own natural timing.

- *Acceptance and Commitment Therapy (ACT)*

ACT is described by its creators as "a behaviour-analytically-based psychotherapy approach that attempts to undermine emotional avoidance and increase the capacity for behaviour change" (Hayes and Wilson, 1994, p. 289). Where a lot of talking therapies may focus on challenging the thoughts and feelings preceding or leading to 'problematic' behaviours, ACT sets its primary goal as seeking to address emotional avoidance. The way that this is achieved is by establishing a mindful awareness of thinking processes as they occur (Hayes et al., 2013). One of the techniques that is taught in ACT is 'defusion' which means to separate out one's self from the thought. A way to achieve this might be as the observer of a thought to thank the mind for offering up whatever thought it was. Other defusion strategies might be to 'watch' a thought come and go as if it were floating past like a leaf on a stream, or to keep repeating a word or phrase so many times that the meaning becomes lost in the sounds. Alternatively, a client might be taught to label the process of thinking; for example using the phrase "*I have noticed that I am having the thought that ...*)" (Hayes et al., 2013). In terms of efficacy of ACT as an intervention, in a meta-analysis of 18 randomised controlled trials comparing ACT with control groups, ACT was found to be "more effective than control conditions across several disorders, but there was no evidence that it was more effective than established treatments" (Powers, Vörding and Emmelkamp, 2009, p. 73).

Mindfulness knowledge

Russ Harris has become known more recently as the person responsible for making ACT more accessible as a therapy to a wider population of practitioners and clients. He describes ACT as a 'mindfulness-based behavioural therapy', and explains it as being a process whereby symptom reduction occurs more as a 'by product' rather than a target of therapy. He argues that "the goal of ACT is to create a rich and meaningful life, while accepting the pain that inevitably goes with it" (Harris, 2006, p. 70). ACT seeks to help clients change their relationship with what have previously been considered to be threatening, painful or unacceptable feelings, thoughts and memories. This is done by focusing on a mindful awareness of those inner experiences in order to develop what is referred to as 'psychological flexibility'. The six core principles of ACT are:

- Defusion
- Acceptance
- Being present
- The observing self
- Values
- Committed action

Some of the techniques to establish defusion have already been discussed. Acceptance has also been touched on in passing as it relates to not struggling against painful or unwanted inner experiences, but 'sitting with' or 'turning towards' as is predicated in traditional mindfulness practice. Being present is also one of the familiar ingredients of any mindfulness approach, as we have noted previously, as is the observing self. In ACT particularly, the observing self is given attention to develop and understand, so that the process of observing thoughts and the activities of defusion can be engaged with. The final two principles listed here are values and committed action, and it is these two, perhaps more than any others that really characterise the uniqueness of the ACT approach. The first four principles relate more directly to the process of learning to accept previously rejected inner or 'private' experiences, whereas the latter two have a focus on making a commitment to engage in action in line with the core values held (Harris, 2019). Typically an ACT practitioner may work with a client to sift through lists of values, often with pre-printed suggestions to aid the client in this process. Gradually these values lists are whittled down to a primary three values. Establishing and acknowledging these core values for the client serves to form a starting point from where all decisions about subsequent action to take will be in accord. Setting goals and taking action towards those goals enables the client to find a place of congruence in their behaviour which is ultimately intended to be more fulfilling.

This section on third wave therapies has highlighted some of the most common therapeutic interventions that have mindfulness as one of their core components. In the case of MBSR, MBCT and MSC, mindfulness is 'front and centre' in the name of the therapy, although as you can see each draw on mindfulness practices in their own unique ways. Whilst DBT and ACT do not have mindfulness in the name, nevertheless they still draw very heavily on mindfulness as a core premise within the approach.

Compassionate mindfulness for trauma

In addition to its original modification in the West for treating stress and depression, mindfulness is now often recommended for use with people who have experienced psychological trauma. Mindfulness involves training the mind to stay in the present moment, 'letting go' of worrying thoughts about the future and ruminations about the past. It also teaches people to be aware of their physical bodies and not so wrapped up in over-thinking. There are a number of benefits of practicing mindfulness that have been identified for individuals who have experienced trauma. These are:

- Decrease in associated depressive symptoms
- Decrease in rumination
- Shift to non-judgemental decentred view of thoughts
- Increased psychological flexibility
- Enhanced emotional regulation
- Decreased avoidance (Brown, Ryan and Creswell, 2007)

However, there are limitations to standard mindfulness exercises in relation to the possibility of triggering further distress for those who have experienced psychological trauma. Trauma is a huge issue in mental and physical healthcare, with vast amounts of money being spent on research into working effectively with people who have experienced trauma. Trauma can be a single incident such as a car accident or it can be over a period of time such as for war veterans, victims of childhood abuse, domestic violence or displacement. As such it is hugely prevalent. It is known that trauma creates stress, and that mindfulness is an effective intervention for reducing stress; therefore, it is logical that mindfulness would be an appropriate resource for reducing anxiety and stress symptoms in those who have been exposed to trauma. However David Treleaven (2018) among others cautions that mindfulness practice can act as a catalyst for PTSD symptoms and traumatic stress reactions, because during practice the person directs their attention to internal experiences that had been previously avoided. Becker-Blease (2017) warns that her students who have themselves experienced trauma, often speak of mental health professionals guiding them in mindfulness techniques for anxiety that are either ineffectual or make their symptoms worse.

With this cautionary message in mind, it is not necessary that mindfulness should be abandoned, but rather that consideration needs to be given to the ways in which mindfulness practice can be adapted to make it trauma-sensitive and trauma-responsive, so that any potential risks may be avoided or minimised (Treleaven, 2018). Additionally, most of the literature to date that has taken account of the need for this adaptation has suggested variations to the way that group programmes are taught in order to make it safer for traumatised people to engage. The difference with the approach of the TIM model is that it is intended to be used primarily in one-to-one interactions. The exercises generally are much shorter and more focused than many mindfulness courses for depression or anxiety, and importantly they are titrated in collaboration with the client to suit their stage of skill development. In a way, TIM can be thought of as a kind of 'personal trainer' approach to helping someone integrate mindfulness practice into their life. In seeking to adapt mindfulness exercises to suit the individual needs of particular clients better who are suffering from the ongoing effects of psychological trauma, a key consideration is to link mindfulness practice very closely to self-compassion.

The three clusters of symptoms of post-traumatic stress disorder (PTSD) are arousal, avoidance, and intrusions. These symptoms are closely related to the fight/flight/freeze stress responses as well as to responses to internal stressors such as self-criticism. It is logical therefore that developing and cultivating self-compassion is likely to be a valuable resource in seeking to calm this threat system. For a traumatised individual, practicing a kinder and more compassionate relationship to themselves has a calming effect on the autonomic system that otherwise may be maintained in a state of hyper-arousal. The commonality between mindfulness and self-compassion is an emphasis on a gradual movement away from resistance towards acknowledging and even embracing emotional pain. Where mindfulness provides a way to turn towards those things that are painful, gradually desensitising them, self-compassion adds an explicit aspect of comfort and warmth to the process. Brought together, mindfulness and self-compassion provide a way of engaging with difficult thoughts, feelings and sensations openly and kindly (Germer and

Neff, 2015). The difference between mindfulness and self-compassion is that where mindfulness tends to focus on the question of curiosity about 'what you are *experiencing*', self-compassion focuses more on the question 'what do you *need?*' For those who have experienced trauma, particularly if it has been over an extended period of time, it may be very difficult for them be able to know what they need or to be kind to themselves. In these cases initially at least it may be necessary for the therapist to keep the questions in mind until the client is able to do so for themselves (Germer and Neff, 2015).

Bessel van der Kolk has stated, "the essence of trauma is feeling godforsaken, cut-off from the human race" (2014, p. 335). In relation to childhood emotional abuse, research has indicated a connection with subsequent low self-compassion, and also that people with low self-compassion experience more emotional distress and are more likely to abuse alcohol or attempt suicide (see for example Vettese, Dyer, Li and Wekerle, 2011). However, developing self-compassion has the potential to improve emotional dysregulation. Research indicates that individuals who have experienced early abuse in their lives and who are also able to develop self-compassion are better able to cope with upsetting events than those who have not developed self-compassion strategies (Vettese et al., 2011). As an example, the results of a pilot study designed to understand the efficacy of compassionate mind training with clients in a hospital day programme who were experiencing shame and self-criticism suggested a significant decrease in levels of shame, depression, feelings of inferiority and self-attacking (Gilbert and Procter, 2006). Self-compassion is also thought to be an important element in protecting against the development of PTSD through the process of decreasing avoidance of emotional discomfort (Germer and Neff, 2015). Thus, for those who have been affected by psychological trauma, it is proposed within the TIM model that mindfulness practices are both adapted and titrated to ensure that they are accessible without triggering adverse reactions, and that an attitude of self-compassion is woven throughout.

Summary

This chapter initially introduced the basic tenets of mindfulness from the Buddhist tradition, explaining how it fits as one of its key principles. In this sense, the spiritual legacy of mindfulness as a practice within a larger framework of principles for 'right living' is honoured. From this starting point, the Westernisation of mindfulness as a beneficial practice that has been introduced into clinical settings to help people to manage a range of psychological difficulties has been outlined. In doing so several 'third wave' psychological interventions have been briefly introduced and described; these are MSBR, MBCT, MSC, DBT and ACT. Finally, a short overview is offered on the need for a tailored adaptation of existing mindfulness-based approaches for people who are experiencing ongoing negative symptoms resulting from psychological trauma. This is contextualised within a self-compassion framework, with an explanation offered as to the need for combining self-compassion with mindfulness practice, especially with this population.

References

Baer, R. A. (2003). Mindfulness training as a clinical intervention: A conceptual and empirical review. *Clinical Psychology: Science and Practice, 10*(2), 125–143.

Beaumont, S. L. (2011). Identity styles and wisdom during emerging adulthood: Relationships with mindfulness and savoring. *Identity: An International Journal of Theory and Research, 11*(2), 155–180.

Becker-Blease, K. A. (2017). As the world becomes trauma-informed, work to do. *Journal of Trauma and Dissociation. 18*(2), 131–138, DOI: 10.1080/15299732.2017.1253401

Brand, S., Holsboer-Trachsler, E., Naranjo, J. R., & Schmidt, S. (2012). Influence of mindfulness practice on cortisol and sleep in long-term and short-term meditators. *Neuropsychobiology, 65*(3), 109–118.

Brown, K. W., & Ryan, R. M. (2003). The benefits of being present: mindfulness and its role in psychological well-being. *Journal of Personality and Social Psychology, 84*(4), 822.

Brown, K. W., Ryan, R. M., & Creswell, J. D. (2007) Mindfulness: Theoretical foundations and evidence for its salutary effects. *Psychological Inquiry, 18*(4), 211–237.

Bryant, F. B., & Veroff, J. (2007). *Savoring: A new model of positive experience.* Mahwah, NJ: Erlbaum.

Carlson, L. E., Speca, M., Patel, K. D., & Goodey, E. (2004). Mindfulness-based stress reduction in relation to quality of life, mood, symptoms of stress and levels of cortisol, dehydroepiandrosterone sulfate (DHEAS) and melatonin in breast and prostate cancer outpatients. *Psychoneuroendocrinology, 29*(4), 448–474.

Chiesa, A., & Serretti, A. (2009). Mindfulness-based stress reduction for stress management in healthy people: A review and meta-analysis. *The Journal of Alternative and Complementary Medicine, 15*(5), 593–600.

Christopher, M. S., Goerling, R. J., Rogers, B. S., Hunsinger, M., Baron, G., Bergman, A. L., & Zava, D. T. (2016). A pilot study evaluating the effectiveness of a mindfulness-based intervention on cortisol awakening response and health outcomes among law enforcement officers. *Journal of Police and Criminal Psychology, 31*(1), 15–28.

de Mello, A. (1990). *Awareness: The perils and opportunities of reality.* London, United Kingdom: Collins Fount.

Dimeff, L. A., & Linehan, M. M. (2008). Dialectical behavior therapy for substance abusers. *Addiction Science & Clinical Practice, 4*(2), 39.

Duerden, T. (2018). *Teaching mindfulness: Potentially traumatising or detraumatising. Teaching mindfulness safely.* Minding the Gaps conference: Brighton, United Kingdom. Retrieved from http://integratedmindfulness.com/mindingthegap2017/

Eby, L. T., Allen, T. D., Conley, K. M., Williamson, R. L., Henderson, T. G., & Mancini, V. S. (2017). Mindfulness-based training interventions for employees: a qualitative review of the literature. *Human Resource Management Review, 29*, 156–178. doi: 10.1016/j.hrmr.2017.03.004

Fronsdal, D. (2006). *The Dhammapada: A new translation of the Buddhist classic with annotations.* Boston, MA: Shambhala Publications.

Germer, C. (2013). Mindfulness: What is it? What does it matter? In C. Germer, R. D. Siegel, & P. R. Fulton (Eds.), *Mindfulness and psychotherapy* (2nd ed., pp. 3–35). London United Kingdom: Guilford Press.

Germer, C. K., & Neff, K. D. (2015). Cultivating self-compassion in trauma survivors. In V. M. Follette, J. Briere, D. Rozelle, J. W. Hopper, & D. I. Rome (Eds.), *Mindfulness-oriented interventions for trauma: Integrating contemplative practices* (pp. 43–58). New York, NY: Guilford Press.

Germer, C., Siegel, R. D., & Fulton, P. R. (Eds.). (2016). *Mindfulness and psychotherapy.* New York, NY: Guilford Press.

Gilbert, P., & Procter, S. (2006). Compassionate mind training for people with high shame and self-criticism: Overview and pilot study of a group therapy approach. *Clinical Psychology & Psychotherapy, 13*(6), 353–379.

Goetz, J. L., Keltner, D., & Simon-Thomas, E. (2010). Compassion: An evolutionary analysis and empirical review. *Psychological Bulletin, 136,* 351–374.

Grossman, P., Niemann, L., Schmidt, S., & Walach, H. (2004). Mindfulness-based stress reduction and health benefits: A meta-analysis. *Journal of Psychosomatic Research, 57*(1), 35–43.

Gunaratana, B. H. (2002). *Mindfulness in plain English: Updated and expanded edition.* Somerville, MA: Wisdom Publications.

Hanh, T. N. (1998). *The heart of the Buddha's teaching: Transforming suffering into peace, joy, and liberation.* New York, NY: Broadway Books.

Hanh, T. N. (2008, June). The Heart of Buddha's teaching. *The Lotus Bud: Magazine of Mindful Living.* Retrieved from http://www.lotusbudsangha.org/downloads/lbs_enews_0806.pdf

Harris, R. (2006). Embracing your demons: An overview of acceptance and commitment therapy. *Psychotherapy in Australia, 12*(4), 70.

Harris, R. (2019). *ACT made simple: An easy-to-read primer on acceptance and commitment therapy* (2nd ed.). Oakland, CA: New Harbinger Publications.

Hayes, S. C., & Wilson, K. G. (1994). Acceptance and commitment therapy: Altering the verbal support for experiential avoidance. *The Behavior Analyst, 17*(2), 289–303.

Hayes, S. C., Levin, M. E., Plumb-Vilardaga, J., Villatte, J. L., & Pistorello, J. (2013). Acceptance and commitment therapy and contextual behavioral science: Examining the progress of a distinctive model of behavioral and cognitive therapy. *Behavior Therapy, 44*(2), 180–198.

Kabat-Zinn, J. (1982). An outpatient program in behavioral medicine for chronic pain patients based on the practice of mindfulness meditation: Theoretical considerations and preliminary results. *General Hospital Psychiatry, 4,* 33–47.

Kabat-Zinn, J. (1990). *Full catastrophe living: Using the wisdom of your body and mind to face stress, pain, and illness.* New York, NY: Delacorte.

Kabat-Zinn, J. (1994). *Wherever you go, there you are: Mindfulness meditation in everyday life.* New York, NY: Hyperion.

Kabat-Zinn, J. (2011). Some reflections on the origins of MBSR, skilful means, and the trouble with maps. *Contemporary Buddhism, 12*(1), 281–306.

Kozasa, E. H., Sato, J. R., Lacerda, S. S., Barreiros, M. A., Radvany, J., Russell, T. A., Sanches, L. G., Mello, L. E., & Amaro E. (2012). Meditation training increases brain efficiency in an attention task. *Neuroimage, 59,* 745–749.

Linehan, M. M. (1993). *Skills training manual for treating borderline personality disorder.* New York, NY: Guilford Press.

Linehan, M. M. (2018). *Cognitive-behavioral treatment of borderline personality disorder.* New York, NY: Guilford Press.

Linehan, M. M., Armstrong, H. E., Suarez, A., Allmon, D., & Heard, H. L. (1991). Cognitive-behavioral treatment of chronically parasuicidal borderline patients. *Archives of General Psychiatry, 48*(12), 1060–1064.

Marchand, W. R. (2012). Mindfulness-based stress reduction, mindfulness-based cognitive therapy, and Zen meditation for depression, anxiety, pain, and psychological distress. *Journal of Psychiatric Practice, 18,* 233–252.

Marchand, W. R. (2014, 28 July). Neural mechanisms of mindfulness and meditation: Evidence from neuroimaging studies. *World Journal of Radiology, 6*(7), 471–479.

Matousek, R. H., Dobkin, P. L., & Pruessner, J. (2010). Cortisol as a marker for improvement in mindfulness-based stress reduction. *Complementary Therapies in Clinical Practice, 16*(1), 13–19.

National Institute of Clinical Excellence (NICE) (2004). *Depression: Management of depression in primary and secondary care*. National Clinical Practice Guidelines, Number 23. London, United Kingdom: HMSO.

National Institute for Clinical Excellence (NICE) (2009). *Depression: The treatment and management of depression in adults (update)*. Clinical Guidelines, CG90. London, United Kingdom: HMSO.

Neff, K. D., & Dahm, K. A. (2015). Self-compassion: What it is, what it does, and how it relates to mindfulness. In M. Robinson, B. Meier, & B. Ostafin (Eds.), *Mindfulness and self-regulation* (pp. 121–139). New York, NY: Springer.

Neff, K. D., & Germer, C. K. (2012). A pilot study and randomized controlled trial of the Mindful Self-Compassion Program. *Journal of Clinical Psychology, 69*(1), 28–44.

Neff, K., & Germer, C. (2018). *The mindful self-compassion workbook: A proven way to accept yourself, build inner strength, and thrive*. London, United Kingdom: Guilford Press.

Powers, M. B., Vörding, Z. V. S., & Emmelkamp, P. M. (2009). Acceptance and commitment therapy: A meta-analytic review. *Psychotherapy and Psychosomatics, 78*(2), 73–80.

Segal, Z. V., Teasdale, J. D., Williams, J. M., & Gemar, M. C. (2002). The mindfulness-based cognitive therapy adherence scale: Inter-rater reliability, adherence to protocol and treatment distinctiveness. *Clinical Psychology and Psychotherapy, 9*(2), 131–138.

Segal, Z. V., Williams, J. M., & Teasdale, J. D. (2013). *Mindfulness-based cognitive therapy for depression* (2nd ed.). London, United Kingdom: Guilford Press.

Taylor, V. A., Grant, J., Daneault, V., Scavone, G., Breton, E., Roffe-Vidal, S., Courtemanche, J., Lavarenne, A. S., & Beauregard, M. (2011). Impact of mindfulness on the neural responses to emotional pictures in experienced and beginner meditators. *Neuroimage, 57*, 1524–1533.

Mindfulness knowledge

Teasdale, J. D., Segal, Z., & Williams, J. M. G. (1995). How does cognitive therapy prevent depressive relapse and why should attentional control (mindfulness) training help? *Behaviour Research and Therapy, 33*(1), 25–39.

Teasdale, J. D., & Williams, J. M. G. (2013). *Mindful way workbook: An 8-week program to free yourself from depression and emotional distress.* London, United Kingdom: Guilford Press.

Treleaven, D. A. (2018). *Trauma-sensitive mindfulness: Practices for safe and transformative healing.* New York, NY: W. W. Norton & Company.

van der Kolk, B. (2014). *The body keeps the score: Mind, brain and body in the transformation of trauma.* London, United Kingdom: Penguin.

van der Velden, A. M., Kuyken, W., Wattar, U., Crane, C., Pallesen, K. J., Dahlgaard, J., Fjorback, L. O., & Piet, J. (2015). A systematic review of mechanisms of change in mindfulness-based cognitive therapy in the treatment of recurrent major depressive disorder. *Clinical Psychology Review, 37*, 26–39.

Vettese, L. C., Dyer, C. E., Li, W. L., & Wekerle, C. (2011). Does self-compassion mitigate the association between childhood maltreatment and later emotion regulation difficulties? A preliminary investigation. *International Journal of Mental Health and Addiction, 9*(5), 480.

Yang, L., & Willis, J. (2017). *Awakening together: The spiritual practice of inclusivity and community.* Somerville, MA: Wisdom Publications.

Zindel V., Segal, J., Williams, M. G., & Teasdale, J. D. (2002). *Mindfulness-based cognitive therapy for depression: A new approach to preventing relapse.* New York, NY: Guilford Press.

CHAPTER FOUR
PERSONAL PRACTICE OF MINDFULNESS
AND SELF-COMPASSION

Chapter contents
• Self-care: mental, emotional, physical, spiritual, relational • Using mindfulness for self-care • Curiosity • Commitment • The two arrows • Mindfulness and loving kindness • Developing self-compassion • Summary

The focus of this chapter is to think first of all about your own self-care. The requirement in TIM for the facilitator to have a mindfulness practice of their own is not just so that you can fully embody what you are teaching, but also so that you can benefit from the significant advantages of having your own mindfulness practice for your own wellbeing. It is so important to think first about your own health, physically, mentally, emotionally and spiritually before and during caring for others. You can only give from your own full reservoir, and if that starts to get dangerously low, you and those that you are seeking to help will suffer as a result. It is my desire that you find a way to love and accept yourself, and to treat yourself well, and to use mindfulness as a gentle wonderful practice to support that journey in your own life. In chapter one (table 1.1) the full specification for learning requirements relating to the seven TIM characteristics was provided. Table 4.1 is a duplicate of the section of that table that relates to Personal practice of mindfulness and self-compassion, and is provided here as a reminder for pedagogical purposes. This chapter explicates in more detail the descriptive elements that relate specifically to this characteristic.

Table 4.1: Trauma-Informed Mindfulness characteristic 3. 'Personal practice of mindfulness and self-compassion' learning aims

	TIM characteristic	Description
3.	Personal practice of mindfulness and self-compassion	• To appreciate the importance of a personal ongoing mindfulness practice • To engage in regular personal mindfulness practice for self-care and awareness building, and to manage the stress of working with traumatised individuals • To utilise personal self-compassion exercises for self-care and development • To draw on this experience reflexively to inform training with others

Self-care

It is extremely important to look after yourself when you are involved in any kind of work that brings you into contact with people who have experienced trauma in their lives. As someone who has chosen the profession that you have, there is a very strong likelihood that you have the personal qualities of being caring and giving and considerate of the needs of others before your own. Such 'selflessness' is celebrated in society as being morally desirable, to the point that not putting others first is considered 'selfish' and therefore accountable. However, self-care is not about being selfish in a morally negative way, but is about loving yourself as much as you love others. This can be a very difficult lesson for many people to accept, as the idea of self-love is often not so much a choice as a matter of not being *able* to love one's self. There is a big difference between loving yourself wholly and fully for who and what you are, and choosing to look after someone else's needs before your own; and having a very low opinion of yourself, which propels you to need to care for others before yourself.

 Pause and consider how you really feel about yourself. Ask yourself completely and honestly whether you can say that you love and accept yourself.

If you are still struggling to think about loving and accepting yourself, at least think about how you could make sure that you are well enough to care for someone else. The primary rule of first aid is to ensure that you as the helper or rescuer are safe enough, and are not putting yourself in danger and risking adding another casualty to the scene. With that in mind, I have separated the components of self-care into five domains: physical, mental, emotional, spiritual and relational. It is not the case that these are actual discrete categories, as they are completely interconnected. However, for the purposes of clarity I have separated them out, and illustrated these domains in the five-pointed star in figure 4.1.

Physical self-care
Physical self-care simply relates to maintaining your physical wellbeing by looking after your body. This includes reflecting on what you put into your body and what you do with it. In terms of what you put into it, there is some truth in the saying 'you are what you eat'. There is no need to be fanatical, but following the basic rules of good nourishment and avoiding consuming things that add too many toxins to your body such as excess sugar, caffeine, alcohol and drugs will go a long way to keeping you physically well. There are many studies that show very strong evidence of the

Personal practice of mindfulness and self-compassion

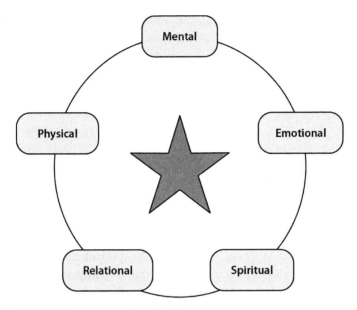

Figure 4.1: The five categories of self-care

brain-body connection. Keeping your body healthy will also help your thoughts and emotions to stay more balanced. In addition to eating and drinking sensibly, getting plenty of rest and sufficient exercise is also what our bodies are designed for, so that they can restore and re-energise. It is amazing how easy it is to lose sight of maintaining good physical health, but how incredibly beneficial it is to you as a whole person to put in place simple ways to keep your body happy and healthy.

Mental self-care
Mental self-care could relate to a number of different things, but in general terms it refers to being your own boss in terms of being able to take charge of what your mind gets up to. Perhaps ask yourself whether your mind is the mental equivalent of a couch potato, just idly allowing input from any source that passes by, or

are you deliberately making good choices about what you feed your mind on. As the computer metaphor states, 'junk in, junk out'; whatever we input into our minds is the raw material for our thoughts and beliefs and ideas. Research shows that 'mind wandering' is the brain's default mode (Raichle et al., 2001; Buckner, Andrews-Hanna and Schacter, 2008). However, the problem is that "a wandering mind is an unhappy mind" (Killingsworth and Gilbert, 2010, p. 932). Although wandering might be the default, that does not mean we have no control, in fact the opposite is true; we have the ability to take charge of our couch potato mind, and train it to think thoughts that will be for our benefit. Physically, mentally, emotionally and in all ways, being able to take care of our minds will enhance our wellbeing in every other area. As a would-be or existing mindfulness facilitator, using mindfulness practices is an excellent way to take charge of this amazingly powerful part of our human make-up. There is an indigenous Indian saying about the mind being like two dogs fighting; there is one part that is kind and thoughtful, and one that is full of anger and destruction. When a young brave approached a wise elder to share with him his struggles with these two parts of himself that felt as though they were at war, he asked his elder which one would eventually win. The wise elder replied "the one that you feed". This is simple, but profound; the thoughts that we dwell on and 'feed' are those that will take root and become hardened beliefs; so let us choose to feed the good ones.

Emotional self-care
In terms of emotional self-care, this is a category of the self that we know to be real, and that we experience daily. However, how do we 'take care' of this aspect of ourselves? A good starting point is to notice. It is a really good practice to start to notice as you go about your day what your emotions are, whether you feel sad or depressed, or anxious or fearful, or happy or expectant. In a lazy

shorthand way, often people simply label their emotions as 'good' or 'bad'. However, if you take a bit of time to be more curious, using mindfulness to 'turn towards' your emotions, you will learn to describe them more accurately. When you learn to differentiate between emotions, you will learn a lot about yourself. You may be jealous rather than angry, or fearful instead of frustrated, or anxious instead of impatient. It is worth looking at your emotions more closely, and as TIM advocates, learn to lean into, to turn towards them so that you find out more about emotions that at first seem prickly or uncomfortable or unwanted. See if you can stay with the feeling, using curiosity to explore where it is in your body, and non-judgement to just allow it to 'be'. Emotional self-care then uses the information you gather to do something about situations where you feel compromised or unhappy. You may be able to choose to do something differently once you acknowledge how you are really feeling.

Spiritual self-care
We are all spiritual as well as physical beings, and so it is just as important to give some time and attention to our spiritual wellbeing. I am using the term 'spirituality' in the widest sense, so that you can relate to this concept in the way that feels most comfortable and meaningful to you. It might be that you already have religious practices in which you engage that support your wellbeing, your sense of hope and security, and this will greatly enhance your resilience in the face of difficult life circumstances. Or you may engage in non-religious spiritual practices such as meditation and ritual. Whatever it is that you do, it is often the meaning behind it that is what gives you a deep sense of purpose and connectedness that is a vitally important aspect of good health and wellbeing. In your spiritual practice you may go within to explore deeper areas of your spiritual self, as well as looking outwards to consider more existentially the meaning of existence

and our relationships with one another. Either way, meaning, contemplation and being true to your core values will help you to feel that your work has purpose and is therefore more satisfying.

Relational self-care
In the literature on resilience, the primacy of maintaining healthy relationships with others in your social and familial network is highlighted as being extremely valuable as a buffer against the stresses and strains of life. In this section on self-care, the underlying premise is that as you attend to maintaining yourself in a good healthy state, you will be more resilient to the challenges of helping people who have experienced trauma. In addition, many people drawn into professions to help others may themselves have been through similar experiences, and that is what draws and motivates them to help others in similar plight. With this in mind, there is all the more reason to look after yourself, as there may be deep-rooted scars and wounds that can be re-opened during your work in professional practice. Relational self-care starts by having respect for yourself, so that you have healthy boundaries in terms of what you will and will not tolerate from other people. Without a healthy sense of self-worth you are vulnerable to being bullied and abused by others. So, in order to have good relational self-care, you need to first know what is appropriate in relationships and develop the self-belief that you are worth other people treating you with thoughtfulness and respect. When you believe this, it will be a lot easier to make sure that the relationships that you do have in your life are beneficial, rewarding and provide you with the support and connectedness that we all need.

 Choosing to commit to practices that enhance and promote self-care is not selfish, but is a sign of self-acceptance, self-value and eventually self-love. This means that when you support others, you do so from a place of strength not weakness, and you do it for their best interest, not to make yourself feel better.

Using mindfulness for self-care

It is well known in the literature that professionals working in the field of mental health are at a high risk of compassion fatigue, burnout or vicarious trauma (Baker, 2003). Healthcare professionals may be good at advising their patients and clients about the benefits of self-care such as relaxation, good sleep and exercise, but many do not extend adequate care to themselves (Bickley, 1998). Thus, the onus is on professionals working in healthcare to take the initiative in making self-care practices part of their daily lives. Regularly using mindfulness practices can increase self-esteem (Brown and Ryan, 2003) and also help those who practice this to engage less with self-critical thoughts (Pepping, O'Donovan and Davis, 2013). One argument to encourage the use of mindfulness is that training programmes should have self-care experiential teaching as part of the curriculum, so as to ensure the self-care message is embedded at an early career stage. Student involvement in MBSR programmes is one way that has been shown to help in reducing stress in health professions such as nursing and medicine (Bruce et al., 2002). Similarly, MBSR has been integrated into some student counselling training to good effect, with students reporting positive changes and a desire to integrate mindfulness into their future profession (Newsome et al., 2006). There may be opportunities either to attend an MBSR course local to where you are based, or if you are involved in education delivery, to find ways to integrate group-based mindfulness programmes into the curriculum.

As an ongoing practice, however, the continued use of mindfulness for stress reduction and improvement in concentration and positive decision-making will necessarily need to become a more routine part of your daily lifestyle to maintain its efficacy. It may be that you are able to carve out regular time for focused sitting or walking meditation where you can spend half an hour or an hour focusing on the breath and allowing your mind to settle. This would be referred to as 'focused attention' type of mindfulness practice. As a form of meditation, there are two broad approaches that can be used in mindfulness practice: 'focused attention' and 'open monitoring' (Lutz et al., 2008). Often someone new to practicing meditation might find the 'focused attention' approach the best starting point to help direct and develop their skills in controlling their attention (Malinowski, 2013). However, it is often then possible to move on to the kind of mindfulness practice that can be incorporated into everyday life by developing a moment-by-moment awareness of surroundings and sensations that come into focus in one's immediate awareness (ibid.). In addition to, or perhaps instead of, using 'focused attention' mindfulness meditation, another way to incorporate mindfulness in a beneficial way into your lifestyle is through the 'open monitoring' form of mindfulness practice. In this respect, mindfulness becomes something that can be tailored to suit your own particular pressures, demands and time commitments. Utilising this kind of mindfulness practice is not onerous as it does not require setting aside special time each day for focused practice. However, it does require remembering to do it, which is the first challenge in the early stages. With regular practice though, it can begin to become more routine.

Another way to think about the 'open monitoring' form of mindfulness is to become more aware of the everyday ordinary things in life. This distinguishes it from formal 'focused attention' mindfulness practices that involve deliberately setting time aside in the day for mindfulness meditation. Open monitoring mindfulness is something that you can just introduce moment by moment as you go through your day, heightening your awareness of, and sensitivity to, the details of what you can see, hear, taste, feel and smell. The way that this becomes a fun and enjoyable process is by keeping an attitude of curiosity. This is not a task, it is an exploration of life, a new way of seeing the world and experiencing it, as if you had just switched to high definition on your TV. To help us become more alert and present in every moment of our lives, we can intentionally bring this attitude of curiosity to anything that we are doing. Open monitoring mindfulness is especially suited to the mundane, everyday activities like breathing, walking, driving, eating and talking that we so often can do on 'automatic pilot'. By setting your intention to bring your awareness to these everyday activities you will find that it gradually becomes more effortless to be mindful, and you will spontaneously become more aware of the details of life around you without even trying during the day.

Curiosity

It is through the process of being genuinely curious and interested in whatever we experience, that we engage with it in a deeper way. In particular, curiosity focuses our attention on the present moment, where we can be "fully aware and receptive to whatever exists and might happen" (Kashdan and Silvia, 2009, p. 368). As Foucault stated, curiosity "evokes the care one takes of what exists and what might exist" (Foucault, 1988, p. 328). Curiosity is by definition 'approach-oriented', and is a motivational state that is closely connected with the idea of exploration. By having an attitude of curiosity and exploration we learn new things, and build our knowledge by learning to think in new ways. When we are being curious, we are not being controlled by pressures to conform to what we should or should not do, but are simply exploring things for their own sake (Kashdan and Silvia, 2009). Some authors even argue that curiosity can also be a way of contesting the written and unwritten rules about how we are meant to respond or act in certain situations (Phillips, 2014). Curiosity creates opportunities to experience and discover new things about what we would normally think of as simply mundane or taken for granted. We can intentionally bring this attitude of curiosity to anything that we are doing. Some of the simple everyday things about which we can begin to foster a newfound sense of curiosity might be the bubbles in the washing up or bath water, the subtle colours and textures in a piece of fruit, the way that the light casts interesting shadows on the ground or walls, or the way that the clouds move and shape-shift in the sky. By re-engaging with what has become overly familiar and un-note-worthy, we can retrain ourselves to regain that innate curiosity. Kashdan and Silvia (2009) argue that "people who are regularly curious and willing to embrace the novelty, uncertainty, and challenges … are at an advantage in creating a fulfilling existence compared with their less curious peers" (2009, p. 367). By deliberately giving attention to seemingly mundane experiences, and challenging our own assumptions, curiosity can be a gateway towards greater wellbeing (Phillips, 2014).

Stop and take a moment to be curious about something close to you where you are now that is very familiar to you. When you look at it again with deliberate curiosity what do you notice?

Another exercise that you can use to help you start to become more mindful of ordinary things is to focus on your breath. As you allow your awareness and attention to focus on your breath, notice the way that your body feels. Notice where you can feel your breath in your body and see if you can notice it in your chest and abdomen, perhaps in your nostrils as you breathe in and out. Simply notice the movement that you feel. Notice the little pause between breathing in and out and that exact moment as it turns around. You can follow each breath from when it first starts as you breathe in and follow it all the way around until the end of the out breath. Take an interest and curiosity in each breath. Be aware of its texture, its temperature (perhaps cooler on the in-breath and warmer on the outbreath), and its rhythm. Every time your mind wanders gently, bring your attention back to being interested in your breath again and refocus your awareness. Notice what happens as you start to take a genuine interest in your breath.

Commitment

As someone either using mindfulness for your own benefit or as someone seeking to incorporate mindfulness into your work to help others, it is good practice to make a commitment to engage in mindfulness practice regularly. There are a number of activities listed below that are designed to help you make a start on using mindfulness in the 'open monitoring' way that can become a regular part of your everyday informal mindfulness. It can also be helpful for you to include your experiences of your mindfulness practice in a reflective journal. You may try just some suggested activities in table 4.2, or maybe all of them, but whichever you choose remember to bring an attitude of gentle curiosity to whatever you do. As well as the ones listed there are many that you can create on your own.

Table 4.2: Suggested ideas for incorporating open monitoring mindfulness into your everyday life (overleaf)

Trauma-Informed Mindfulness

1.	In the morning when you wake up, before you get out of bed, just notice how your body feels. You can stretch or move, and notice how the bed feels, the temperature, the texture of the bedding. Notice your skin, your muscles and your breathing
2.	During the day, take a moment to 'check in' with your body. In particular, notice the points of physical contact between you and your surroundings, such as the feeling of your feet on the floor, your back leaning against the chair, or your arms resting on your desk
3.	Throughout the day, take a few moments to bring your attention to your breathing. You can use a mindfulness app or set your own timer to remind yourself to bring your awareness back to being present, and reconnecting with your breath. For a couple of minutes just be aware of it coming in and going out, and the sensations in your body
4.	As you move through your day, take time to tune into and notice the particular sounds around you such as the sound of the wind or rain, the sound of birds singing or an aeroplane overhead, traffic outside, or the sound of a clock or the heating system. Just tune into them with a curiosity and spend a few moments focusing your awareness on them before you carry on with what you were doing or thinking
5.	Whenever you eat or drink something, take a moment to really connect with it. Pause and notice how your body feels, whether you are hungry or thirsty. As you eat or drink, really connect with the sensory experience, being curious about the taste, the smell, the texture. Notice when you chew what happens, and when you experience the urge to swallow
6.	As you walk or stand, become aware of how your body is positioned, how your posture is, where your weight is distributed, and how you are using the space you are occupying. Feel the movement of each part of your body if you are walking, and notice if you are rushing. Bring your awareness back to each individual step that you take

7.	Be aware of any points of tension or tightness in your body during the day. You can briefly scan your body and become aware of your neck, shoulders, stomach, jaw, hands and feet. If you find tension anywhere allow yourself to let go on each out breath
8.	Bring your awareness to noticing the way that you perform your habitual daily activities such as brushing your teeth, styling your hair, putting on your clothes, having a shower, washing the dishes, making a drink. Bring curiosity and awareness to each activity and see what you notice
9.	As you get ready to go to sleep at night, bring your attention to your body and your breathing. In particular, scan your body for any tension and let it go, noticing how the bed supports your whole body

The two arrows

One of the simple underlying truths of mindfulness is that there is always pain in life. Pain is part of life, because we love and we care, so losses and bereavements for example, are painful and common to everyone. However, mindfulness helps us to see that the way that we react to these events can, if we let it, create even more suffering. An analogy of the two arrows is sometimes used to explain this: the first arrow is the pain that we experience from things that happen to us as we go through our lives, and these are the things that are common to humankind. The second arrow, however, is not one that is shot at us, but one that we choose to pick up from the ground and proceed to stab ourselves with. The second arrow is when we resist the initial pain and struggle to search for an explanation about why it has happened. This mental resistance is born from a mistaken belief that understanding the pain of the first arrow will somehow offer relief.

1. Take a minute to jot down some of the 'first arrow' things that you have experienced. Perhaps you were made redundant or had an accident or a relationship break-up.

2. Next consider some of the 'second arrow' responses that you had to those experiences. Perhaps you blamed yourself for what happened, or let yourself think that you must be useless and not worth anyone wanting to be with anyway?

3. These are all really common 'second arrow' responses to the painful events that we all experience in life. Think for a minute about how much additional suffering you have brought upon yourself by engaging in those painful second arrow responses, and perhaps whether you can let some of them go.

The Buddhist teaching is that there is no relief from the first arrow pain, and searching for an explanation does not make it better. As we beat ourselves up, we might admonish ourselves for not getting out of the way, for not seeing the first arrow and ducking, or for being weak and pathetic because we feel the pain of the first arrow. In this act of using the second arrow against ourselves, we are adding another layer of pain to the original pain, and creating further suffering. It is this extra layer of suffering that we bring upon ourselves. However, the answer in mindfulness is to 'let go' of resistance and struggle against the first arrow. Mindfulness argues not to punish yourself further, but encourages kindness and self-compassion, and by helping to let go of those negative judgements.

Bhikkhu (1997) states:

> when touched with a feeling of pain, the uninstructed run-of-the-mill person sorrows, grieves, and laments, beats his breast, becomes

distraught. So he feels two pains, physical and mental. Just as if they were to shoot a man with an arrow and, right afterward, were to shoot him with another one, so that he would feel the pains of two arrows.

The words 'uninstructed' and 'run-of-the-mill' in this quotation from Buddhist teaching indicate clearly the value placed on making an effort to enforce structure or control over the mind. Without giving in to thoughts that take over and exaggerate the problems of the first arrow, the person is less likely to continue in suffering, but will able to ride out the waves of the first arrow pain until it gradually subsides.

Mindfulness and loving kindness
A typical component of mindfulness programmes that focuses on developing compassion is the 'loving-kindness' exercise. This is a meditation that involves bringing to mind in turn, an acquaintance, someone you know very well, and someone you dislike, and to intentionally 'send' thoughts and feelings of loving kindness towards them. My mindfulness teacher Suryacitta Malcolm Smith taught this exercise in the following way (The Happy Buddha, 2011) by starting with the self:

1) After settling into a meditation focusing on the breath, focus on your heart area and say to yourself the phrase '*may I be happy, may I be well'*. Notice any responses, such as self-criticism, and kindly bring your attention back to the heart. After a few minutes allow yourself to bring the phrase to mind again and relax into noticing your breathing.

2) When you feel ready, bring to mind a good friend, and repeat the same exercise saying '*may you be happy, may you be well'*. Again, keep your focus on the heart area, and just notice what comes up for you whatever that might be. After a few

minutes allow the friend to step aside and bring your awareness gently back to your breath.

3) Next, bring to mind a 'neutral' person, someone you do not really know very well, but see during your day, perhaps a bus driver or receptionist. Use the loving-kindness phrase again with them in mind, *'may you be happy, may you be well'*. Be aware of what you notice about your reactions without judgement. Bring your awareness back to your breath and your heart area, and let that person step aside.

4) Repeat the process, this time bringing to mind a person that you find difficult, again wishing them well with the phrase, *'may you be happy, may you be well'*. Allow your attention to dwell in the heart area, and notice any thoughts or emotional response with kindness and non-attachment. Then let them step aside and focus again on your breath.

5) The final step is to bring together all of the people that have just been involved in your loving-kindness meditation, yourself, your friend, a neutral person and someone you find difficult. As they are gathered together as a group, gently lean into the phrase again *'may you be happy, may you be well'*. Allow yourself a few minutes to notice your reactions kindly and gently and then, as you focus back on your breath, let go of your images or impressions of the people you called to mind.

Interestingly, perhaps like many others, I found that starting with the self was quite tricky. I was fairly well practiced at that time in thinking compassionate thoughts towards others, but had never used an exercise like this to think about myself before. It may be that you prefer to adapt this exercise and do fewer of the components in one sitting, and perhaps start with someone else, and end with yourself. See what works for you. What this exercise does reveal is not just how we feel about others, but how we feel about ourselves. In the introduction to Suryacitta's second book on mindfulness and self-compassion, he states, "there is a saying in the mindfulness tradition – how we relate to one thing is how we relate to everything. When we are compassionate towards ourselves, with sympathy for our own shortcomings and pain, we cannot be anything else to other people" (The Happy Buddha, 2015, p. 8). I believe that this is true, and again, this serves as another motivator for us to find ways to develop a more self-compassionate attitude towards ourselves.

Developing self-compassion
An interesting distinction in the literature has been made between 'avoidance' behaviour and 'approach' behaviour, with avoidance being defined as motivated by, and directed towards, an aversive possibility, and approach behaviour being directed towards a positive possibility (Elliot, 1999). The role that self-compassion plays in supporting beneficial approach behaviour is that those who practice it are better able to cope adaptively with situations that might invoke a feeling of a fear of failure (Hjeltnes et al., 2015). The fear of failure by definition has a self-critical aspect to it; the focus is on one's own short-comings or flaws. However, if we can be less harsh and critical of ourselves, and increase our self-compassion, we can engage more often in 'approach' behaviour. The following section describes a valuable exercise that can be used to help yourself or a client identify areas where they may be less self-compassionate, so that you or they can begin to work on those areas. The key difference between being self-compassionate and being mindful is that the focus of mindfulness is to bring awareness to what we are *experiencing*. The subtle difference in self-compassion work, that follows on very nicely from bringing awareness to experience is to think about what we *need* to help us to feel better. In effect, the self-compassion component is the practical next step that looks for the answer to what can be done to

help. This process of building on mindful awareness to self-compassionate action is illustrated in figure 4.2.

As this figure shows, there is a clear relationship between mindful awareness and the need for a self-compassionate response to that increased self-awareness. Similarly, there is a value in maintaining a mindful 'approach' attitude towards what we experience because, "we need to be able to turn towards and acknowledge when we are suffering, to 'be' with our pain long enough to respond with care and kindness" (Neff and Germer, 2018, p. 11). However, the risk of increasing self-awareness is always that we shine a light on ourselves and become even more acutely aware of what we see as our faults and failings. Without simultaneously engaging the skills of non-judgement, self-compassion and letting go, we could potentially get sucked into the vortex of a negative thought spiral. This is a good moment to refer back to the TIM attitude of courage that was introduced in chapter one. It takes a certain amount of courage to be willing to 'turn towards' the pain or unwanted aspects that we see in ourselves, and to stay with that challenge long enough to respond to it with self-compassion and kindness.

A useful framework for thinking about the need for courage is Johari's window (Luft and Ingham, 1955). This is a model that shows how there are some things about ourselves that only we know but others do not, some things that we know about ourselves and others also know, some things that others know about us about which we are not aware, and finally some things that neither we know about ourselves, nor do other people. I find this to be a helpful model to use when thinking about the process of developing mindful self-awareness, as inevitably in mindful self-reflection we become more aware of things we already knew about ourselves (and potentially feel negatively about), as well as potentially starting to see areas about ourselves that were previously hidden

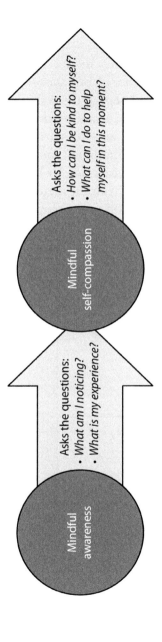

Figure 4.2: Building from mindful awareness to self-compassionate action

to our conscious awareness. An illustration of Johari's window is provided in figure 4.3.

The 'hidden self' in this model refers to those aspects of ourselves that we are aware of but choose not to make known to others. A motivation for keeping these things hidden may be that we feel ashamed or embarrassed by these aspects of ourselves. During mindful meditation we may start to think more about these things, and doing so with kindness and compassion will save us from either moving into avoidance, or becoming self-critical and depressed. As you can see from the arrows that have been added, there is an expected direction of developmental travel in terms of

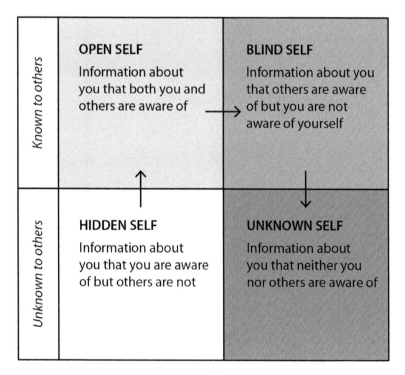

Figure 4.3: Johari's window (Luft and Ingham, 1955) (arrows added)

awareness building. The square that relates to the hidden self may always contain hidden information that a person does not want to share with others, and this is often appropriate. Using Johari's window as a reflective tool, however, it is possible to consider these choices, how they are made, and whether any adaptations might be helpful either to disclose more or less of the hidden self to others.

The 'blind self' box in Johari's window is also known as the 'blind spot'. This model is sometimes used to think about ways to enhance self-awareness of what is consciously available to others but not to the self, and also to enhance self-awareness of the unconscious part of the self (the unknown self). One of the key transitions as it applies to mindfulness is that between the 'open self' and the 'blind self'. There may be many reasons why someone has aspects of the self that unconsciously they have made inaccessible to themselves, and mindfulness is an excellent tool for being able to draw attention to that blind spot, and bring the information within it into the open self area. Thus, Johari's window might be a tool that you find useful for your own reflections about how mindfulness practice may encourage and facilitate your own conscious growth in better self-awareness. You may use it alone or with a trusted supervisor as an aid to your own personal development. A primary reason that Johari's window is being discussed in this section is that bringing awareness to hidden aspects of the self and previously unknown aspects of the self takes a degree of courage. Happily, there may be extremely positive qualities to be found there. Equally however, there may be aspects of the self that are hidden and are less easy to accept when they move into conscious awareness. Either way, awareness at least allows the possibility of arriving at a point of honest knowledge of what is. The need for self-compassion in undergoing this process should now be evident, and as the figure in 4.2

indicated, self-compassion asks the questions, *'how can I be kind to myself?'* and *'what can I do to help myself in this moment?'*

In my experience, asking these self-compassionate questions takes practice, as many people start asking rather unhelpful questions at this point of awareness such as 'why me?' and 'what did I do wrong?' So perhaps even writing the self-compassionate questions on small cards, Post-it™ notes or in your diary or phone can act as reminders not to get on to the 'why me?' spiral, but to ask more solution-focused questions about how to help yourself. One easily implemented activity that could be the answer to the self-compassionate question *'what can I do to help myself in this moment?'* is the self-compassion break. When giving yourself a self-compassion break you can cross your arms or hands over your chest or heart and take a deep breath, and say out loud or in your head (depending where you are) *'This is a moment of suffering, suffering is part of life, may I be kind to myself in this moment, may I give myself the compassion I need.'* This is a simple and effective technique that validates your moment of struggle and suffering without self-blame, and reminds you that your intention is to be kind and compassionate with yourself in your pain.

A more structured exercise in compassion that you can use for yourself in the first instance, and can also be very helpful for using with clients is the compassion circles (adapted from Lowens, 2015). Figure 4.4 shows the numbering used from 1–10, and the six segments that represent aspects of compassion that are to be assessed: sensitivity, sympathy, non-judgement, empathy, distress tolerance and wellbeing. This exercise can be used first to ask yourself (or your client) how you rate yourself from 1–10 on each of the six dimensions, using an imaginary scenario as reference point. This will assess where you stand at present in relation to 'other-compassion'. The exercise can then be repeated using yourself (or for the client to use themselves), as the object of inquiry, and again measure from 1–10 on each dimension where you stand in relation to self-compassion. Some examples of scenarios that you might use for the 'other-compassion' and 'self-compassion' exercises are provided in tables 4.3 and 4.5 (see pp. 140 and 142).

- **Step one**
Choose either one of the examples from the list of scenarios suggested for the other-compassion exercise in table 4.3 or one of your own. Next, go to the six compassion rating statements that

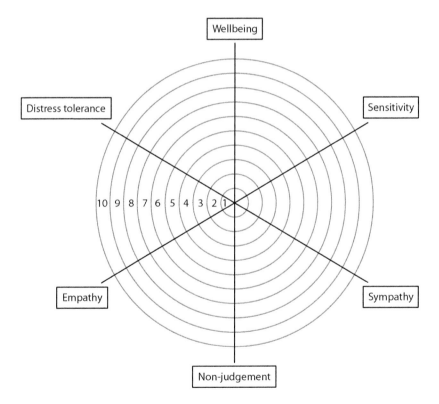

Figure 4.4: Self and other compassion circle

are listed in table 4.4 and read each of the left hand column questions used in the other-compassion exercise. As you read each question that relates to one of the six compassion dimensions of sensitivity, sympathy, non-judgement, empathy, distress tolerance and wellbeing, give yourself a rating score between 1 and 10. In this case 10 represents you feeling that the statement would be completely true of how you would feel, and 1 would mean that statement was not true at all. You could photocopy or redraw the concentric circles in figure 4.4 to map your compassion rating on to each dimension visually by plotting the score on to the circle that corresponds to your rating. This will give you an immediate picture of which areas are more or less developed, and help you have an idea of which areas you might want to focus your attention on. Alternatively, you can complete the exercise by just making a written note of the six self-compassion dimensions from table 4.3 and write your rating from 1–10 next to them.

Table 4.3: Example scenarios for other-compassion exercise

Scenario 1.	• You are waiting to catch a train and the woman next to you starts to get agitated and upset and says that she has left her purse and tickets on the train that she has just got off, which has now departed
Scenario 2.	• You are walking through town and you see a boy crying in the middle of the path. He has got lost and does not know where his parents are
Scenario 3.	• You are sitting on a bench in the park when you see an elderly gentleman fall over on the gravel path. He looks injured and is struggling to stand up

Table 4.4: Self- and other-compassion rating statements

Compassion dimensions	For use in other-compassion exercise	For use in self-compassion exercise
	Rate how accurate on a scale of 1–10 with 10 being completely true and 1 being not true at all	
Sensitivity	I would notice that the person was distressed	I notice when I am distressed
Sympathy	I would feel moved to help the person	I have a sense of wishing to help myself when I am distressed
Non-judgement	I would accept the person in their distress	I accept rather than judge myself when I am distressed
Empathy	The person's feelings would make sense to me	I am able to make sense of my feelings
Distress tolerance	I would be able to tolerate being with the person	I am able to tolerate my distress
Wellbeing	The person's wellbeing would be important to me	I actively invest in my own wellbeing

- **Step two**

After you have completed the whole 'other-compassion' exercise, you can then complete the exercise again for 'self-compassion'. In this case choose one of the examples from the list of scenarios suggested in table 4.5 (overleaf), or you can use another one of your own. When you have chosen an imaginary scenario, go to the six compassion rating statements in table 4.3 and rate yourself on a scale from 1–10 on each of those dimensions (make sure that you ask yourself the self-compassion questions in the right hand column). Again, you can either photocopy or redraw the concentric circles figure to add your ratings visually or you can jot down your answers in written form.

Table 4.5: Example scenarios for self-compassion exercise

Scenario 1.	• You have gone out to post a letter. Just as you let go of the letter into the letter box you realise that you have not put a stamp on it
Scenario 2.	• You have been for an interview for a job that you really wanted, but have just had a phone-call to say that, unfortunately, you have been unsuccessful on this occasion
Scenario 3.	• A close friend of yours contacted you and asked to spend some time with you. You were busy and said that you would see them the next day. However, the next day you find out that your friend was involved in an accident

 Pause to compare the ratings you gave yourself for 'other-compassion' and 'self-compassion' in this exercise, and reflect on what similarities and differences you notice.

This exercise can be helpful as a reflective tool for self-assessment of how able you are to feel compassionate towards yourself or others. Also bear in mind that if you have scored lower than you would have liked on either scale, there is a possibility that you may be experiencing 'compassion fatigue'. Compassion fatigue "reduces our capacity or our interest in bearing the suffering of others" (Figley, 2002, p. 1434) and is a common experience for healthcare practitioners and professionals involved in frequent care of people who have experienced trauma. Research shows that in order to avoid or combat compassion fatigue, practitioners need to "invest time and energy into nurturing the self" (Boyle, 2011, p. 5) through compassionate self-care (Larson and Bush, 2006). If it is a possibility that you are experiencing compassion fatigue, it may be valuable to remind yourself of the compassionate questions introduced earlier; *'how can I be kind to myself?'* and *'what can I do to help myself in this moment?'*

Summary

This chapter has covered material aimed at encouraging and supporting you to develop and maintain a rich and beneficial compassionate mindfulness practice of your own. In service of this aim, an introduction was provided outlining the importance of self-care when working with clients who have experienced psychological trauma, addressing the dimensions of mental, emotional, spiritual, physical and relational self-care. The topic of fostering curiosity was outlined as a way to develop a new sense of engagement with the present, and as a springboard to being able to commit to a regular practice of mindfulness, whether that is through focused attention or open monitoring meditation. The analogy of the two arrows was described as a way to help you to understand that some of the greatest harm and pain that we experience is often self-inflicted, and that if we learn to be more self-compassionate and avoid this kind of self-attack, we may manage the difficult circumstances of life more graciously. Finally some compassion exercises have been provided to help bring awareness to this facet of your make-up at present, together with a guided instruction on employing loving-kindness meditation to develop kindness towards self and others.

References

Baker, E. K. (2003). *Caring for ourselves: A therapist's guide to personal and professional well-being.* Washington, DC: American Psychological Association.

Bhikkhu, T. (1997). *The Arrow Sallattha Sutta* (SN 36:6). Dhammatalks.org. Talks, writings and translations of Thānissaro Bhikkhu. Retrieved from https://www.dhammatalks.org/suttas/SN/SN36_6.html

Bickley, J. (1998). Care for the caregiver: The art of self-care. *Seminars in Perioperative Nursing, 7,* 114–121.

Boyle, D. A. (2011). Countering compassion fatigue: A requisite nursing agenda. *The Online Journal of Issues in Nursing, 16*(1), 1–13.

Brown, K. W., & Ryan, R. M. (2003). The benefits of being present: mindfulness and its role in psychological well-being. *Journal of Personality and Social Psychology, 84*(4), 822.

Bruce, A., Young, L., Turner, L., Vander Wal, R., & Linden, W. (2002). Meditation-based stress reduction: Holistic practice in nursing education. In L. Young & E. Virginia (Eds.), *Transforming health promotion practice: Concepts, issues, and applications* (pp. 241–252). Victoria, BC, Canada: F. A. Davis Company.

Buckner, R. L., Andrews-Hanna, J. R., & Schacter, D. L. (2008). The brain's default network. *Annals of the New York Academy of Sciences, 1124*(1), 1–38.

Collins Dictionary (2019). Grounding. Retrieved from https://www.collinsdictionary.com/dictionary/english/grounding

Elliot, A. J. (1999). Approach and avoidance motivation and achievement goals. *Educational Psychologist, 34*(3), 169–189.

Figley, C. R. (2002). Compassion fatigue: Psychotherapists' chronic lack of self care. *Journal of Clinical Psychology, 58*(11), 1433–1441.

Foucault, M. (1988). *Politics, philosophy, culture: Interviews and other writings 1977–1984* (Trans. A. Sheridan). New York, NY: Routledge.

Happy Buddha, The (2011). *Happiness and how it happens: Finding contentment through mindfulness.* Brighton, United Kingdom: Leaping Hare Press.

Happy Buddha, The (2015). *Mindfulness and compassion: Embracing life with loving kindness.* Brighton, United Kingdom: Leaping Hare Press.

Hieronymi, P. (2006). "Controlling Attitudes". *Pacific Philosophical Quarterly, 87*, 45–74.

Hjeltnes, A., Binder, P. E., Moltu, C., & Dundas, I. (2015). Facing the fear of failure: An explorative qualitative study of client experiences in a mindfulness-based stress reduction program for university students with academic evaluation anxiety. *International Journal of Qualitative Studies on Health and Well-being, 10*(1), 27990.

Kashdan, T. B., & Silvia, P. J. (2009). Curiosity and interest: The benefits of thriving on novelty and challenge. *Oxford Handbook of Positive Psychology, 2*, 367–374.

Killingsworth, M. A., & Gilbert, D. T. (2010). A wandering mind is an unhappy mind. *Science, 330* (6006), 932.

Larson, D. G., & Bush, N. J. (2006). Stress management for oncology nurses: Finding a healing balance. In R. Carroll-Johnson, L. Gorman, & N. J. Bush (Eds.). *Psychosocial nursing along the cancer continuum* (pp. 587–601). Pittsburgh, PA: Oncology Nursing Society.

Lowens, I. (2015). *Compassion circles.* Personal discussion.

Luft, J., & Ingham, H. (1955). The Johari window, a graphic model of interpersonal awareness. *Proceedings of the western training laboratory in group development.* Los Angeles, CA: University of California, Los Angeles.

Lutz, A., Slagter, H. A., Dunne, J. D., & Davidson, R. J. (2008). Attention regulation and monitoring in meditation. *Trends in Cognitive Science, 12,* 163–169.

Malinowski, P. (2013). Neural mechanisms of attentional control in mindfulness meditation. *Frontiers of Neuroscience, 7,* 8.

Neff, K., & Germer, C. (2018). *The mindful self-compassion workbook: A proven way to accept yourself, build inner strength, and thrive.* London, United Kingdom: Guilford Press.

Newsome, S., Christopher, J. C., Dahlen, P., & Christopher, S. (2006). Teaching counselors self-care through mindfulness practices. *Teachers College Record, 108*(9), 1881.

Pepping, C. A., O'Donovan, A., & Davis, P. J. (2013). The positive effects of mindfulness on self-esteem. *The Journal of Positive Psychology, 8*(5), 376–386.

Phillips, R. (2014). Space for curiosity. *Progress in Human Geography, 38*(4), 493–512.

Raichle, M. E., MacLeod, A. M., Snyder, A. Z., Powers, W. J., Gusnard, D. A., & Shulman, G. L. (2001). A default mode of brain function. *Proceedings of the National Academy of Sciences, 98*(2), 676–682.

CHAPTER FIVE
PRIORITISATION OF
CLIENT SAFETY AND CHOICE

Chapter contents
• Lack of safety and control in traumatic situations • Working in a trauma-informed way • Creating safety before introducing mindfulness practice • Supporting choice in mindfulness practice • Summary

The central key message of this book and this approach to using mindfulness with anyone who has experienced trauma is to bear in mind the importance of the two primary initiatives of safety and choice. These are important to consider both at the start of any work with someone who has experienced trauma, as well as being an essential reference point to continue to bear in mind. This chapter starts by raising our awareness of the fact that in traumatic situations there is, by definition, typically a lack of safety and a lack of control or choice for the person caught up in that situation. In addition to offering a short introduction to what it means for an organisation to work in a trauma-informed way, this chapter offers some suggestions about how to create safety for your client within the five dimensions of environmental, bodily, relational, cultural and process safety. The discussion about the importance of creating safety before introducing mindfulness practice serves as a backdrop to the more detailed explanations of the actual intervention that will be provided in later chapters. There are a number of helpful theories that can offer a useful explanatory position for psycho-education about maintaining a safe mindful practice. One of these is the transactional model of stress, which is

Table 5.1: Trauma-Informed Mindfulness characteristic 4. 'Prioritisation of client safety and choice' learning aims

	TIM characteristic	Description
4.	Prioritisation of client safety and choice	• To appreciate the importance of safety and choice for people who have experienced trauma • To be familiar with ways of supporting and encouraging safety and choice for traumatised individuals • To understand that safety needs to be developed environmentally, relationally, culturally, in the body and in relation to the process of the intervention • To be aware of the impulse towards avoidance for traumatised clients, and to ensure that they feel safe and supported and sufficiently resourced to engage in practice • To be aware of the prevalence of dissociation within traumatised individuals, and to be able to use skills to avoid or manage dissociation

explained in this chapter with figures to illustrate. Some concrete examples of how to support clients in feeling more in control during their mindfulness practice include negotiating and offering choice about when appointments are arranged, explaining what the mindfulness exercises will involve in advance of practicing them, and agreeing communication about when a client needs to stop or take a break. In chapter one (table 1.1) the full specification for learning requirements relating to the seven TIM characteristics was provided. Table 5.1 is a duplicate of the section of that table that relates to the prioritisation of client safety and choice, and is provided here as a reminder for pedagogical purposes. This chapter explicates in more detail the descriptive elements that relate specifically to this characteristic.

Lack of safety and control in traumatic situations
In the *DSM-5* (APA, 2013) the descriptor of what constitutes a 'criterion A' traumatic stressor is that the person has been either exposed to 'death, threatened death, actual or threatened serious injury, or actual or threatened sexual violence'. It is not difficult to imagine that the primary experience of any person exposed to a situation like this would be to feel unsafe. Those who work specifically with children who have experienced trauma confirm, "unfortunately, the defining experience of any child who has experienced complex trauma is that of feeling unsafe" (Bath, 2008). It is this sense of being unsafe peri-traumatically that causes a huge surge of physiological biochemical responses in the body correlating to the fight/flight/freeze/flop responses typical of trauma reactivity. Additionally, the impact of peri-traumatic helplessness can continue to exert its influence throughout life. Traumatised children are likely to continue to harbour a deep mistrust of others, especially adults, and develop numerous behavioural strategies to protect themselves and keep adults at a safe distance (Seita and Brendtro, 2005). As Judith Herman has stated "the essential features of psychological trauma are disempowerment and disconnection from others" (1998, p. 98). Therefore the process of recovery needs to address these two issues of reconnection in relationships and empowerment (Herman, 1992).

Young people who have been exposed to chronic adversity can develop beliefs that they have little control or influence over what happens to them, and that they are just at the mercy of fate (Quinton and Rutter, 1988) or that there is "nothing they could do to affect what happened to them" (Rutter, 2012, p. 338). Knowing this facilitates an understanding of some of the basic needs of traumatised adults and children alike, and can be extremely helpful when supporting these individuals both formally and informally. For example Bruce Perry (2006) advocates the importance of enabling children to have as much control over decision-making as is practically and developmentally possible. It is therefore logical to conclude that the two overarching aspects of experiencing trauma that affect people most are a feeling of having no control over what is happening, and of being unsafe and in danger. Although some practitioners and clients may be of the opinion that working with trauma involves working in states of high distress, this is not actually very effective whilst the client feels unsafe (Rothschild, 2004). Therefore learning to lower arousal is necessary for both facilitator and client before engaging in trauma processing elements of therapy. This means that when working with people who have experienced trauma, whether they meet all of the criteria for a PTSD diagnosis or not, it is *essential* to bear in mind the need to create a safe environment in which the person can feel a degree of control over what is happening.

 By definition, when a person has experienced a traumatic event in their lives, they felt unsafe, and had no control or choice about what was happening.

Working in a trauma-informed way

One of the key groups who recognise the impact of trauma and its ripple effect on many aspects of a person's life is organisations who work with people who have become homeless. In the UK the organisation Homeless Link understands that often trauma has been the precipitating factor that has led to a complex array of additional difficulties socially and economically, and has now adopted a similar trauma-informed care model to that which was instigated by the US National Centre for Trauma-Informed Care (NCTIC) in 2008. The NCTIC clearly states that trauma-informed organisations "understand the importance of power differentials and ways in which clients, historically have been diminished in voice and choice and are often recipients of coercive treatment. Clients are supported in shared decision-making, choice and goal setting to determine the plan of action they need to heal and move forward" (SAMHSA, 2014a, p. 11). This statement demonstrates an understanding of the fundamental challenge when working with people who have experienced trauma, which is that there is usually a profound experience of being powerless, unsafe and having no choice that accompanies the traumatic experience. Therefore, both Homeless Link (The Innovation and Good Practice Team, Homeless Link, 2017), and other homelessness services in the US (SAMHSA, 2012b) who are utilising a trauma-informed care model state that these four elements are key to working in this way. These are:

1. *Trauma awareness* – service providers are encouraged to make learning about trauma an integral part of their staff training
2. *Emphasis on safety* – service providers are encouraged to consider ways in which they can ensure the physical and emotional safety of their clients
3. *Opportunities to rebuild control* – service providers are encouraged to find ways to provide environments and services that are predictable, and to increase the client's opportunities to exercise choice and control
4. *Strengths-based approach* – service providers are encouraged to support people in identifying their own personal strengths and adaptive coping mechanisms

The same message about safety, control and choice is re-emphasised here. These are the key elements that appear to come through repeatedly in the good practice guidelines for working with trauma, and are certainly the main aspects that I have seen in clinical practice. So it is evident that when introducing mindfulness practices to individuals who have experienced trauma, these factors really need to be heeded. It is also worth mentioning at this point that often people do not disclose a trauma early on in any professional relationship, if ever. This means that there may be clients in services who are affected by trauma but who do not yet feel safe enough to disclose it. So, not just for those for whom their traumatisation is evident, but also for those who prefer to keep it hidden, these principles continue to apply. In terms of how a person's belief system is affected by trauma and how their sense of safety is severely damaged, it is worth turning to the literature to illuminate what the processes are that might cause this to happen.

Janoff-Bulman (1992) proposed an accessible and helpful theory which is referred to as the theory of 'shattered assumptions'. Due to the severe challenge to a person's existing core beliefs about himself or herself, others and the world, a person who has experienced a traumatic event can find these beliefs 'shattered' by what has happened (ibid.). Where previously a person may have felt relatively safe in a public place such as a shopping centre or bar, if for example, they had been exposed to a major incident that threatened their safety in one of these locations, their beliefs about being safe in similar situations may subsequently be significantly damaged. Indeed, if we return to the diagnostic criteria for PTSD, symptoms of hyper-vigilance and reactivity accompanied by avoidance of potentially 'triggering' stimuli are classic symptoms for a person affected by trauma. Therefore when seeking to introduce mindfulness practice to individuals with trauma-related hyper-vigilance and reactivity, creating an environment where the person can begin to feel safe is even more important than usual. Notably, as Sandra Bloom points out "safety and comfort are not necessarily the same thing" (Bloom, 2019, n.p.). By this, she means that creating safety may require organisations to enter a process of change, which may initially feel uncomfortable.

Creating safety before introducing mindfulness practice

As agreed, the first priority when working with someone who has experienced psychological trauma is to facilitate a sense of safety for them. There are however, different ways that a person may feel unsafe, and these can vary depending on the specific experiences that each person has encountered that have contributed to their heightened awareness of potential dangers. Babette Rothschild has devised a list of ten foundations that she presents from experience, as being an essential framework for engaging in safe trauma therapy. These are summarised in table 5.2.

Table 5.2: Rothschild's (2003) ten foundations for safe trauma therapy

	Foundation	Description
1.	Establish safety for the client within and outside the therapy	In order to work therapeutically with the trauma that a client has experienced, there is a need to help the client 'loosen' their defence mechanisms. The client needs to be living in a relatively safe environment and to feel relatively safe within the therapy room, in order to manage this without making themselves too vulnerable and thereby risking de-compensation
2.	Develop good contact between the therapist and client	It is essential for the client to feel sufficiently safe within their relationship with their therapist to be able to face the terror of their past experiences.

		The therapeutic alliance is one of the strongest predictors of good outcomes in therapy. Potentially, developing this level of trust may take months or even years
3.	Both client and therapist need to be confident that they can apply the 'brake' to therapy if needed	Working with trauma can be unpredictable and potentially volatile, and a myriad of factors may act as triggers unbeknown consciously to either therapist or client. A characteristic of PTSD is that memories can be very easily triggered. Helping a client to find ways to 'put the brakes on' this when it happens helps give the client courage to engage in the therapy, as well as more confidence in having some control over their experiences
4.	Identify and build on the client's internal and external resources	Resources are the protective factors that can act to balance out the symptoms and difficulties. Building on those that exist and developing new ones can facilitate resilience
5.	Instead of removing current coping strategies/defences, build new ones so that more choices are created	However 'dysfunctional' or problematic a client's existing coping strategies seem, it does not serve them to remove these defences when there is nothing in their place, as this could actually make matters worse. The safest strategy is to help the client develop new coping strategies, so that the client does not just have one 'problematic' defence that they revert to, but they have some control and options

6.	Work to reduce the 'pressure' of trauma rather than increase it	Any kind of provocative intervention or confrontation with the client's already very fragile system may be re-traumatising. It is better to work on increasing resources and reducing pressure
7.	Adapt the therapy to the client	This requires the therapist to be adept in drawing upon a number of different trauma-informed intervention models, so that the therapy can be tailored to the individual client. If only one therapy is provided, and for whatever reason this does not suit the client, they are at risk of feeling that it is them that has failed
8.	Have a broad knowledge of the theory of the physiology and psychology of PTSD and trauma	Having a broad knowledge of theory and approaches affords the therapist with more scope in terms of the kinds of interventions and psycho-education that can be offered to the client. This knowledge also enables the therapist to tailor a specific combination of interventions that will best suit an individual client
9.	Appreciate each client is different and remain non-judgemental about a particular intervention being ineffective, or with the client's non-compliance	Do not focus on looking for where the client may be 'resistant' or there may be 'secondary gains' for the client in not progressing in therapy. Each client is different and no therapy will work the same on two different clients. Treat each client without blame or shame and continue to work on creating an intervention that will suit that particular client

10.	Be prepared to put aside techniques and just talk to the client	Although it is necessary in trauma-work to have a wide range of tools and techniques available, it is also important to acknowledge yourself as the therapist being a primary source of positive human contact. Be prepared to be fully present as a caring listening being

I have presented these ten foundations fully, although paraphrased from the original, as I agree that these provide excellent practical guidance for anyone working in this area. I believe these are widely applicable, and therefore it will be no surprise that similar themes re-emerge during the presentation of TIM throughout this book. For the purposes of focusing specifically on how to develop safety for your client, I have divided the topic into five areas where the client may feel unsafe: feeling unsafe in the environment, feeling unsafe in their own body, feeling unsafe interpersonally or relationally, feeling unsafe culturally, and feeling unsafe with the process. These are in many ways artificially delineated, but serve fairly well for the purpose of helping us to think about building safety in each of these domains, as much as is practicable. In terms of safety beyond the small environment that we have control over in the place where we work, there may be little that we can do. If a client is truly at risk, then it may be more appropriate in the first instance to work with or refer to other agencies who may be able to help provide shelter, food or protection. This may mean involving social services or the police if there are safeguarding concerns. Table 5.3 (overleaf) is provided as a reference point to extrapolate a little further on the five safety categories:

Table 5.3: Aspects of feeling unsafe for the traumatised individual

Location of perceived danger	Description
Perceiving danger in the environment	This aspect of safety relates to the actual physical environment that the person is in. For example, some people may not feel safe in a room that has no clear and easy exit, such as an easily accessible nearby door and clear route to leave the building. Often people who have been traumatised feel safer if they know that there is a physical 'escape route' should they feel the need to leave
Perceiving danger in their own body	This aspect of safety relates to the relationship that the person has with their physical body. Many people who have experienced physical trauma especially, feel disconnected from their body, and do not feel safe being asked to pay attention to, and deliberately experience sensations of embodiment. This is particularly important to consider given our understanding of how trauma is not just a process that happens in the brain, but is also held somatically in the body
Perceiving danger relationally	This aspect of safety relates to the relationship that the person who has experienced trauma has with other people, including their friends, family, colleagues and therapist. If the person has experienced an interpersonal trauma where they have been hurt emotionally, physically or sexually by another person, it can be extremely difficult for them to 'let down their guard' sufficiently and feel safe enough to interact with others

Prioritisation of client safety and choice

Perceiving danger in cultural differences	This aspect of safety relates to the imposition of the beliefs and practices of a dominant culture on a minority culture in such a way as to render the oppressed minority culture powerless. Such imposition of values, norms and practices can be in themselves deeply traumatising to those individuals. Attending to cultural safety is important in order to redress this power imbalance, and instead to honour the practices and belief systems of those minority groups, which in turn can provide a safe basis for healing.
Perceiving danger in the process	This aspect of safety relates to the actual process of work that is being facilitated to help the client heal or manage their trauma symptoms. It is known that many people fear starting trauma therapy, or drop out part way through as it can bring back memories and associated emotions and cognitions that the client finds too difficult to cope with. Developing safety on the process involves collaborating with the client before any work is started to find ways to pace the sessions, and for the client to be able to slow down or stop the momentum if it becomes too painful Note the discussion in chapter eight about dynamic stabilisation

Bearing in mind that a person who has experienced trauma is likely to feel unsafe to a greater or lesser extent in relation to each of the categories listed, it is important to consider how to manage each of them. By attending to each of these areas in turn, you will have a better chance of creating a 'space' physically and interpersonally within which the individual can begin to learn, and ultimately make use of the beneficial techniques that mindfulness practice can offer. It is not just during the teaching or training part of the process that safety needs to be worked towards, but it is also important for the person as they learn to integrate mindfulness practice into their daily life to find ways to create these elements of safety in the variety of idiosyncratic situations, environments and relationships that they inhabit.[iv] Related to the categories already outlined about safety, the following questions may help to establish what it is about the environment, the body, the relationship and the process that may not feel safe for your client, so that you can work on addressing those aspects. This is not intended to be an exhaustive list, but may be a starting point to help you consider each of these areas in more detail:

Environment:

- Does the other person look fidgety, ill at ease, are they looking around?
- Might they feel safer if they sat in a different place?
- Is there clear access for the person to leave the room if they choose to?
- Are there security locks on any of the doors between this room and outside?
- Can you overhear people outside the room, or could they overhear you?
- Are there windows where other people can see in?

[iv] Please note that in some situations, such as where there may be ongoing domestic violence, or where a person still inhabits an active war zone, or where a person may be homeless or does not have safe physical shelter, it may not be possible to create a 'safe place'. It is important, therefore, to recognise that safety is a relative term, and that threats to safety are not just about perception, but may actually be real and present dangers that need to be acknowledged and managed appropriately. Note also that any safeguarding concerns need to be raised and addressed immediately and in line with available protocols.

Body:

- Do you know from what they have already said that they have experienced physical trauma?
- Are you aware of which parts of their body might be affected?
- Do they struggle with intrusive thoughts or images that might mean focusing on thoughts makes them feel unsafe?
- Do they use detrimental coping strategies such as self-harm or using drugs or alcohol to 'block out' physical, mental or emotional experiences that do not feel safe?
- Do they have other perceptual challenges such as hearing voices or seeing figures that might mean that they feel less safe?
- Do you know if they dissociated from their body peri-traumatically, or use dissociation as a form of coping strategy now?[v]
- Could you provide objects in the room to help them to be more grounded and to manage possible dissociation?[vi]

Relationship:

- Has the person got a history of difficult or broken relationships personally and professionally?
- Do you know anything about their attachment style?
- Have they experienced interpersonal trauma that may leave them feeling vulnerable?

---

[v] There are helpful assessment tools to evaluate the person's level of dissociation such as the Dissociative Experiences Scale (DES) (Bernstem and Putnam, 1986; Ross et al., 1989) and adolescent version (ADES) (Armstrong et al., 1997).

[vi] Useful items to have to hand include playdough, colouring pencils, pebbles, bubble wrap, stress balls, reusable heat pads or ice packs, shells or other small items or toys to hold or manipulate, depending on their age.

- Is there anything about you (age, gender, ethnicity, power, etc.) that may remind the person of someone with whom they felt unsafe previously or who had abused them?
- Have they expressed that they find it difficult to trust people?
- Are there things that you can do to be more predictable (consistent about when and where you meet, doing what you say you will do, being consistent in your behaviour and attitude)?
- Could you use self-disclosure judiciously to let them know something about you to help them trust you more? Conversely would it be better for the client for you to withhold self-disclosure so that they don't start to feel concerned about you?

Culture:
- Thinking about your own cultural background, ideology, beliefs and cultural norms and mores, on which aspects are you not flexible?
- How might your own cultural beliefs and practices differ from the other person?
- In what ways might your actions and assumptions create a power imbalance between you and the other person?
- What can you do to help the other person feel that their cultural background and worldview is acceptable and respected?
- What can you do practically to conduct yourself in a way that honours the other person's cultural values and helps them to feel safer with you?
- Are there ways in which you can practice TIM with this person that fit better with their cultural mores?

Process:
- Has the person given consideration to whether they are ready to start this process now?
- Are there any destabilising factors in their life at the moment such as problems with accommodation or relationships that might indicate this is not a good time?[vii]
- Have you explained to them anything about how trauma affects people to normalise their experiences and symptoms?
- Have you explained what the benefits of learning about TIM might be for them?
- Do they know exactly what is going to be involved?
- Have they really agreed or just consented because they are either too scared or too embarrassed to say no?
- Have you thought about revisiting these questions regularly, not just at the start?

Creating environmental safety
The first of the nine building blocks for safe trauma treatment advocated by Peter Levine is to create an environment of 'relative' safety. The way that Levine describes this kind of safety relates both to providing a "therapy room that promotes feelings of calm" (Levine, 2010b, p. 9), but also to the therapist's centredness and physical position within that environment relative to the client. The issue of considering physical proximity in relation to developing a greater feeling of safety for the client is very pertinent. Although in this discussion I have separated environments, physical, relational and cultural safety for the sake of thinking about the whole topic in more detail, it is in this area perhaps more than others that there is a clear overlap between these categories. With

---

[vii] This may not be a reason to avoid engaging in TIM, but it is included so that facilitators are aware of any factors that may make it more difficult for the client to self-regulate emotionally.

physical proximity there is a real possibility that your client will feel very anxious if they perceive you as being 'too close'. This can be a challenge if you have a very small space to work in, but within the environment that you have, consider what scope there is for the client to choose where to sit (even if that means sitting in 'your' chair!), and whether they can move the chairs slightly further apart or at a different angle if that makes them feel more at ease. Take care with standing over or behind clients who have experienced trauma, as this can often be extremely un-nerving and potentially triggering. Similarly, take care with sudden or exaggerated movements, or movements that are quite close to the client. For someone who has experienced physical abuse for example, this could remind them of movements from a perpetrator. Also think about practical things like whether your conversation can be overheard by people in another room, or if there are any windows in the room, which mean that other people can look in. In some places where I have worked with young people, other staff coming into the room unbidden, or other young people pulling faces through the windows, or the extraneous sounds of alarms or screaming can be extremely unsettling. Similarly, I have worked in community spaces where the therapy rooms could only be accessed through a series of locked doors. For some clients such as military veterans with PTSD, the thought of not being able to 'escape' elevates their anxiety levels to such an extent that therapy is not possible. In any environment you will have constraints that you cannot change, but as much as possible work to make it feel as safe as you can for your client.

Creating body safety
Talking about their research in working with mindfulness groups for people at risk of suicide, Williams and colleagues (2017) reported that their participants often struggled with exercises that involved turning their attention towards their bodies, as their clients

had previously spent very little time connecting with themselves physically in a positive way. They explained that focusing attention on the body often awakened their awareness of sensations in their bodies that were associated with trauma. One way that Williams and colleagues found could help participants to tolerate the exercises more comfortably was to offer choice about whether they engaged in a practice or not, and choice about where in their body their focus of attention was placed (ibid.). Recovery from trauma is not just about becoming more in control of the mind and emotions, but also of the body's responses (van der Kolk, 2014). A very useful field of work for consideration of how to help a client feel more safe in their body is that of somatic experiencing (SE), which is a trauma therapy intervention developed by Peter Levine that "helps to create physiological, sensate and affective states that transform those of fear and helplessness. It does this by accessing various instinctual reactions through one's awareness of physical body sensations" (Levine, 2010a, p. 10). The premise of SE is to guide clients to be aware of their kinaesthetic, proprioceptive and interoceptive experiences, and to provide advice about how mindfulness practices can be modified to facilitate clients in processing trauma memories (Payne, Levine and Crane-Godreau, 2015). Whilst there are a number of specialist trauma therapy interventions that focus particularly on the body or somatic experience, considering how you can be aware of how safe your client feels in their body will help you whatever approach you are using. When using TIM, an awareness of your client's sensitivity to physical sensations acting as triggers to trauma memories may help you to agree collaboratively the level of proximal titration to use, potentially starting with exercises that are outside the body.

Creating relational safety
Judith Herman asserts that recovery from traumatic experiences cannot occur in isolation but must necessarily happen within the

context of a relationship (1998). Herman goes on to address the issues of those individuals who have experienced trauma, especially complex or ongoing trauma that stems from childhood, which can be very challenging to work with. The reason for the difficulty in making steady progress is that these clients have very extreme patterns of relating to others, displaying extreme dependency and neediness or withdrawal and rejection. This can push therapists to question the limits of their own abilities and capacity, as well as forcing questions of personal ethics and beliefs (Herman, 1998). However, there is a great deal of evidence to suggest that the relational factors between the therapist and client are more significant determinants of a successful outcome than the intervention itself. According to Lambert and Barley (2001), who reviewed more than a hundred studies and combined the results, approximately 40% of change is due to factors outside of therapy, and that within therapy 30% of positive change is attributable to therapist 'common factors' of empathy, warmth and congruence. They state that "the main curative component is the nature of the therapeutic relationship" and therefore "improvement of psychotherapy may best be accomplished by learning to improve one's ability to relate to clients and tailoring that relationship to individual clients" (Lambert and Barley, 2001, p. 357).

Many experienced therapists will testify that the need to stay centred and grounded, to have a well-developed personal care regime, and to make good use of clinical supervision are all essential in working with traumatised clients. Peter Levine (2010a) states that when working with a traumatised client, the facilitator's "ability to stay centered, present and calm are critical" (p. 9). Arguably, one can only genuinely maintain this kind of calm and centred stance in the face of possible dissociation, fragmentation, projection and distress, when one is diligently aware of and in control of one's own inner thoughts, emotions and bodily responses. This is a key reason why mindfulness is strongly advocated as a self-care and self-awareness tool for therapists working with clients who have experienced trauma. In order not to react in unhelpful ways to a client's chaos and distress, the therapist should assume a "neutral, accepting stance, not just at the emotional and cognitive level, but at the body level as well" (Levine, 2010a, p. 9). This requires therapists to be embodied during their work, so as to manage any of their own defences against the client's dysregulation. Being able to be authentically in control of oneself as a trauma therapist is the keystone for providing relational stability and safety for the client.

The building of trust for a traumatised client will typically take a long time, and is not easily earned (Chu, 1988); however, with patience, consistency, good boundaries and limits, it is possible to provide the kind of relational security within which a client can start to make the difficult journey of unveiling their vulnerability to make therapeutic progress. For clients who have experienced abusive relationships, whether through sexual, physical or emotional abuse, bullying, torture, slavery or domestic violence, their 'blueprint' of relating is one of power control and coercion from the perpetrator, and submission compliance and exploitation as the victim. This dynamic of power and force over helplessness and submission will be a well-trodden path that is potentially the most familiar or only pattern of relating that they have. Clients with this kind of mental patterning can flip between helpless states of passive endurance to agitated states of aggressive dominance, with little capacity to experience anything more stable in between these extremes. In a therapy session the transference process may act in such a way that the client expects or acts as though you as the therapist will behave in a controlling or authoritarian way, and therefore a hugely therapeutic aspect of the work may be to help the client to work collaboratively. This notion of egalitarianism and partnership may be quite alien, and can take time to develop. Because trauma damages a person's capacity to enter into a relationship built on mutuality and trust, there will be predictable difficulties on both sides in building a healthy working alliance. However if these challenges are understood and anticipated from the outset, success will be more likely (Herman, 1998).

According to Steven Porges's polyvagal theory (see Porges, 2007), the autonomic nervous system (ANS) has three divisions (it had been previously thought to have only two), the first being the sympathetic nervous system (the fight/flight response) and the second and third being in effect two branches of the parasympathetic nervous system. The parasympathetic nervous system is primarily controlled by a major nerve called the vagal nerve which has two branches: the dorsal, which induces a 'shut-down' response in the nervous system, and the ventral (the more recently proposed third component of the ANS) which Porges proposes controls 'social engagement'. The suggested purpose or function of the ventral vagus is to promote parasympathetic 'rest and recover' response through interacting in social connection with others (Porges, 2007). In application, knowledge that social interaction can promote the engagement of the parasympathetic rest and recover response is very relevant to creating safety through relationship in a therapeutic encounter with someone who is highly aroused. In the somatic experiencing approach, Levine makes explicit reference to using social engagement activities deliberately, such as making eye contact and modulating the voice, in order to activate the client's ventral vagus and thus encourage a sense of safety and balance in the nervous system (Payne, Levine and Crane-Godreau, 2015).

Bath (2008) states that creating safety when working with traumatised children is "the first imperative" (p. 19). Research also clearly indicates that when working with individuals who have experienced trauma, it is vital to develop a safe therapeutic relationship (Kohlenberg and Tsai, 1991). For clients who have had very little if any positive experiences of safe relationships in the past, it is arguably an absolute prerequisite for engaging in any therapy that addresses their trauma history to first establish a safe and contained therapeutic relationship (Follette, Palm and Pearson, 2006). This stage may take some time to establish before more formal therapy can commence, but is vital for the success of any therapy that this safe space is first built (Greenwald, 2005). In terms of developing a sense of interpersonal safety, aspects that are helpful to cultivate are availability, honesty, predictability, reliability, consistency and transparency (Bath, 2008). When thinking more carefully about what relational safety might include for children and young people, Bath suggests considering both peer relationships and adult relationships, and that adult relationships are beneficial where there is compassion, empathy and acceptance.

For people who have experienced interpersonal trauma for an extended period of time and/or in multiple situations or relationships, they may experience particular challenges regarding relational safety. For example, it may not feel safe for someone to show kindness towards them, and this may not feel tolerable for them to experience. In this case, take care to titrate your demonstration of kindness. As Bessel van der Kolk (2014) has argued, the sense of safety with other people is probably the single most important aspect of mental health, as those safe connections are a fundamental aspect of ensuring a meaningful and satisfying life. This is an argument that has been put forward by many researchers who have studied the variables that predict successful outcomes in counselling and psychotherapy. There is now a body of evidence to support the claim that "the therapist is a key change ingredient in most successful therapy" (Blow, Sprenkle and Davis, 2007, p. 298).

Creating cultural safety

'Cultural safety' is a term that originated from the context of Maori nursing education in New Zealand, but has now transcended national boundaries to receive widespread recognition as an area that needs to be considered in healthcare provision (Smye, Josewski and Kendall, 2010). The main concern of the impetus to promote cultural safety is to redress the inequalities in health and social justice caused by the imposition of Western colonial approaches on indigenous peoples, without respect for their existing health beliefs and practices. Cultural safety is an approach that promotes positive recognition of diversity and requires practitioners from majority cultural backgrounds to challenge their stereotypical ideas about people from minority and/or displaced cultures. By critically challenging these dominating colonial ways of understanding health and illness, and taking an active position to promote cultural safety, practitioners seek to redress the inherent power differences that have been created.

In order to create cultural safety, practitioners are encouraged to consider their own sociocultural, historical and economic background (Anderson et al., 2003) especially when that is the majority or dominant culture, and to acknowledge the differences that may exist in the culture of the people that they work with. Such reflective awareness can help raise the conscious awareness of practitioners so that they do not continue to impose their own cultural beliefs and systems on the people they work with, particularly those of minority communities. The issue of safety from a cultural intelligence perspective is to protect minority clients from the oppressive imposition of beliefs and practices by practitioners from a dominant culture (Gray, Hughes and Klein, 2003). As Bath notes in relation to being aware of developing or maintaining cultural safety with children and young people, recognition and attention needs to be given to considering a young person's "cultural priorities, needs, language and behaviours"

(Bath, 2016, p. 4). The way that this happens is to focus carefully on how a particular cultural group is perceived and treated, not just on the differences in what that people think or do (Polaschek, 1998), but also the privilege that is given to societal structures that dominate.

Creating process safety
Babette Rothschild (2004) states that she has learned that when working in the area of trauma therapy it is essential that the client first feels confident that the "flow of their anxiety, emotion, memories, and body sensations can be contained at will" (p. 42). In other words, it is important, before starting to focus on any aspect of trauma symptomology, that the client knows that they have control over the amount of emotional or physical reactivity that may be triggered during a session. Often clients feel very frightened by their belief that if they start to think about or focus on what has happened to them it will open a 'Pandora's Box' of emotions and thoughts that will flood over them in a completely uncontained and unmanageable way. The fear of annihilation is what often leads to clients taking whatever measures they can to keep a very firm lid on any such emotional outbursts. What is important in supporting such clients is to help them to build a degree of confidence in their own ability to 'let out' only a little of that distress at a time, like releasing the pressure valve on a steam cooker or the lid of a soda bottle that has been shaken up.

From experience we all know that where a huge amount of steam or carbonation has built up, to open it in one go causes a volcanic eruption and the contents are spilt, and everything around is ruined with the overflow. Instead, by just allowing a tiny bit of steam or fizz out at a time, we can gradually release the pressure, and catastrophe is averted. I often use a soda bottle metaphor to help a client to understand the process when explaining this aspect of the work. The way that Rothschild (2004) describes this is to teach the client how to use their 'trauma brakes' before hitting the accelerator in therapy. The concept of trauma brakes is a good one because it describes well the importance of the client being able, and knowing that they are able to control the process of therapy. Many clients fear what will happen when the therapist takes over and drives the therapy car too fast too soon, which can understandably cause them to dig in their heels and become resistant or avoidant.

The more productive and ethically safer approach is to work with the client to facilitate their learning where the brakes are and to give them back the control to use them whenever needed. In reality this means learning to have a degree of control over their trauma memories, rather than the trauma memories having control over them, flooding into their awareness unbidden and unwanted. However, the client is not the only one who can use the brakes. Just like a learner driver has the use of the brakes, but the instructor in specially adapted learning vehicles also has a brake on their side of the car. This is crucial if an emergency stop is needed, or where slowing down heading into a bend would be much safer. Many clients, at least early in their therapy, struggle with having the confidence to assert that they want to take a break or stop the work. Therefore, it is really important that the TIM facilitator is attentive enough to put the brakes on when things are getting a little too overwhelming for the client, and to reduce the titration of the exercise. The benefit of working very slowly and incrementally with the exercises in TIM is that clients are offered a lot of control over this process. Nevertheless, having a client 'stop' button or signal is an essential part of any trauma work.

It can take a bit of practice as a therapist to learn to tune into the subtle signals that a client may be displaying when they are starting to feel that the process is becoming too much, especially if the client has experienced extended periods of abuse and has learned to present a very effective 'mask' facially and posturally that they are OK. Such pretence in the past may have served a protective function where any indication of vulnerability may have made the client a target. By the time they are in treatment, this pretence of not showing any weakness or vulnerability may be very well established, and hard to 'read'. This is where an open discussion about how you are learning to understand your client may be helpful, and if appropriate a validation that you understand their defence mechanism of masking their true feelings.

Having said all this, by careful observation a facilitator can watch for signs of distress in the client's tone of voice, colouration, movements or breathing. For example, someone may go pale, or start to say less, change their breathing pattern or hold their breath or change their speed or tone of voice. They may be sitting very still, but their feet or hands might belie small 'tells' that they are feeling anxious. Often clients start to feel much warmer when anxious, and may start to shift in their seat, or look flushed, or start to develop a pink patch on their neck. When any of these indicators of sympathetic nervous system arousal are observed they are signs that you may need to put the brakes on for them. You can do this by inviting the client to take a break, change the subject, do some grounding or paced breathing, or open a window to cool down, or take a sip of water, and to then titrate the TIM exercises down to make them less challenging. If they sigh, yawn, breathe more deeply or slowly or start to cry, these are usually signs of the parasympathetic nervous system starting to be more involved, and the distress being dissipated. Whilst these are general indicators, you will need to take note of each client individually as people respond differently, and children may have more behavioural signs of anxiety than adults. The process of learning to interpret your client's physical manifestations of distress can also be very helpful for the client themselves if this is done collaboratively. Many clients are unaware of these changes, and learning to be aware of them can be a helpful starting point to noticing in a more physically associated way, when their distress is increasing beyond their window of tolerance.[viii] Awareness is the starting point for learning to have more control.

Supporting choice in mindfulness practice
Typically when someone has experienced a traumatic event they will have felt powerless to do anything to stop it, and been in a position where they had no control or choice. Especially in the case of complex trauma where a person has encountered repeated traumas, this can affect a person's sense of volition more generally. Logically therefore, helping someone to feel that they do have choices, and there are things in their life they do have some control over, can help significantly in re-building a person's sense of autonomy and self-worth. Additionally, talking with someone specifically about what they have experienced is likely to precipitate the physiological, emotional and cognitive trauma-responses that occur when the person reconnects with those memories. This is an extremely frightening experience, and one that most people will work hard to avoid at any expense. Therefore, it is important as someone introducing mindfulness as a distress management tool, to take care to ensure that the person has control over what they do and when. The transactional model of stress (Lazarus, 1993) can be helpful to consider as a theoretical basis to understanding this more clearly. The following is a simple definition of this model:

> Coping is defined as on-going cognitive and behavioural efforts to manage specific external and/or internal demands that are appraised as taxing or exceeding the resources of the person. (Lazarus, 1993, p. 237)

The transactional model of stress (Lazarus and Folkman, 1987) proposes that stress, or inability to cope, is the result of an

---

[viii] The window of tolerance is described more fully in chapter seven.

imbalance between resources and demands. People become stressed when the demands (pressure) outweigh the resources (ability to cope). There are two options according to this model as to how to rectify the imbalance of too much demand and not enough resource to cope:

1. *Problem focused change*: this intervention is to reduce the demands or pressure either externally in the environment or internally
2. *Resource focused change*: this intervention is to increase the inner resources or ability to cope (Duerden, 2018)

What matters in this model is the way that a person *perceives* both the demands being placed on them, and their assessment of how well they can cope with or manage those demands. In this respect a third possibility for intervention could be introduced in addition to the two already described. This would be to work with the client on altering their *perceptions* of either the demands or their resources to be more realistic and to help build their confidence. Of relevance to the current discussion about responses to traumatic events, a key ingredient in whether a person experiences an extreme stress response is whether they feel they have any control. A felt sense of having control forms part of the perceived resources available to mitigate the threat or stressor. A diagrammatic illustration of this using a seesaw metaphor is provided in figure 5.1 (overleaf).

As stated, this model does not just take into account 'actual' resources versus demands, but rather the *perception* the individual has about these two aspects. It may be true that a person can cope with what they perceive as overwhelming, but it will take time for them to change their perspective from one of anticipated overwhelm to anticipated capacity to manage. In order to achieve this, a person will need to gain confidence in their resources, and confidence that their resources are at least equal to the challenge faced. From a TIM perspective the resources that are built are an inner confidence to know that it is possible to turn towards

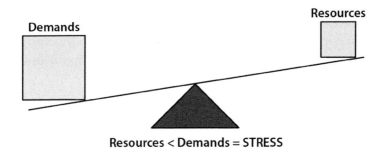

Resources < Demands = STRESS

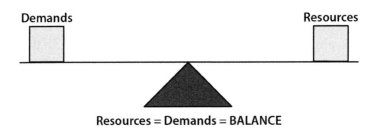

Resources = Demands = BALANCE

Figure 5.1: Diagrammatic representation of the transactional model

thoughts and experiences in the body without becoming overwhelmed or collapsing. In therapy, a common way to help someone to build confidence in their perceived ability to cope with stressors is through the process of graded exposure. The starting point with any graded exposure intervention, no matter how aspirational the goals are, is that the person needs to start where they are right now. Or rather where they perceive themselves to be right now. If their current perception is that they do not have the resources to focus on their breath without stopping breathing, then that is the starting point that needs to be accepted.

The notion of *dialectic* that is used in DBT (Linehan, 2018) is a helpful one to think about at this point. Working with the dialectic means to maintain a balance at the mid-point between *acceptance* and *change*. In other words, accepting where a person is right now, and also working towards a positive change that will be helpful for them in the future. Returning to our dual concepts of safety and choice, it is best to start where a person is now in their (relative) safety zone. Challenging them to move out from a place of safety is going to feel frightening for anyone, and so this needs to be done incrementally and collaboratively, so that the client is in agreement about the pace and size of the change that is sought. That is the premise behind the titrated exercises in TIM. In this way clients are being given back some control over themselves and their choices, which will feel more doable or achievable by having someone supportive to help them with that challenge. Not only does taking this incremental approach to gradual exposure help the person to gain a feeling of achievement or success, it allows them to build mastery and to also gain a sense of self-efficacy.

Summary
This chapter has introduced the very important topic of how to consider the safety of your client in a number of dimensions: environmental, bodily, relational, cultural and process. Some questions and suggestions relating to each of these areas have been provided together with an acknowledgment of the literature in this area. The other primary message of this chapter has been to discuss the issue of control or choice from the perspective of the client. You have been encouraged to reflect on the ways in which you could work collaboratively with your client to offer them choices wherever possible as one way to develop a sense of equality therapeutically and to avoid replaying previous relational dynamics of power and control. The chapter has briefly introduced the concept of trauma-informed care to illustrate the fact that taking this perspective is multifaceted and exists at both individual and organisational levels. This will be revisited in more detail in

chapter six. The transactional model of stress has also been introduced during this discussion as a theoretical framework to relate to the concepts of safety and choice.

References

American Psychiatric Association (APA) (2013). *Diagnostic and statistical manual of mental disorders, Fifth edition DSM-5*. Washington, DC: APA.

Anderson, J., Perry, J., Blue, C., Browne, A., Henderson, A., Khan, K. B., Reimer Kirkham, S., Lynam, J., Semeniuk, P., & Smye, V. (2003). "Rewriting" cultural safety within the postcolonial and postnational feminist project: Toward new epistemologies of healing. *Advances in Nursing Science, 26*(3), 196–214.

Armstrong, J. G., Putnam, F. W., Carlson, E. B., Libero, D. Z., & Smith, S. R. (1997). Development and validation of a measure of adolescent dissociation: The Adolescent Dissociative Experiences Scale. *The Journal of Nervous and Mental Disease, 185*(8), 491–497.

Bath, H. (2008). The three pillars of trauma-informed care. *Reclaiming Children and Youth, 17*(3), 17–21.

Bath, H. (2016, August). *The three pillars of transforming care: Healing in the 'other 23 hours'*. Retrieved from http://www.twi.org.au/3PHealingInTheOther23Hours.pdf

Bernstem, E. M., & Putnam, F. W. (1986). Development, rehability and validity of a dissociation scale. *Journal of Nervous and Mental Disease, 174*, 727–735.

Bloom, S. L. (2019). *The Sanctuary Model®*. Retrieved from http://sanctuaryweb.com/TheSanctuaryModel.aspx

Blow, A. J., Sprenkle, D. H., & Davis, S. D. (2007). Is who delivers the treatment more important than the treatment itself? The role of the therapist in common factors. *Journal of Marital and Family Therapy, 33*(3), 298–317.

Chu, J. A. (1988). Ten traps for therapists in the treatment of trauma survivors. *Dissociation, 1*(4), 24–32.

Duerden, T. (2018). *Mindfulness: Potentially traumatising or detraumatising*. Minding the Gaps conference, Brighton, United Kingdom. Retrieved from http://integratedmindfulness.com/mindingthegap2017/

Follette, V., Palm, K. M., & Pearson, A. N. (2006). Mindfulness and trauma: Implications for treatment. *Journal of Rational-emotive and Cognitive-behavior Therapy, 24*(1), 45–61.

Gray, N. J., Hughes, F. A., & Klein, J. D. (2003). Cultural safety and the health of adolescents. *British Medical Journal, 327*(7412), 457.

Greenwald, R. (2005). *Child trauma handbook: A guide for helping trauma-exposed children and adolescents.* New York, NY: The Haworth Maltreatment and Trauma Press.

Herman, J. L. (1992). *Trauma and recovery.* New York, NY: Basic Books.

Herman, J. L. (1998). Recovery from psychological trauma. *Psychiatry and Clinical Neurosciences, 52*(S1), S98–S103.

Innovation and Good Practice Team, The, Homeless Link (2017). *An introduction to psychologically informed environments and trauma-informed care briefing for homelessness services.* London, United Kingdom: Innovation and Good Practice Team.

Janoff-Bulman, R. (1992). *Shattered assumptions: Toward a new psychology of trauma.* New York, NY: The Free Press.

Kohlenberg, R. J., & Tsai, M. (1991). Functional analytic psychotherapy: *Creating intense and curative therapeutic relationships.* New York, NY: Plenum Press.

Lambert, M. J., & Barley, D. E. (2001). Research summary on the therapeutic relationship and psychotherapy outcome. *Psychotherapy: Theory, research, practice, training, 38*(4), 357.

Lazarus, R. S. (1993). Coping theory and research: Past, present, and future. *Psychosomatic Medicine, 55,* 234–247.

Lazarus, R. S., & Folkman, S. (1987). Transactional theory and research on emotions and coping. *European Journal of Personality, 1,* 141–169.

Levine, P. A. (2010a). *In an unspoken voice: How the body releases trauma and restores goodness.* Berkeley, CA: North Atlantic Books.

Levine, P. A. (2010b). *Instructor's Manual for Resolving trauma in psychotherapy: A somatic approach.* Retrieved from https://www.psychotherapy.net/data/uploads/5113e38c831c3.pdf

Linehan, M. M. (2018). *Cognitive-behavioral treatment of borderline personality disorder.* New York, NY: Guilford Press.

Payne, P., Levine, P. A., & Crane-Godreau, M. A. (2015). Somatic experiencing: Using interoception and proprioception as core elements of trauma therapy. *Frontiers in Psychology, 6,* 93.

Perry, B. (2006). Applying principles of neurodevelopment to clinical work with maltreated and traumatized children. In N. Webb (Ed.), *Working with traumatized youth in child welfare* (pp. 27–52). New York, NY: Guilford Press.

Polaschek, N. R. (1998). Cultural safety: a new concept in nursing people of different ethnicities. *Journal of Advanced Nursing 27*, pp. 452–457.

Porges, S. W. (2007). The polyvagal perspective. *Biological Psychology, 74*(2), 116–143.

Quinton, D., & Rutter, M. (1988) *Parenting breakdown: The making and breaking of inter-generational links*. Aldershot, United Kingdom: Avebury.

Ross, C. A., Heber, S., Norton, G. R., Anderson, D., Anderson, G., & Barchet, P. (1989). The dissociative disorders interview schedule: A structured interview. *Dissociation, 2*(3), 169–189.

Rothschild, B. (2003). *The body remembers casebook: Unifying methods and models in the treatment of trauma and PTSD*. New York, NY: W. W. Norton & Company.

Rothschild, B. (2004). Applying the brakes. *Psychotherapy Networker, 28*(1), 42–45.

Rutter, M. (2012). Resilience as a dynamic concept. *Development and psychopathology, 24*(2), 335–344.

Seita, J., & Brendtro, L. (2005). *Kids who outwit adults*. Bloomington, IN: Solution Tree.

Smye, V., Josewski, V., & Kendall, E. (2010). *Cultural safety: An overview* 1(28). Ottawa, Canada: First Nations, Inuit and Métis Advisory Committee, Mental Health Commission of Canada.

Substance Abuse and Mental Health Services Administration (SAMHSA) (2014a). *SAMHSA's Concept of Trauma and Guidance for a Trauma-Informed Approach*. Rockville, MD: Substance Abuse and Mental Health Services Administration (Publication No. (SMA) 14-4884). Retrieved from https://ncsacw.samhsa.gov/userfiles/files/SAMHSA_Trauma.pdf

Substance Abuse and Mental Health Services Administration (SAMHSA) (2014b). *Trauma-informed care in behavioral health services. Treatment Improvement Protocol (TIP) Series 57.* HHS Publication No. (SMA) 13-4801. Rockville, MD: Substance Abuse and Mental Health Services Administration. Retrieved from http://store.samhsa.gov/product/TIP-57-Trauma-Informed-Care-in-Behavioral-Health-Services/SMA14-4816

van der Kolk, B. (2014). *The body keeps the score.* New York, NY: Penguin.

Williams, J. M. G., Fennell, M., Crane, R., & Silverton, S. (2017). *Mindfulness-based cognitive therapy with people at risk of suicide.* London, United Kingdom: Guilford Press.

CHAPTER SIX
AVOIDANCE OF HARM

Chapter contents
• Harmed by the healer • A trauma-informed model of care • Vulnerability and resilience • Potential iatrogenic consequences of PTSD treatment • Tailored trauma-interventions • Summary

This chapter begins by introducing the concept of iatrogenic harm, or unintended harm that is the consequence of an intervention designed to heal. Harm can be caused at an individual or at an institutional level where risk and behaviour management procedures can sometimes override client welfare. In this chapter an alternative approach to the behaviourist model of management is introduced. This is discussed by contrasting models of care provision that follow a sanctions and rewards model, with those that take a trauma-informed, rehabilitation approach. The concepts of trauma-informed provision of service and trauma-informed care models are introduced. Trauma-informed care is often implemented as a whole service approach to managing challenging client behaviours in a way that acknowledges the trauma aetiology and works to provide services in a trauma-sensitive way. As such, a discussion is provided regarding the ways in which trauma symptoms, and ways of coping with those symptoms may present behaviourally.

This chapter will also consider research that investigates what might make one person more vulnerable to being affected by experiencing a traumatic event than another. In parallel with this discussion is the related topic of what might make one individual

Avoidance of harm

more resilient than another. A lot of research effort has been spent on trying to establish what these parameters might be in order to try to predict reliably which individuals in society might be more or less affected by trauma. This topic is introduced briefly in order to contextualise the discussion for the place interventions that take a trauma-informed perspective after consideration of the potential iatrogenic consequences of PTSD treatment. In chapter one (table 1.1) the full specification for learning requirements relating to the seven TIM characteristics was provided. Table 6.1 is a duplicate of the section of that table that relates to Avoidance of harm, and is provided here as a reminder for pedagogical purposes. This chapter explicates in more detail the descriptive elements that relate specifically to this characteristic.

Table 6.1: Trauma-Informed Mindfulness characteristic 5. 'Avoidance of harm' learning aims

	TIM characteristic	Description
5.	Avoidance of harm	• To understand how trauma symptoms may present behaviourally and in what coping behaviours a traumatised person may engage • To have an awareness of vulnerability and resilience factors • To appreciate the possibility of iatrogenic effects from trauma treatments • To be aware of what it means to work in a trauma-informed way • To have an understanding of how and why using mindfulness could potentially re-traumatise someone if triggers are not carefully attended to, and safety procedures followed

Harmed by the healer

The term *iatrogenic* means 'harm caused by the healer', and is usually used to refer to unintended harm such as complications or disease that arise after surgery or medical procedures. It is used in this context to refer to the unintended harm that might arise in relation to working with people who have experienced trauma. Many institutions such as custodial services, pupil referral units, inpatient units, drug and alcohol rehabilitation services work with adults and children who are engaged in harmful and socially undesirable behaviour. It is often the case that behaviour management in these settings is the primary focus of attention before treatment or rehabilitation, simply because it is apparently the most immediately urgent need. Management of the challenging behaviour of individuals in these services has historically been built on the premise of the rewards and sanctions behaviourist model. However, it is also the case that many people in these environments have also experienced significant trauma in their lives. I am using the term iatrogenesis in this chapter because I believe that for the most part, those who commission, manage and work within these environments have in their hearts a desire to help their clients move towards recovery and rehabilitation. Thus, any 'harm' that is caused by a lack of understanding about trauma and its management is truly unintentional. It is my hope, therefore, through presenting this aspect of TIM, that those readers who work in such settings may glean some helpful knowledge about the impact of trauma on human beings, and that this may possibly influence the way that these patients/inmates/pupils/ service users are understood and treated.

Having worked in secure inpatient settings, I have found it heart-breaking to come across very well-intentioned staff firmly holding to the reward and sanction model when working with severely traumatised patients struggling with immobilising flashbacks and frightening psychotic symptoms. In many instances I have witnessed staff presenting ultimatums to patients that if they manage to 'behave', they will be able to access certain privileges. Typically in these situations 'behaving' means to manage their behaviour so as not to cause harm or put themselves or others at risk. Whilst I absolutely appreciate that risk management is essential for staff and patient safety, there may be different ways to manage risk without re-traumatising the individual or setting wholly inappropriate goals that they will inevitably fail to attain. A little understanding and compassion can go a very long way to preventing re-traumatisation. However, many staff in these challenging work settings are absolutely stretched to their limits, working 12-hour shifts with massive demands, staff shortages and little opportunity to take breaks or engage in self-care. It is little wonder perhaps that when wrung out to such an extent, staff have minimal resources left to maintain a compassionate attitude towards their clients, let alone themselves. So, my encouragement to work together to find ways to move from a risk and behaviour management model to a trauma-informed, rehabilitation model comes from a place of appreciating the very immediate problems that exist in the real world.

A trauma-informed model of care
There are several of different definitions of what being trauma-informed means, and sometimes the term 'trauma-sensitive' is used to mean the same thing. There are now a growing number of organisations and institutions, particularly in the United States that promote a trauma-informed understanding of their service user group, and an approach to responding to their needs that is trauma sensitive. The framework for this is called 'trauma-informed care' (TIC). However TIC itself has also been described as "an amorphous concept" (Hanson and Lang, 2016), with a lack of clarity around what trauma-informed care might actually look

like in practice, or what an organisation might need to do to establish itself as 'trauma-informed'. The definition that I find most efficiently and succinctly encapsulates the core components is:

> Trauma-Informed Care is a strengths-based framework that is grounded in an understanding of and responsiveness to the impact of trauma, that emphasizes physical, psychological, and emotional safety for both providers and survivors, and that creates opportunities for survivors to rebuild a sense of control and empowerment. (Hopper, Bassuk and Olivet, 2010 p. 82)

The US Substance Abuse and Mental Health Services Administration's (SAMHSA) National Centre for Trauma-Informed Care (NCTIC) claim in a recent review document that trauma-informed care has reached a 'tipping point' in the US, and that there has been a significant shift in the cultural responsiveness to this model (SAMHSA-HRSA, 2020). At a 2019 conference hosted by the Community Resilience Initiative (CRI), Jane Stevens led a session entitled 'Reaching the Tipping Point' in which she made a plea for organisations to adopt a trauma-informed approach. She stated;

> We REALLY need to reach a tipping point – ASAP! – in educating people about ACEs science, engaging organizations in the ACEs movement, and in helping them start the process of integrating trauma-informed and resilience-building practices throughout their work. (Stevens, 2019)

At present in the UK, there is not a national body that promotes the practice of trauma-informed care, but the National Health Service (NHS) has made a commitment to providing trauma-informed services in its long-term strategic development plan (Alderwick & Dixon, 2019). There are also a growing number of organisations that are adopting and adapting the model designed by the NCTIC in the US. For example, Homeless Link, in recognition of the complex needs of homeless people, have recently outlined a document advocating both psychologically informed environments (PIE) and trauma-informed care (TIC) as best practice for supporting homeless people in the UK (The Innovation and Good Practice Team, Homeless Link, 2017). For children who have been affected by trauma, many child services providers are now advocating the need to understand the connection between the pain of trauma and the behavioural responses that are symptomatically exhibited, and for adults working with these children to "understand the pervasive impact of their experiences" (Bath, 2008, p. 20) by engaging in a trauma-informed programme that has the potential for healing and growth.

It is recognised that TIC is not a trauma treatment intervention per se, but a framework to support people to make sense of their symptoms as being the product of trauma, and to ensure that services that are provided to offer help do not inadvertently re-traumatise people through lack of understanding of these principles. In fact Homeless Link state clearly that, "it could be considered more dangerous not to work in a trauma or psychologically informed way, than to do so" (The Innovation and Good Practice Team, Homeless Link, 2017, p. 6). David Treleaven (2018), in writing about trauma-sensitive mindfulness has adopted the 'four R's' definition of trauma-sensitive practice put forward by the US National Centre for Trauma-Informed Care. According to the four R's approach, there are several criteria that need to be borne in mind when adapting any programme to be 'trauma-sensitive'. These are listed below:

- Trauma-sensitive practice **realises** that the experiences of trauma and its impact are widespread, and understands that there are different potential paths that lead to recovery.

- Trauma-sensitive practice **recognises** what the symptoms and indications of traumatisation are in individuals, families and organisations
- Trauma-sensitive practice **responds** appropriately by integrating the knowledge of how trauma affects people into all of its practices, policies and procedures.
- Trauma-sensitive practice actively seeks to prevent further harm by engaging in unhelpful practices that may be further **re-traumatising**

When faced with challenging or antisocial behaviour, a common response is to attempt to control the behaviour using incentives and sanctions. This behaviourist model of behaviour management has been prevalent across multiple institutions, organisations and care settings. In child-care environments, children's problematic behaviour has typically been met with controlling or punitive sanctions from those who are in positions of responsibility to care for them (Bath, 2008). In adult settings such as inpatient units or custodial facilities, a similar picture of behaviourist interventions is often prevalent. However, treating behaviour as if it were the product of deliberate disobedience rather than the symptom or manifestation of underlying trauma can actually cause greater problems. Sandra Bloom, author and creator of the Sanctuary Model has referred to the social practices that contribute to the generation of traumatic acts, as 'traumatogenic forces' (Bloom and Reichert, 1998; Bloom, 2019). By failing to recognise these forces, environments may be created that feel very unsafe for the traumatised individual, whose behaviour would be better understood as a reflection of their inner pain (Anglin, 2002). It is this inner pain that a trauma-informed approach argues to have as its primary focus. In other words, by "dealing with primary pain … without unnecessarily inflicting secondary pain … through punitive or controlling reactions" (Anglin, 2002, p. 55). This focus on working to heal the initial wound from trauma without causing further harm is the primary theme of this chapter on avoiding harm, and of the TIM characteristic of the same name.

The central issue in the argument to take a more humane trauma-informed approach to managing socially 'problematic' behaviour is that it appreciates the behaviour is a reaction to unendurable pain, and not simply a morally apprehensible choice. Just as a person in excruciating physical pain may not be able to stop themselves from crying out and writhing around until pain relief is administered, a person in emotional pain may not be able to stop themselves from acting in certain ways until the emotional pain is treated. If a person in terrible physical pain were treated with threats, bribery, restraint or seclusion to stop their screaming and writhing, we would be appalled. In the same way, the emotional pain that is caused by intolerable trauma and abuse cannot be simply 'stopped' by such measures. In fact, we should be equally appalled by such treatment, as these measures can cause even greater damage and harm, and can re-traumatise someone further. Our first responsibility as civilised human beings ought therefore to be to treat one another with compassion and dignity, to recognise emotional suffering more readily, and to utilise interventions that recognise and understand the suffering of others. The medical term for causing unintentional harm in the process of trying to treat someone to help them get better is 'iatrogenesis'. The term iatrogenesis is adopted throughout this chapter to reference the unintended harm that can be caused by trauma interventions designed to relieve suffering, including mindfulness. As Treleaven (2018) reminds us in the four R's mnemonic of trauma-sensitive practice, we need to take active steps to teach people how to recognise where behaviour is symptomatic of underlying trauma, to ensure no further harm befalls those who are already vulnerable by engaging in behaviour management strategies that are re-traumatising. In an attempt to consolidate the necessary components for a service model to claim to be legitimately trauma-informed, Hanson and Lang (2016) conducted a review of the literature, and further consultation and opinion scoping exercises amongst experts in the field of trauma. They found that there were 15 consistent thematic components that characterised trauma-informed care provision across three domains. A simplified list describing these domains and components is presented in table 6.2.

Table 6.2: Components of trauma-informed care (adapted from Hanson and Lang, 2016)

Domain		Component
Workforce development	1.	Staff training on the impact of abuse or trauma
	2.	Measurement of staff ability to demonstrate psychological trauma knowledge and practice
	3.	Processes to address or reduce secondary traumatic stress among staff
	4.	Development of staff knowledge and skills in how to access and refer service users for evidence-based trauma focused interventions
Trauma-focused services	5.	The use of standardised, evidence-based screening or assessment measures to identify trauma history and trauma-related symptoms in service users
	6.	The inclusion of a service user's trauma history in the case record or service plan
	7.	The availability of clinicians trained in providing evidence-based trauma-focused interventions
Organisation environment and practices	8.	Service coordination, collaboration, and sharing of information related to trauma-informed services between professionals within the organisation

	9.	Service coordination, collaboration, and sharing of information related to trauma-informed services amongst professionals in other agencies or organisations
	10.	Systems in place to reduce the risk of re-traumatising service users
	11.	Procedures in place for service users to have input into trauma-informed service development
	12.	The provision of strengths-based services
	13.	The provision of a safe and positive physical environment
	14.	Written policies explicitly supporting trauma-informed ways of working
	15.	A defined trauma-informed care position or job role

Trauma-informed care for children

A helpful model for working with traumatised children is the 'Three Pillars' approach developed by Harry Bath who was the inaugural commissioner for children in Australia's Northern Territory from 2008 until 2015. The model was created primarily as a framework for people who work with or who live with children and young people who have experienced trauma, but who are not necessarily qualified as people who would engage with those young people in formal therapy. The pillars are representative of what are proposed to be the core characteristics necessary to provide a social environment that is conducive to the promotion of growth and healing. The three pillars of 'safety, connections and coping', are based on what are referred to by Bath as "trauma-related needs" (Bath, 2016, p. 3). They are:

Pillar One – Safety: This relates to creating a safe environment within which a young person can engage in age-appropriate developmental activities without fear of threat or harm

Pillar Two – Connections: This relates to the need for developing trusting interpersonal relationships with adults both in their care environment and the community, having opportunity to also develop a sense of belonging and connection to their cultural heritage

Pillar Three – Coping: This relates to the development of skills and strategies for the young person to better manage their emotions and impulses

This is a simple model, designed for non-professionals in order to be able to think about ways in which these components can be created in a variety of situations and settings. These are the basic principles that anyone can adopt to help children, young people and adults take the first steps in healing from their traumatic experiences.

Vulnerability and resilience

One of the things that research in the area of psychological trauma has highlighted is that different people respond to and cope with traumatic experiences in different ways (Bonnano, 2004; Wilson and Drozdek, 2004). A term that is often used to discuss the factors that exist in relation to this individual variability is *resilience*. Although our focus is largely on the negative impact of trauma, according to Bonnano (2009), resilience is the more common reaction to traumatic experiences. The study of what makes some people more resilient to coping with the potentially devastating impact of experiencing trauma is therefore of particular interest, as it holds the potential for perhaps not only being able to predict who may be more vulnerable to the negative effects of trauma, but also perhaps, who may be better able to cope. There are therefore two sides to this area of study: on one side is the investigation of vulnerability factors that might make someone *less* psychologically robust in the face of trauma, and on the other side is the investigation of resilience factors that might make someone *more* psychologically robust in the face of trauma.

Vulnerability

There are a number of factors that have been investigated with regard to what might make a person more susceptible or 'vulnerable' to the negative effects of being impacted by a traumatic experience. One of the variables is that lower IQ tends to be correlated with vulnerability to antisocial behaviour in what are referred to as 'at risk' groups of adolescents and children (Masten et al., 1999). A well-established body of research that has investigated vulnerability factors relates to what are now referred to as ACEs or 'adverse childhood events' which are a wide range of stressful events that are known through empirical study to have a negative impact on children's development. The kinds of stressors that ACEs cover include parental separation and being a 'looked after child' (LAC). Many studies that have examined adverse childhood events have indicated that childhood abuse, neglect and family dysfunction often occur together (Rosenberg et al., 2007). An informative review of the literature that examined a total of 46 research studies suggested a significant correlational relationship between childhood sexual abuse and adult post-traumatic stress disorder (Kendall-Tackett, Williams and Finkelhor, 1993). Some critics of early ACE studies argue that when much of the data were collected, participants were typically aged in their 50s, and were therefore retrospectively constructing the adversities that they felt they experienced during their childhood (Finkelhor et al., 2013).

Resilience

The more recent trend has been an overall redirection of focus away from seeking to identify risk factors, towards seeking to identify strengths (Richardson, 2002). In an attempt to define what resilience is, the dictionary definition denotes it as an ability to "recover quickly from difficulties" or "spring back into shape" (*Oxford English Dictionary*, 2018, n.p.). The term 'resilience' is often used in the literature as if it is a quantifiable and measurable variable that is either intrinsic to a person, or can be behaviourally learned (Agaibi and Wilson, 2005). It is also considered by some researchers to be an adaptive 'consequence' of positive human development (Caffo and Belaise, 2003). Others have favoured conceptualising resilience in terms of a person's capacity to adapt to their environment and circumstances effectively, and be able to return to their previous level of functioning once a stressful period has passed (Richardson, 2002). In other words, the capacity to 'bounce back' to the same pre-trauma performance levels (Lazarus and Folkman, 1984). In a systematic review of the literature Agaibi and Wilson (2005) distinguished five different working definitions used by researchers in this area:

1. **Lexical:** A dictionary definition of psychological resilience refers to the properties of an object, which after being temporarily distorted by external pressure is able to return to its original form
2. **Base-line:** This definition of psychological resilience refers to the non-context-specific aspects of an individual including affect-regulation, cognition, perception, and information processing
3. **Adverse conditions:** This definition refers to those particular psychologically resilient behaviours that a person might engage in that are effective as determined by the outcome
4. **Adaptive coping:** This definition refers to the capacity to adapt and cope effectively within adverse situations and environments
5. **Protective factors:** This way of defining resilience refers to the particular factors thought to be important in enabling coping in the face of trauma, such as social support. It also considers individual differences, and the potential for variability over a lifespan as personality and environmental factors interact

It seems to be that the research on resilience overall concludes that it is not an individual characteristic or trait (Rutter, 1999), but is a multidimensional construct (Block and Kremen, 1996). Having reviewed the research on resilience, Richardson (2002) proposed that there are three core approaches that can be taken to studying resilience in order to understand and predict it more easily:

1. Identification of the unique characteristics or traits of individuals who appear to cope well in the face of adversity
2. Identification of the processes by which resilience appears to develop through life experiences
3. Identification of the cognitive mechanisms that appear to be key in directing adaptive responses

In Richardson's approach, the foundational premise is that these three areas of study – individual characteristics, developmental experiences, and cognitive mechanisms, are likely to illuminate what it is about certain individuals that appears to make them more resilient to stressful life events than others who may be more vulnerable to being adversely affected. It is thought that if we could understand what makes some people more resilient, it might be possible to first of all predict who those individuals are (perhaps for recruitment purposes to certain professions), and second perhaps to discover whether some of these mechanisms can be taught to and learned by others who are naturally less resilient. When reviewing the literature in this area, there are three characteristics of resilience that appear repeatedly (Caffo and Belaise, 2003). These are:

1. The intrinsic qualities or characteristics of the individual
2. The severity, chronicity and accumulation of external stressors

3. The behavioural adaptability of the individual to the external stressor

Taking these findings and the previous definitions into account, and bearing in mind the core areas of debate regarding the degree to which the internal intrinsic or innate traits of an individual interact with their behavioural responses to environmental stressors, I have developed a tripod model of representing resilience. I have deliberately not separated out psychological resilience from physical resilience, as I believe that the two are inseparably connected. For example, research clearly indicates that chronic and significant stress, places demands on the body that can frequently lead to physical health problems (Schnurr and Green, 2004). I have therefore simply referred to 'resilience', acknowledging the fact that psychological stress has a considerable physical impact on the body and vice versa. This model takes into account the aforementioned variables of individual differences and the individual, cognitive or behavioural responses, and adds in a component that also acknowledges the amount and severity of the external stressors. The proposed tripod model of resilience is illustrated in figure 6.1. As the model suggests, it seems that taking into account all three of these variables is sensible when assessing resilience.

In line with this tripod model of psychological resilience, each facet is described further in table 6.3.

The first of these variables relates to the innate characteristics of an individual. The second variable relates to the event itself, which cannot be changed after the fact. However, the possibility of potentially changing the perspective of the person experiencing the event relates to the third variable of cognitive and behavioural adaptation.

Avoidance of harm

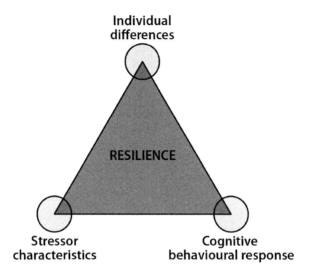

Figure 6.1: The tripod model of resilience

Table 6.3: Description of the facets of the tripod model of psychological resilience

Label	Resilience facet	Description
Individual differences	The intrinsic qualities and characteristics of the individual	Individual differences that are the personal attributes of an individual including values, beliefs, cognitive schemas, worldview, flexibility of thinking, temperament, physical health, sense of self, emotional connection and expression, level of embodiment and perception and meaning-making frameworks. These tend to be innate characteristics, but are also changeable over time and as a result of life experiences

Stressor characteristics	The severity, chronicity and accumulation of external stressors	This takes into account all that is known about 'large T' and 'small t' traumas together with the *DSM* and the *ICD* definitions of criterion A trauma regarding trauma severity. It also acknowledges the impact of chronicity of trauma and extreme stress over time, together with frequency of trauma exposure accumulated during a lifespan
Cognitive behavioural response	The cognitive and behavioural adaptability of the individual to external stressors	Cognitive appraisals and behavioural responses to external stressors that enable an individual to adapt and respond to adverse, stressful and traumatic situations and environments in ways that support personal wellbeing. This also includes an individual's capacity to learn and utilise new strategies and skills and to effectively engage with positive social support

This is probably the main variable that is a more realistic option to be addressed as a target for interventions focused on strengthening or developing resilience. Research indicates that the coping mechanisms people employ tend to be dependent on the particular situation, with environmental and situational variables interacting with personality variables (Parkes, 1986). For example, children may demonstrate resilience when faced with certain adverse events and stressors but not others (Rutter, 1999). Additionally, children and adolescents cope better with adverse life events when there are protective factors in place, such as experiencing stable, nurturing care from others (Agaibi and Wilson, 2005). Similarly, research shows that even those children who have not had those kinds of relationships early in life can 'catch up' to some extent if provided with stable nurturing care later. The classic studies of UK adopted Romanian orphans conducted in the 1990s are good examples of this, where very young children who had experienced extreme physical and cognitive deprivation were found to return to 'normal' developmental trajectories several years later post-adoption (Rutter, and the English and Romanian Adoptees Study Team, 1998).

The same team who conducted those initial studies have continued to follow up the adopted children, and found that although many children made remarkable recoveries, there were also "major persistent deficits in a substantial minority" (Rutter and O'Connor, 2004, p. 81). The conclusions are interesting, because although there was a clear correlation between the length of time the child had remained in a deprived environment, and their capacity to recover from its damaging effects, there were still individual differences for which there was no accounting. More recent studies from the same research group have suggested an interaction between early life deprivation, genetic predisposition, and stressful life events later in life (Kumsta et al., 2010). Other research findings have shown that a vital component for children's development of resilience is to have a positive connection with a caring adult such as a teacher or mentor (Benard, 2004; Rutter, 2013). Indeed, research has consistently indicated that one of the main factors associated with resilience is attachment and interpersonal support (Masten, 2015). Given the different factors that relate to resilience and vulnerability, a helpful psycho-education aid to support advice about developing resilience is the stress-vulnerability model.

The stress-vulnerability model
The stress-vulnerability model was developed by Zubin and Spring (1977) as a way to extract the common factors of other

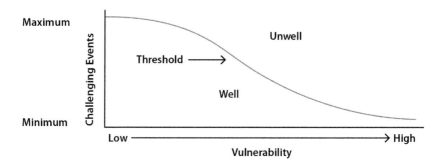

Figure 6.2: Diagram of the relationship between vulnerability and challenge in the stress-vulnerability model (from Zubin and Spring, 1977)

explanatory models for schizophrenia. Although originally designed as a model to draw together disparate explanations for schizophrenia, the stress-vulnerability model is now used for understanding and explaining the role of stress in a range of mental illnesses and is also useful for "identifying and treating relapses of mental illness" (Goh and Agius, 2010, p. 198). According to this model there is a direct relationship between vulnerability and challenging events. In other words, a person's threshold for managing greater challenges decreases proportionally in relation to their vulnerability. An illustration of the model is provided in figure 6.2 to demonstrate this relationship.

According to the stress-vulnerability model, people who are more vulnerable (due to the combined influence of environmental, biological and psychological factors), tend to have a lower *threshold* to becoming unwell when faced with challenging events or circumstances. People who are low on the scale in terms of vulnerability conversely have a greater capacity to endure challenging events without becoming ill. What the stress-vulnerability model adds to our understanding so far is a greater appreciation of individual differences by taking a bio-psycho-social perspective. This approach combines our understanding of the biological, psychological and social influences that have affected, and are likely to continue to increase the probability of experiencing a mental health difficulty. The notion of 'vulnerability' relates to people who have a greater number of pre-existing elements that when combined together are likely to reduce their ability to coping with challenges.

Another way that this relationship between vulnerability and challenge can be explained to a client is using the metaphor of the 'stress bucket'. A diagram of the model is provided in figure 6.3 (overleaf). This has been represented for illustrative purposes in three stages: first the size of the 'bucket' relates to a person's current degree of vulnerability to stress, second the 'rain' denotes the number, size and frequency of challenging events or circumstances that the person is or has been exposed to, and third are the possible solutions. Three are listed, which are to increase the size of the bucket (increase resilience and lessen vulnerability), to reduce the number or size of the life challenges, or to learn ways to 'release' the pressure in the bucket so that it does not overflow. The analogy of the bucket overflowing is akin to the idea of a person being overwhelmed and unable to cope with the current demands in their life.

As it is not always possible to have direct control over reducing the size or number of challenging life events, a focus on increasing resilience (reducing vulnerability) and learning ways to release stress is usually a more practical solution.

Increasing resilience
There has been a change in contemporary positive psychology from a focus on the identification of risk factors to vulnerability,

Figure 6.3 (overleaf): Illustration of the 'stress bucket' analogy

The first stage of the model is the size of the bucket	
This relates to the person's overall vulnerability level – the smaller the bucket the greater the vulnerability.	
The second stage of the model is number of 'life challenges' that go into the bucket	
The water droplets filling the bucket each relate to different life circumstances and challenges that are 'raining down' on the person. Those with a smaller bucket (the more vulnerable) can cope with fewer of these challenges before their bucket is full, than people with less vulnerability. The bigger the bucket = the more 'rain' you can cope with before your bucket starts to overflow.	
The third stage of the model relates to possible solutions	  = bigger = less = release

200

> The possible solutions to becoming overwhelmed are threefold: by increasing the size of a person's 'bucket' by decreasing vulnerability and increasing resilience, by reducing the amount of 'rain' or challenging events in a person's life, or by finding ways to 'release' excess water in the bucket and lessening the impact of the challenging events by learning ways to release the tension.

and an interest instead on what factors may build resiliency (Richardson, 2002). In relation to the inherent characteristics of the individual, perhaps these latent aspects are less available to manipulation, and may potentially constitute an underlying vulnerability. The second relates to the chronicity and severity of stressful events, and again is not always easy to change. However, the third element, that of behavioural adaptation, is exactly the component or variable that is definitely open to being worked with and strengthened. Bear in mind however, that whatever the person has been using as a coping strategy up to this point has provided them with a level of functional relief from their distress. Therefore, whatever support is offered is best considered as *additional to* rather than *instead of* to start with. What this means is that we are not trying to take away current coping strategies, as harmful as they could be, but rather to offer additional strategies, so that the person begins to have a choice of options that can be used in a given situation. Eventually, as the new, more helpful or less harmful strategies prove to be effective, the person can then voluntarily choose to use them more often, and gradually lessen their need to keep using the older more problematic strategies.

What is known about some of the factors that can promote resilience is that a sense of control and choice can be instrumental in both facilitating strength in the face of adversity, and in making sense of what has happened afterwards. Talking about the experience of post-traumatic growth, which is a positive outcome that many people experience as a result of trauma, Tedeschi, Park and Calhoun found that those who have "even modest control, are more likely to have transformative experiences" (1998, p. 226). Indeed Masten (2001) shares the same view. She advocates that resilience is a 'normative process' and observes that "choices at crucial junctures play an important role in the life course of resilient individuals" (Masten, 2001, p. 227). This element of choice is a recurring theme across the trauma literature, and is something that has been covered in more detail in chapter five as a primary characteristic of delivering TIM. The American Psychiatric Association (2019), suggests ten ways to increase resilience. For convenience, these are represented in table 6.4.

Table 6.4: Ten ways to develop resilience (APA, 2019)

Resilience factor	Description
Make connections	Make good connections through relationships with friends and family. Social support strengthens resilience by accepting help and being listened to. Joining groups such as a faith-based organisation or groups that share similar interests can help. Also, if you are able to reach out to help someone else in need, it can benefit the person offering the help as well
Avoid seeing crises as insurmountable problems	Adopting this attitude means that although you cannot change the fact that very stressful things happen, you can have some control over how you respond to those events. One way is to try to look past the current pain to a time in the future when things may be a little better. If you take notice, you may see the subtle ways in which you are beginning to feel a little bit better whilst you are still dealing with difficult situations
Accept that change is a part of living	It may well be that some of your previous goals are no longer possible to attain as a result of the adversity that has been experienced.

	However, by learning to accept those circumstances that cannot be changed, you can place your focus more on those circumstances over which you can have some influence
Move toward your goals	Start by creating new realistic goals. When you have the key is to take action towards your goal regularly, even if what you do is only a tiny step. Each tiny step will add up and your overall direction of travel is towards the accomplishment of your goals. Instead of placing your attention on trying to do things that seem unachievable, focus on what you *can* do
Take decisive actions	Take action in whatever way that you can in relation to any adverse situations in your life. Instead of just detaching from problems and stresses, hoping they will go away, take decisive actions to do something about them
Look for opportunities for self-discovery	As a result of struggle and loss people often find that they learn something new about themselves and may grow in other ways too. When people have experienced hardship or tragedy they can find that they have greater strength than they knew, even though they also felt vulnerable. Going through very difficult situations can increase self-worth, improve relationships, develop more spirituality and instil a greater appreciation for life
Nurture a positive view of yourself	When you develop more confidence in your ability to solve problems and to trust your instincts, this also helps to build resilience
Keep things in perspective	Even when you are facing very painful events, if you try to think about the stressful situation you are going through in relation to the

	broader context it will help you to focus on the longer-term perspective. As bad as it is, take care to try not to lose sight of the bigger picture
Maintain a hopeful outlook	When you hold on to an optimistic perspective, this enables you to change your expectancy so that you expect that good things will happen. It is better to try to visualise what you want to happen, rather than worrying about what you fear
Take care of yourself	Finally, it is always very important to look after yourself and to give attention to your own needs and feelings. You can do this by taking part in activities that you find enjoyable or relaxing. Taking care of yourself, maybe by exercising regularly, helps to keep your mind and body well so that you are much more able to cope with situations that require resilience

Potential iatrogenic consequences of PTSD treatment

The unintended adverse or iatrogenic impact of PTSD treatment is not something that has received a great deal of research attention. Although there is data to indicate that some psychological interventions may induce harm, it is unclear whether there is in fact a systematic approach to routinely collecting information about any adverse effects in clinical trials (Jonsson et al., 2014). One of the few studies that has sought to investigate the collection and reporting of data that might indicate unintended harm in psychological interventions for PTSD was conducted by Bisson and colleagues (2013), who examined 70 previously published studies of treatments for people with PTSD, but found that there was very little information about any reported outcomes that may have been problematic. In fact, not one of the 70 studies investigated reported on any negative reactions to the treatment, and only 11 of them discussed treatment dropout. In conclusion the authors advised "there is insufficient evidence to show whether or not psychological therapy is harmful" (Bisson et al., 2013).

Similarly, Jonsson and colleagues concluded from their systematic review of harm-reporting in studies published between 2010 and 2014 that "important information about harms is not reported systematically within this research field, suggesting that the risk of reporting bias is nontrivial in conclusions about the risk-benefit ratio of psychological treatments" (2014, p. 2). This concern about not having adequate data to compare the risks against the benefits of certain treatment options does indeed appear to be a significant obstacle to providing a full and comprehensive picture to would-be clients about different treatment options. The only concrete data that is currently available about the possible iatrogenic impact of trauma treatments is the lack of uptake and dropout. Lack of uptake may be due to fear, lack of knowledge, mis-information, stigma, and lack of trust in the therapeutic relationship (Young, 2009). It is known that common anxieties for clients anticipating engaging in trauma treatment are that they will be re-traumatised (Vincent et al., 2013) and/or that the treatment will fail (d'Ardenne and Heke, 2014). This is arguably not a completely unfounded concern, as the primary recommended therapies for PTSD, whether trauma-focused cognitive behavioural therapy (tf-CBT) or EMDR both require "bringing distressing trauma-related images, beliefs, and bodily sensations to mind" (Bisson et al., 2013, n.p.). Less is known about dropout reasons; however, a characteristic of trauma therapy is that clients are required to repeatedly revisit their past trauma in detail as a way to process the memory (Brewin and Holmes, 2003). This repeated revisiting of acutely painful memories may prove to be too challenging for many, and thus clients drop out from therapy at the point that this happens.

In terms of mindfulness-based interventions, these too are potentially not without adverse effects. However, the same problem of reporting is present in the literature on mindfulness-based studies. As Cebolla and colleagues argue, "it seems that the expansion of mindfulness in the West has been associated with a gentle, positive vision of the technique, without the necessary balance related to the negative consequences of any practice" (2017, n.p.). Several other authors have also noted that a problem with the way that many mindfulness studies are reported is that they often fail to state whether there have been any adverse effects. For example, in a review of 47 trials of meditation-based interventions, the authors noted that very few had mentioned any negative outcomes from the interventions (Goyal et al., 2014). In seeking to rectify this omission, a recent study by Schlosser and colleagues (2019) involving an international sample of 1,232 participants who meditated regularly, asked participants about whether they had experienced any unpleasant meditation-related experiences. In total, 315 participants (about a quarter) reported that they had experiences that included an altered sense of the self or the world, fear, anxiety, and distortions in thoughts or emotions.

In another study of predominantly Spanish participants (Cebolla et al., 2017), 25% reported experiencing 'unwanted effects' (UEs) from meditation. Although most of these unwanted effects were reported to be quite mild, this is not always the case. A study in 2018 by Vieten and colleagues found quite a wide range of experiences that were disturbing to the participants. In this online study of 1,120 meditators the majority of participants reported experiencing "anomalous and extraordinary experiences" (Vieten, 2018, n.p.). However, only half shared their experiences with their teachers, indicating perhaps that in the general population of meditators including those practicing mindfulness meditation, more people may be experiencing 'anomalous' events during their practice of which we are currently unaware. Some of the experiences encountered by participants in the Vieten and colleagues (2018) study were physical and perceptual sensations that were apparently not related to the physical environment. These included changes in temperature, feelings of pressure and tingling sensations, seeing visions, images or lights, experiencing somatic sensations of floating or heaviness/lightness, missing body parts, hearing buzzing sounds, humming or singing, out of body experiences, and the feeling of changes in body shape or size (60–90% of participants), and smelling or tasting things not actually present (35%). In addition, meditators reported experiencing distortions of time, being in the future or re-experiencing the past (86%). Importantly, this last anomalous experience of time distortion was reported by 60% of participants to occur either 'many times', or 'almost always'. Finally, 32% of participants surveyed also described feeling 'fear, dread, or terror' either during meditation or shortly after. Taken together, this array of symptoms does appear worryingly similar to many symptoms experienced by individuals suffering from PTSD. It is possible therefore that if trauma-symptomatic individuals were to engage in similar meditation practices, they may feel very frightened by the similarity between these anomalous meditation experiences and their familiar PTSD symptoms. Considering the possibility for such abreactions to mindfulness-based interventions amongst post-trauma clients, an ethical approach to such interventions that takes account of such possibilities, is prudent.

Tailored trauma-interventions
In response to the usual recommendations to adopt a phased treatment approach, which is discussed in detail in chapter eight, the conclusion that some authors are starting to put forward is that treatment should move away from a 'one-size-fits-all' method of

trauma-treatment (Steenkamp, 2016), and "towards developing interventions that are tailored to meet the specific PTSD and co-morbid symptoms profiles" (Murphy et al., 2019, p. 1). The research by Murphy and colleagues (ibid.) suggests that although all PTSD sufferers share the same symptoms, some experience certain symptoms in more extreme ways than others. Their conclusion is therefore that if certain symptoms, such as avoidance for example, are more prominent, this should be considered in relation to what treatment is offered. Another way of tailoring interventions has been offered by Galovski and colleagues (2012) who found positive benefits in their plot trial of tailoring the number of sessions of PTSD therapy to between four and 18 sessions, dependent on the client. Another way to tailor treatment options is to provide multiple trauma-treatment sessions during a one week 'intensive' which Ehlers and colleagues (2010) suggest is more difficult for clients to avoid, and offers a quicker opportunity to return to normal life. There are additional new approaches to working with specific populations (Kiyimba, 2019), such as Accelerated Resolution Therapy (ART), which is a brief intervention that has good evidence of efficacy with military veterans suffering from PTSD and co-morbid traumatic brain injury (TBI) (Kip et al., 2019). Also psychiatrists Corrigan and Hull have written about the benefits of the Comprehensive Resource Model (CRM) developed by Lisa Schwartz in treating complex post-traumatic stress disorder (CPTSD) (Hull and Corrigan, 2019). These advances in creating new approaches to relieving trauma symptoms in particular client groups is a welcome step forward in understanding the heterogeneous nature of trauma experiences.

Summary
In summary, this chapter has addressed the key components required within TIM for a trauma intervention that is designed to take care to avoid harm. This has been achieved by explaining initially that many behaviours traumatised individuals engage in as a reaction to, or way of managing their symptoms may not be understood as such. Therefore, the value of adopting a trauma-informed approach within organisations, and interventions that work with these clients, is advocated and explained. In addition, this chapter explains some of the factors that might increase a person's vulnerability to being adversely affected by traumatic experiences, and those factors that might support and promote resilience. Although there has been much research into effective trauma interventions, there has been far less attention paid to the potential for harm to be caused in the course of engaging in those treatments. Thus, this chapter has also introduced the concept that iatrogenic or unintended harm may be caused in the application of interventions for people suffering from trauma-related difficulties. This awareness is the backdrop for promoting a trauma-informed approach to any therapeutic intervention that also bears in mind the possibility for traumatisation or re-traumatisation in its application. The TIM characteristic of avoidance of harm is applied to the possibility that inappropriately managed mindfulness interventions for trauma may increase risk of abreaction if due care is not given to issues of safety, choice and titration of practices. It is not intended that by drawing awareness to these issues, would-be TIM facilitators are frightened of working with trauma clients or that the work is presented as over-complicated and only to be attempted by experts. However, it is offered as a sober reflection on the need to take appropriate measures to work with caution, sensitivity and due diligence. This chapter provides a rationale for the need for titration of practice, which is the topic of chapter seven.

References

Agaibi, C. E., & Wilson, J. P. (2005). Trauma, PTSD, and resilience: A review of the literature. *Trauma, Violence and Abuse, 6*(3), 195–216.

Alderwick, H. & Dixon, J. (2019). The NHS long term plan. *BMJ, 364.* l84. Retrieved from https://doi.org/10.1136/bmj.l84

American Psychiatric Association (2019). *Ten ways to build resilience.* Retrieved from https://www.apa.org/helpcenter/road-resilience

Anglin, J. P. (2002). *Pain, normality, and the struggle for congruence: Reinterpreting residential care for children and youth.* New York, NY: Haworth Press.

Bath, H. (2008). The three pillars of trauma-informed care. *Reclaiming Children and Youth, 17*(3), 17–21.

Bath, H. (2016, August). The three pillars of transforming care: Healing in the 'other 23 hours'. Retrieved from http://www.twi.org.au/3PHealingInTheOther23Hours.pdf

Benard, B. (2004). *Resiliency: What have we learned?* San Francisco, CA: WestEd.

Bisson J., Andrew M., Lewis C., Cooper R., & Roberts N. (2013, 13 December). Psychological therapies for chronic post-traumatic stress disorder (PTSD) in adults. *Cochrane Database Systematic Review, 12.*

Block, J., & Kremen, A. M. (1996). IQ and ego-resiliency: conceptual and empirical connections and separateness. *Journal of Personality and Social Psychology, 70*(2), 349.

Bloom, S. (2019). *Traumatogenic forces in society.* The Sanctuary Model. Retrieved from http://sanctuaryweb.com/PublicHealth/TraumatogenicForcesinSociety.aspx

Bloom, S. L., & Reichert, M. (1998). *Bearing witness: Violence and collective responsibility.* Binghamton, NY: Haworth Press.

Bonnano, G. A. (2004). Loss, trauma and human resilience: Conceptual and empirical connections and separateness. *American Psychologist, 59*(1), 20–28.

Bonnano, G. (2009). *The other side of sadness: What the new science of bereavement tells us about life after a loss.* New York, NY: Basic Books.

Brewin, C. R., & Holmes, E. A. (2003). Psychological theories of posttraumatic stress disorder. *Clinical Psychology Review, 23*(3), 339–376.

Caffo, E., & Belaise, C. (2003). Psychological aspects of traumatic injury in children and adolescents. *Child and Adolescent Psychiatric Clinics of North America, 12*(3), 493–535.

Cebolla, A., Demarzo, M., Martins, P., Soler, J., & Garcia-Campayo, J. (2017). Unwanted effects: Is there a negative side of meditation? A multicentre survey. *PloS One, 12*(9), e0183137.

d'Ardenne, P., & Heke, S. (2014). Patient-reported outcomes in post-traumatic stress disorder Part I: Focus on psychological treatment. *Dialogues in Clinical Neuroscience, 16*(2), 213.

Ehlers, A., Clark, D., Hackmann, A., Grey, N., Liness, S., Wild, J., Manley, J., Waddington, L., & McManus, F. (2010). Intensive cognitive therapy for PTSD: A feasibility study. *Behavioural and Cognitive Psychotherapy, 38*(4), 383–398.

Finkelhor, D., Shattuck, A., Turner, H., & Hamby, S. (2013). Improving the adverse childhood experiences study scale. *Journal of the American Medical Association Pediatrics, 167*(1), 70–75.

Galovski, T. E., Blain, L. M., Mott, J. M., Elwood, L., & Houle, T. (2012). Manualized therapy for PTSD: Flexing the structure of cognitive processing therapy. *Journal of Consulting and Clinical Psychology, 80*(6), 968.

Goh, C., & Agius, M. (2010). The stress-vulnerability model how does stress impact on mental illness at the level of the brain and what are the consequences? *Psychiatria Danubina, 22*(2), 198–202.

Goyal, M., Singh, S., Sibinga, E. M., Gould, N. F., Rowland-Seymour, A., Sharma, R., Berger, Z., Sleicher, D., Maron, D. D., Shihab, H. M., & Ranasinghe, P. D. (2014). Meditation programs for psychological stress and well-being: A systematic review and meta-analysis. *JAMA Internal Medicine, 174*(3), 357–368.

Hanson, R. F., & Lang, J. (2016). A critical look at trauma-informed care among agencies and systems serving maltreated youth and their families. *Child Maltreatment, 21*, 95–100.

Hopper, E. K., Bassuk, E. L., & Olivet, J. (2010). Shelter from the storm: Trauma-informed care in homelessness services settings. *The Open Health Services and Policy Journal, 3*(2), 80–100.

Hull, A. M., & Corrigan, F. M. (2019). The Comprehensive Resource Model®: Overview of basic affects in adversity & effective treatment for complex reactions to trauma. *Counselling and Psychotherapy Research, 19*(2), 130–137.

Innovation and Good Practice Team, Homeless Link, The (2017). *An introduction to psychologically informed environments and trauma-informed care briefing for homelessness services.* London, United Kingdom: The Innovation and Good Practice Team.

Jonsson, U., Alaie, I., Parling, T., & Arnberg, F. K. (2014). Reporting of harms in randomized controlled trials of psychological interventions for mental and behavioral disorders: A review of current practice. *Contemporary Clinical Trials, 38*(1), 1–8.

Kendall-Tackett, K. A., Williams, L. M., & Finkelhor, D. (1993). Impact of sexual abuse on children: A review and synthesis of recent empirical studies. *Psychological Bulletin, 113*(1), 164.

Kip, K. E., Berumen, J., Zeidan, A. R., Hernandez, D. F., & Finnegan, A. P. (2019). The emergence of accelerated resolution therapy for treatment of post-traumatic stress disorder: A review and new subgroup analyses. *Counselling and Psychotherapy Research, 19*(2), 117–129.

Kiyimba, N. (2019). Moving forward: New frontiers in treatments for psychological trauma. *Counselling and Psychotherapy Research, 19*(2), 102–104.

Kumsta, R., Stevens, S., Brookes, K., Schlotz, W., Castle, J., Beckett, C., Kreppner, J., Rutter, M., & Sonuga-Barke, E. (2010). 5HTT genotype moderates the influence of early institutional deprivation on emotional problems in adolescence: Evidence from the English and Romanian Adoptee (ERA) study. *Journal of Child Psychology and Psychiatry, 51*(7), 755–762.

Lazarus, R. S., & Folkman, S. (1984*). Stress: Appraisal, and coping.* New York, NY: Springer.

Masten, A. S. (2001). Ordinary magic: Resilience processes in development. *American Psychologist, 56*(3), 227.

Masten, A. S. (2015). *Ordinary magic: Resilience in development.* New York, NY: Guilford Press.

Masten, A. S., Hubbard, J. J., Gest, S. D., Tellegen, A., Garmezy, N., & Ramirez, M. (1999). Competence in the context of adversity: Pathways to resilience and maladaptation from childhood to late adolescence. *Development and Psychopathology, 11*(1), 143–169.

Murphy, D., Ross, J., Busuttil, W., Greenberg, N., & Armour, C. (2019). A latent profile analysis of PTSD symptoms among UK treatment seeking veterans. *European Journal of Psychotraumatology, 10*(1), 1558706.

Oxford English Dictionary (2018). Retrieved from https://en.oxforddictionaries.com/definition/resilience

Parkes, K. R. (1986). Coping in stressful episodes: The role of individual differences, environmental factors, and situational characteristics. *Journal of Personality and Social Psychology, 51*(6), 1277.

Richardson, G. E. (2002). The metatheory of resilience and resiliency. *Journal of Clinical Psychology, 58*(3), 307–321.

Rosenberg, S. D., Lu, W., Mueser, K. T., Jankowski, M. K., & Cournos, F. (2007). Correlates of adverse childhood events among adults with schizophrenia spectrum disorders. *Psychiatric Services, 58*(2), 245–253.

Rutter, M. (1999). Resilience concepts and findings: Implications for family therapy. *Journal of Family Therapy, 21*(2), 119–144.

Rutter, M. (2013). Annual research review: Resilience–clinical implications. *Journal of Child Psychology and Psychiatry, 54*(4), 474–487.

Rutter, M., & the English and Romanian Adoptees Study Team (1998). Developmental catch-up and deficit following adoption after severe global early privation. *Journal of Child Psychology and Psychiatry, 39*, 465–476.

Rutter, M., & O'Connor, T. G. (2004). Are there biological programming effects for psychological development? Findings from a study of Romanian adoptees. *Developmental Psychology, 40*(1), 81.

SAMHSA-HRSA (2020). Trauma. Centre for Integrated Health Solutions. Retrieved from https://www.integration.samhsa.gov/clinical-practice/trauma-informed

Schlosser, M., Sparby, T., Vörös, S., Jones, R., & Marchant, N. L. (2019). Unpleasant meditation-related experiences in regular meditators: Prevalence, predictors, and conceptual considerations. *PloS One, 14*(5), e0216643.

Schnurr, P., & Green, B. (2004). *Trauma and health: Physical consequences of exposure to extreme stress.* Washington, DC: APA Books.

Steenkamp, M. M. (2016). True evidence-based care for posttraumatic stress disorder in military personnel and veterans. *JAMA Psychiatry, 73*(5), 431–432.

Stevens, J. (2019). Reaching the Tipping Point: 2019 BPT Big Idea Session by Jane Stevens. ACE's Connection. Retrieved from https://www.acesconnection.com/blog/reaching-the-tipping-point-2019-bpt-big-idea-session-by-jane-stevens

Tedeschi, R., Park, C., & Calhoun, L. (Eds.) (1998). *Posttraumatic growth: Positive changes in the aftermath of crisis.* London, United Kingdom: Lawrence Erlbaum Associates.

Treleaven, D. (2018). *Trauma sensitive mindfulness: Practices for safe and transformative healing.* New York, NY: W. W. Norton Publishers.

Vieten, C., Wahbeh, H., Cahn, B. R., MacLean, K., Estrada, M., Mills, P., Murphy, M., Shapiro, S., Radin, D., Josipovic, Z., & Presti, D. E. (2018). Future directions in meditation research: Recommendations for expanding the field of contemplative science. *PloS One, 13*(11), e0205740.

Vincent, F., Jenkins, H., Larkin, M., & Clohessy, S. (2013). Asylum-seekers' experiences of trauma-focused cognitive behaviour therapy for post-traumatic stress disorder: A qualitative study. *Behavioural and Cognitive Psychotherapy, 41*(5), 579–593.

Wilson, J. P., & Drozdek, B. (2004). *Broken spirits: The treatment of traumatized asylum seekers, refugees and war and torture victims.* London, United Kingdom: Routledge.

Young, K. (2009). Cognitive therapy for survivors of torture. In N. Grey (Ed.), *A casebook of cognitive therapy for traumatic stress reactions* (pp. 247–264). London, United Kingdom: Routledge.

Zubin, J., & Spring, B. (1977). Vulnerability: A new view of schizophrenia. *Journal of Abnormal Psychology, 86*(2), 103.

CHAPTER SEVEN
WORK WITH TITRATION

Chapter contents
• The window of tolerance • Dissociation as a psychological defence • Dissociation and awareness • Increasing awareness with mindfulness • The risks of awareness • Working with avoidance • Being in the body • Titration • Summary

The term 'titration' is used throughout this chapter as a way to explain the different ways in which exercises in TIM can be adapted and adjusted in a gently graded way, so as to be more challenging gradually and incrementally. The concept of the window of tolerance is also introduced in companionship with this approach, as it offers a useful framework to visualise when a client is in a stable state of arousal, neither hyper- nor hypo-aroused. When a client is in a stable arousal state, this is the most conducive state to taking on board the new information being introduced. This chapter also engages in a discussion of the relationship between dissociation and awareness. Dissociation is a common coping strategy for people who have experienced trauma, and often serves as a protection against the pain of external and internal reminders of the event. In contrast, mindfulness activities by their nature are designed to increase awareness of the present moment and of the sensory, cognitive, emotional and somatic experiences of being totally present.

In relation to the wider issue of the need to titrate TIM exercises in a way that will not trigger a client to 'pop out' of their window of tolerance into a hyper-state abreaction or hypo-state dissociation, the topic of how awareness and dissociation relate to one another is explored. This is further examined through a discussion regarding avoidance as a trauma symptom, and how best to work with avoidance in a way that does not collude with the problem, and yet faces the avoided triggers in a sensitive and titrated way in order to break the maintenance cycle that avoidance can create. Having laid the theoretical foundations, the latter part of this chapter takes a more pragmatic approach to considering exactly how TIM exercises can be titrated both through proximity (in the outside environment, in the body, or inner processes) and by time (through incrementally increasing the length of practice or frequency). In chapter one (table 1.1) the full specification for learning requirements relating to the seven TIM characteristics was provided. Table 7.1 is a duplicate of the section of that table that relates to work with titration, and is provided here as a reminder for pedagogical purposes. This chapter explicates in more detail the descriptive elements that relate specifically to this characteristic.

Table 7.1: Trauma-Informed Mindfulness characteristic 6. 'work with titration' learning aims

	TIM characteristic	Description
6.	**Work with titration**	• To have an understanding of the need for titrating mindfulness practice at the pace of the individual, so as to minimise the risk of re-traumatisation • To commit to always working collaboratively with a client to establish titration levels and choice of practices

		<ul><li>To understand the need to balance the dialectics of challenge and validation</li><li>To try not to work with too many skills of mindfulness in one practice, but to develop them incrementally</li><li>To take a strengths-based approach, so that the individual is able to build mastery before moving to the next level</li></ul>

The window of tolerance

The window of tolerance is a tool used to help explain the optimal level of stress or arousal that is ideal to function healthily, and was first proposed as a model of autonomic arousal by Dan Siegel (Siegel, 1999). It relates to the Yerkes-Dodson law (Yerkes and Dodson, 1908), which demonstrated that humans perform at their best when they have a certain amount of physiological or mental arousal. The term 'eustress' has been coined to explain this beneficial level of stress (Lazarus, 1974), and is a combination of the Greek *eu* meaning good, with stress; i.e. 'good stress' or in other words 'stress without distress' (Selye, 1974). However, if the stress level goes too high, performance decreases. It is when stress levels go above the optimum range for effective healthy functioning that distress occurs, and a person becomes *hyper*-aroused. Hyper-arousal is associated with recognisable physiological symptoms, including increased heart rate, sweating, shallow breathing, a dry mouth and stomach churning. When arousal levels drop too low, a person is described as being *hypo*-aroused, which is recognisable by behaviours such as loss of interest, lack of concentration, difficulty feeling motivated, and generally feeling 'flat'. These two extremes are detailed more fully in table 7.2.

Table 7.2: Descriptions of the differences between hyper-arousal and hypo-arousal

Level of arousal	Physiological response system	Description
Hyper-arousal (too much arousal)	The sympathetic nervous system response	This is related to states that are commonly known as the 'fight or flight' responses. Typically, it is associated with feelings of anxiety, panic or tension, accompanied by racing thoughts, intrusive imagery, feeling unsafe, tense, and engaging in hyper-vigilant or impulsive behaviour
Hypo-arousal (too little arousal)	The parasympathetic nervous system response	This is related to states that are commonly known as the 'freeze or flop' response. Typically, it is associated with feelings of emotional numbness or emptiness, with difficulty concentrating or remembering, lacking in energy, passivity and of a physical sense of paralysis or immobility

Siegel (1999) proposed that between the extremes of hyper-arousal from the over-activity of the sympathetic nervous system, and hypo-arousal from the over-activity of the parasympathetic nervous system, there is an optimal 'window' within which balance can be achieved. Within this window affect is subjectively felt to be manageable, and experiences can be integrated. When a person maintains their equilibrium at a level that is within this optimal range, the level of stress is experienced as sufficient to encourage engagement, motivation and focused attention, without being so extreme as to trigger overwhelm or collapse. In this balanced state a person is able to think and to feel, to experience empathy, to be aware of the present moment, to respond in a way appropriate to the situation, to be cognisant of their own and other people's boundaries, and to have the capacity for openness and curiosity. The proposition that holding one's self within this optimal window as a way to manage these distressing fluctuations is now widely accepted as a helpful heuristic to understand the importance of maintaining a healthy, balanced level of eustress. When people are within this optimal range they are in the best physiological and mental position to be able to take in, process and integrate new information. It is also the optimal state to aim to maintain in order to have the best chance of effectively managing the challenges and demands of day-to-day life. Figure 7.1 represents diagrammatically how the window of tolerance can be explained simply.

The notion of the optimal range of arousal for healthy functioning that is at the core of the window of tolerance model is an important concept to work with in relation to people who have experienced trauma. Characteristically, these clients tend to

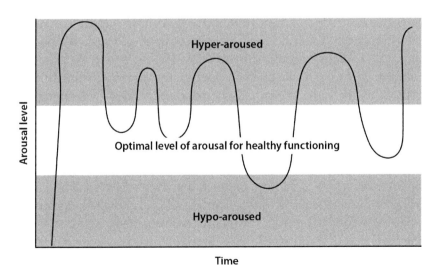

Figure 7.1: Diagrammatic representation of the window of tolerance

present clinically with stress symptoms that fluctuate unpredictably and rapidly (Ogden, Pain and Fisher, 2006). Additionally, Perry (2006) has noted that even when there is no external threat, children who have experienced complex trauma seem to "reset their normal level of arousal" so that in effect "they are in a constant state of alarm" (p. 32). This is very helpful to bear in mind, as such a child will perhaps be at the top end or above the optimal range in the window of tolerance most of the time due to their hyper-aroused threat system. Safe trauma therapy hinges on being able to accurately assess the state of the client's autonomic nervous system: to be aware of whether they are becoming hyper- or hypo- aroused, and to use body-focused tools to address that imbalance (Rothschild, 1999). Managing your own expectations therefore about how much change is realistic to achieve at any one time will be important. For some clients, only very small steps will be tolerable to start with, and appreciation and validation of how difficult their experience is to live with will help your client to feel heard and to feel more able to trust you as you work together.

There are several important things to bear in mind when using the window of tolerance as a psycho-education tool with people that you are sharing mindfulness with who have also experienced trauma. The first is to assess whether the planned mindfulness activity is likely to be something that your client can engage in from within their optimal zone that feels comfortable and will not trigger a reaction that will 'pop' them out into a hyper- or hypo-aroused state. This can be difficult to judge, as clients who have been managing their trauma symptoms for many years will have developed ways of hiding or masking their distress. The safest thing to do is to start with very simple TIM exercises that you feel relatively confident that the client will manage without being triggered, and set at the lowest level of titration (which will be discussed in more detail later in this chapter). In addition, as Babette Rothschild advocates, it is always good to agree how to apply the 'brakes' with a client before starting any trauma work (Rothschild, 2010). This just means that you have a conversation with the client to agree a stop sign or a way to communicate with each other if the exercise is too much and you need to stop and have a break, or do some grounding work to reset.

When using titration in mindfulness exercises, bear in mind that the objective is to ensure that you start the exercises just inside what feels comfortable for the client in relation to their window of tolerance – neither hypo- nor hyper-aroused. With practice, mindfulness exercises can be used to help someone return to the optimal range within their individual window.

With more practice, a client can be supported to use TIM exercises to enable them to move from a slightly hyper- or hypo-aroused state that is just outside their optimal range in the window. Notably, a person is probably only going to be able to cope with using mindfulness if they are only just on the border of their optimal zone. The further away they are from the optimal range within the window of tolerance, in hyper- or hypo-arousal, the less easily accessible it will be for them as a useful tool. My experience is that when a client is far away from their window of tolerance, other techniques are more effective than mindfulness in edging them closer to their optimal range. In these instances, other interventions (such as energetic activity or a sudden change of temperature) are best utilised as a first line, and then mindfulness can be introduced potentially as a secondary skill once the person has got much closer to being within range of their optimal zone. Of course, all of this relies on the person having developed sufficient awareness to start to identify where they are at any given time relative to their optimal zone, and this awareness building may need to be established first.

In relation to working with the window of tolerance with trauma-affected clients, Levine (2010a) introduced the concept of 'pendulation'. The definition of pendulation in this context is to work on the edge of the window of tolerance and to 'dip in and out' of experiences that are just outside the optimal zone (Levine, 2010a). This relates particularly to working physically or somatically with the body to release trauma; however, the principles are the same whether the work is at a cognitive, emotional or physical level. Levine also uses the term titration to describe the need for incrementally supporting the client to tolerate more of their experiences that have previously been outside their window of tolerance, and thereby gently increasing the size of the optimal or manageable zone of arousal.

Dissociation as a psychological defence
Dissociation is an interesting phenomenon in that it is something that everyone experiences to some extent, and has been conceptualised as one extreme end of a continuum between dissociation and full awareness (Braun, 1988). In cognitive neuroscience it is widely understood that there are two broad categories of mental processes, which are those that are under conscious control and those that are unconscious or automatic. Those processes that fall into the category of 'automatic' may either be that way innately, or they may have become *automated* over a period of time through repetition. In terms of thought processes that have become automatic, these tend to follow well-worn neural pathways and are largely unconscious, which makes them inherently difficult to identify and challenge (Raz and Buhle, 2006). There is a difference in the neurobiology of dissociation from the fight or flight response that involves the activation of the central nervous system. Although there is an increased release of epinephrine, there is also increased tone in the main nerve connected to the heart (the vagal nerve), which causes a drop in

blood pressure. Research into this occurrence in animal studies refers to this event as 'defeat' (Perry et al., 1995), and if severe can cause fainting.

Another neurochemical response that is similar in both defeat and dissociation is that endogenous opioids are released, which can affect one's perception of reality, temporality and spatiality (Resick, 2014). It is this chemical reaction that produces excess opioids, combined with an increased release of norepinephrine, that some experts believe is what causes disruption to the normal storage of memory information (van der Kolk, 1996). The impact of this is that there can be an experience of dissociation or amnesia that results in a gap in the explicit or conscious memory of a traumatic event. In 1963, Spiegel proposed six overlapping levels on the attention-dissociation continuum. These are described in Table 7.3.

Table 7.3: The attention-dissociation continuum (Spiegel, 1963)

Level		Description	Function
1.	**Selective inattention (repression)**	This relates to any kind of 'fragmentation' process whereby any undesirable instincts or any anxiety or fear are psychically defended against through processes such as dissociations and amnesia	Function to limit anxiety and fear, and are therefore by nature *constrictive.*
2.	**Expressive implemen-tation of the dissociated**	The main function of this level is in the service of repressing anxiety and fear, but predominantly relates to the consolidation or reinforcement	Tend to be rigid and compulsive

		of the dissociation of what has already been repressed. This category can include observable behaviours such as tics or phobias	
3.	Marginal awareness	This relates to the continuous and automatic 'scanning' that occurs as various stimuli are noted and perceived beyond the central experience. It includes subliminal awareness and any perception of stimuli by the body inside and outside it	Serve to maintain and *sustain* already established adaptive levels of dissociation (from levels 1 and 2)
4.	Automatic activity	This facilitates the ability to maintain central concentration and experience elsewhere, and is the kind of inattention that occurs when conducting routine or familiar tasks, or when attention is otherwise captured	
5.	Expressive uncovering with re-integration (insight)	This level relates to the occurrences of dissociated fragments making their way into conscious awareness in readiness for re-integration. It can be observed in free association links, in slips of the tongue, gestures and dreams	Function in the service of growth, *expansion* and re-integration of previously fragmented or dissociated aspects
6.	Expressive growth	At this level, the dissociated experiences move to a place of maturation and growth as they become integrated, forming new concepts and actions creatively and spontaneously	

Dissociation and awareness

In a dissociated state, a person is temporarily consciously unaware of some aspect of themselves, such as awareness of their physical body, awareness of thoughts, awareness of what is around them, or awareness of what has happened. When thinking about traumatic experiences there are three phases. These are known as pre-trauma (before), peri-trauma (during) and post-trauma (after). As therapeutic practitioners we will usually be working with people in the post-trauma phase, when clients are experiencing negative and problematic symptoms.[ix]

In order to cope with the overwhelming distress of a traumatic event a person may dissociate or disconnect mentally, emotionally or physically whilst it is happening (peri-traumatically). The person may also dissociate after the event whenever something triggers or reminds them of what had happened, as a defence against being flooded again with the same overwhelming feelings of the original trauma. Many people who have experienced trauma will use dissociation as a defence mechanism, and this is mostly an unconscious process that can exist on many different levels. The different levels of dissociation can range from the very everyday and familiar forms that most people use in some way or another when they 'zone out', lose focus, or lose track of time. As such, dissociation tends to be considered to be a spectrum or continuum of experiences.

Increasing awareness with mindfulness

For many individuals, dissociation can become extremely problematic in the long term, and can adversely affect their lives, relationships and work. In dissociated states, individuals may simply become 'inert' for long periods of time, or may behave in

---

[ix] It is acknowledged that in some cases a client may still be in an ongoing traumatic situation such as in the case of war or domestic violence. As such these discrete categories are not as clear.

ways that they are not consciously aware of, such as engaging in harmful behaviours towards themselves or others. Thus, a primary focus for many therapists who work with people who dissociate is to promote their own and others' safety through developing skills to manage and regulate these dissociative episodes. One of the foundational components of mindfulness is conscious present-focused awareness, which could be thought of as effectively the opposite of dissociation. The practice of mindfulness cultivates awareness, which is either explicitly or implicitly part of the process of recovery from trauma (Duerden, 2018). Becoming more aware is a really helpful treatment intervention for someone who dissociates, however, this must be done with an understanding of the fact that dissociation serves a protective function. Increasing awareness helps to mitigate against the risks of dissociation, but brings with it different risk or challenges in the form of now having to face up to what was previously being avoided through dissociation.

The main way in which mindfulness is thought to be effective in diminishing the symptoms of stress, anxiety and depression is through developing an objective awareness of automatic thoughts (Marchand, 2012). By developing objective awareness, it becomes possible to see thoughts as objects to be observed, and thus increases the opportunities to mitigate irrational or unhelpful thoughts and beliefs, or to misinterpret thoughts as 'facts'. Thus, becoming more aware of thoughts is a very helpful starting point as an intervention. However, for someone who unconsciously uses dissociation as a coping strategy to be 'unaware' of distressing emotional, cognitive or physical experiences, understanding and care should be taken, as the dissociation to some extent serves a protective function. TIM can be taught to help people to become more consciously aware of what they are doing, and therefore more in control of when and where these dissociative defences kick in. However, becoming aware requires conscious effort and practice and requires time and patience to learn to use effectively. Building on something that the person already does with focus such as a hobby or aspect of their job can often be a helpful starting point. Some of the ways in which you can work practically with clients who dissociate are to titrate their awareness building, and balance it with simultaneous self-compassion work and emotion regulation.

One of the major benefits of working with TIM with clients who experience dissociation as a coping mechanism, is that it can be extremely useful in helping people to become more consciously aware of their body, their thoughts and emotions. Conscious awareness is the pre-cursor for changing any of these aspects that were previously operating 'under the radar' on the unconscious or automatic level. A central aspect of mindfulness practice is the development of the skill of maintaining focused attention (Tang and Posner, 2009). This development of personal awareness is the necessary precursor to subsequently being able to sustain a non-judgemental awareness of sensory perceptions, emotions and thought patterns (Chiesa and Malinowski, 2011). By becoming more aware of one's thought patterns and emotions, it becomes possible to move into the position of the observer stance, whereby there is less sense of identification with those thoughts and feelings. In doing so, the thoughts and feelings start to lessen their power or control, and negative automatic thoughts become more apparent, and recognisable (Marchand, 2014).

The risks of awareness

Increasing awareness helps to manage unconscious dissociation; however, in doing so different challenges are brought to the fore, as experiences previously avoided through dissociation, come in to awareness. In an interesting piece of research using naturally occurring data (Kiyimba, Lester and O'Reilly, 2018) on online discussion posts and blogs, participants with schizophrenia used mindfulness for managing their symptoms (Brorstrom, 2009). In one of the posts discussed, the participant spoke of the psychosis as being a kind of relief from or even dissociation from the real world: "I associate being present with being hyper-aware. I know everything that's happening in my surroundings. If I escape into my psychosis a bit, it's much more manageable/less intense." Later on the same participant stated, "I feel neither relaxed nor edgy when that happens. It's just very exhausting. I go back into my psychosis a bit to cope with it" (p. 42). In this extract, the 'being present' that mindfulness trains its practitioner into being more aware of, felt too intense and exhausting to stay with for any length of time, and so the psychosis was seen as a retreat, a relief. As the author of the study reiterates, "the use of the word 'escape' (Extract 22) constructs schizophrenia as something he uses in order to deal with his experiences of being hyper-aware" (Brorstrom, 2009, p. 43). Tim Duerden (2018) has some useful guidelines for engaging in trauma-sensitive mindfulness practice in groups, to help manage some of these potential challenges of introducing mindful awareness with clients. These are summarised in table 7.4.

Table 7.4: Safe management of group trauma-sensitive mindfulness practice (from Duerden, 2018)

Consideration	Description
Person centred	Collaboration between teacher and participants with adapted mindfulness practices that emerge from individual need(s) that have been identified
Safe	Easily achievable challenges invited that have a very low chance of failure or shame, and a high degree of personal choice
Relational	The practices are rooted in a relationship of trust between the teacher and participants

Scaffolded	Practices develop initially from experiences that are more familiar with clear explanations provided beforehand about what the practices will involve and short initial 'test-drives' of practices
Gradual	Short practices that are repeated so that skills can be developed in incremental steps
Grounding	Participants are encouraged to keep their eyes open, to be active and moving, and there should be provision of external anchors in the environment

As you can see from the table containing the key recommendations from Tim Duerden about trauma-sensitive mindfulness practice for groups, the same theme of titration is raised. In this case, Duerden uses the phrases 'scaffolded' and 'gradual' to describe the same principles of titration that exist in TIM.

Working with avoidance

There has been quite a bit of research to show that people who have experienced trauma actively avoid particular situations, together with avoiding the thoughts or emotions that relate to those situations, in an effort to minimise or escape the associated distress (Palm and Follette, 2000). Avoidance can also be exhibited behaviourally as people may turn to drugs or alcohol as substances to numb or avoid the acute distress of trauma symptomology. Whilst avoidance is one of the symptoms in the criteria for a diagnosis of PTSD, avoidance may also be a contributing factor to the maintenance of post-traumatic suffering. The empirical evidence indicates a paradoxical effect of avoidance, which can actually cause an increase of intrusive cognitions (Clark, Ball and Pape, 1991; Wegner et al., 1990). Similarly, avoidance behaviours have also been shown to make the experience of negative and distressing emotions worse (Cioffi and Holloway, 1993; Wegner and Zanakos, 1994). Avoidance of the feared stimulus is what is referred to in Cognitive Behavioural Therapy (CBT) as 'safety behaviour'. As the feared stimulus is anticipated, there is an increase in the stress arousal response in the body. Rather than 'staying with', 'riding the wave' or 'turning towards' this feeling of anxiety, as mindfulness might propose, a person with an avoidance response will typically short-circuit the exposure to the feared stimulus through avoidance behaviour. In doing so, they experience a feeling of relief as the stress response physiology is calmed and the anxiety lessens. In the short term this seems to be a helpful adaptive strategy, however when repeated, a form of behavioural conditioning is set in motion whereby the safety behaviour (avoidance) becomes a conditioned response. Behaviourally, this is problematic because it becomes more likely for the person to continue engaging in the safety behaviour every time there is an anticipation of the feared stimulus, thus perpetuating the reinforcement of that behaviour. This is called a maintaining cycle and is illustrated in figure 7.2.

Whilst it might be tempting for family, friends or professionals involved with a person who is actively avoiding

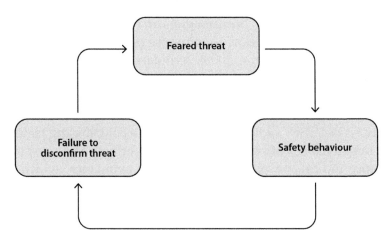

Figure 7.2: The maintaining cycle of avoidance as safety behaviour

certain situations, places, people or other potential triggers, such collusion only feeds into the maintenance cycle. In the long term, due to the fear of the stimuli that is anticipated to act as a trigger, avoidance becomes more ingrained and can generalise to other similar situations. As figure 7.2 illustrates, it is the 'failure to disconfirm the threat' that maintains the cycle. The solution therefore is to have the opportunity to disconfirm a threat. When people experience flashbacks as part of their PTSD symptomology, it feels exactly like they are reliving the event, with exactly the same feelings of terror. The brain mistakenly acts as though the threat is current rather than in the past. Through various therapeutic strategies a person suffering from these experiences is exposed to the memories whilst simultaneously being able to be present in the current moment. This dual processing approach means that the memories are eventually given the appropriate 'time tag' in the brain that the traumatic event happened in the past. In relation to the maintenance cycle model that is being discussed, the opportunity is provided through therapy to be able to disconfirm that the threat is current. When this is achieved, the individual being treated is able to break the maintenance cycle, and no longer has the same need to avoid reminders of the traumatic event that might trigger a trauma re-living experience. What is clear therefore, is the necessity to *avoid avoidance* in order to promote healing.

The reason this topic is being raised in this chapter on titration is that mindfulness is an approach that can be practiced as a way to learn to 'turn towards' certain thoughts or feelings or urges rather than to avoid them. It is also a way of turning towards physical sensations in the body that may otherwise be avoided. However, the risk in turning towards is always that it may be done too quickly or without due care and attention, and result in flooding or re-traumatisation. So the balance needs to be established between not completely avoiding a potential trigger, and not bringing awareness to it too quickly, for too long or without appropriate escape strategies in place. This is where titration comes into planning suitable practice exercises to support the clinical application of the particular TIM skills that involve non-avoidance, which are: Curiosity, Observation, Factual description, Non-resistance, and Turning towards. Practicing each of these particular skills is a way of working with avoidance, and can be practiced in a titrated way. For example practicing curiosity, observation or factual description of an external object starts the titration at a safer proximity level than practicing any of these skills in relation to physical sensations in the body, or a closer proximity titration level, which might be to practice the same skills in relation to internal processes such as thoughts and emotions.

In addition to avoidance being a symptom of PTSD in its own right, it may also contribute to maintaining of post-traumatic suffering. This lack of capacity to be present without having to use avoidance as a defence mechanism can be considered to be a skills deficit, and arguably therefore mindfulness can be a useful approach to facilitating healing by prompting acceptance rather than avoidance of experiences (Folette, Palm and Pearson, 2006). Additionally, the use of mindfulness skills may be helpful in decreasing avoidance and improving exposure treatment efficacy by providing a mechanism whereby clients learn to remain 'in contact' with painful or distressing feelings, thoughts or memories without having to resort to engaging in the usual avoidance strategies (Follette, Palm and Pearson, 2006). One of the advantages of practicing mindfulness is that it decreases avoidance (Brown, Ryan and Creswell, 2007).

Being in the body
Within the body there are different types of sensory receptors that monitor information in the form of stimuli from sources inside and outside the body. The three that relate to TIM practice are

exteroceptors, proprioceptors and interoceptors. A description of each of these is provided in table 7.5.

Table 7.5: Description of the types of sensory receptors in the body

Type of sensory receptor	Description
Exteroceptors:	These provide information about the external environment, like touch, pressure, temperature, light, sound, taste, smell, hearing
Proprioceptors:	These provide information about the position and posture of our body in space. They sense stimuli from the muscles, tendons and the joints
Interoceptors:	These detect stimulus within the body, such as temperature, thirst, blood pressure, blood oxygen or the degree of stretching of the urinary bladder

Although they are listed separately for the purposes of explaining the differences between the different types of sensory mechanisms in the body, they are actually very interrelated. One way that this will frequently be seen is when an external stimulus perceived by the exteroceptors in turn triggers an internal reaction that will be perceived by the interoceptors. For example, externally perceiving the smell of freshly baked bread can stimulate the production of saliva and cause changes in the stomach. In this case, the external stimulus is the smell of fresh bread that is sensed or experienced by the exteroceptors, and the production of saliva and sensations in the stomach are the body's physiological response to that smell, which can be felt or experienced by the body's internal interoceptors. Another example might be a new mother who hears her baby crying through the use of her exteroceptive sense of hearing. Her body's automatic physiological response if she is lactating will be for her to feel and experience in her body a 'let-down' reflex, which will be a felt sense through her interoceptors.

The let-down reflex is the automatic physiological response of her breasts starting the flow of milk ready to feed the baby. A further example is the exteroceptor sense of sight. In a situation perhaps where a person looks at someone that they perceive to be physically attractive, there may be a concurrent automatic physiological response from their internal sexual organs. An internal sensation perceived through interoception may therefore be felt or experienced as a direct result of the connection with the external sensory experience.

 Whilst walking slowly, move your awareness between information being taken in by each of the different sensory mechanisms in turn:
- Exteroceptors
- Proprioceptors
- Interoceptors

 Practice noticing your awareness through your proprioceptor sensory mechanism:
- Try standing on one leg
- Try stretching your arms out to each side
- Try bringing your finger up to touch your nose
- Now do the same with your eyes closed

There has been an increase in research into the function of interoception, and it has been suggested that interoceptive awareness is linked to a sense of self, and is also involved in decision-making and cognition (Payne, Levine and Crane-Godreau, 2015). The empirical literature indicates that the practice of mindfulness has the function of developing interoceptive awareness of bodily sensations (Marchand, 2014). For example, a study using fMRI to investigate interoceptive activity in people trained in MBSR, found that training in mindfulness not only improved their general attention capacity, but also improved their interoceptive attention (Farb, Segal and Anderson, 2013). There have also been a number of research studies that support the premise that mindfulness practice can be a useful tool in supporting and promoting emotional regulation (Marchand, 2014). In traditional mindfulness, a lot of different exercises are used to help people to be 'in the body' rather than 'in the mind'. This can range from breathing exercises to eating something with intense awareness of all the senses. However, what we know about people who have experienced trauma is that often the body has been violated, hurt or injured in some way, and subsequently does not feel like a safe place to be. If mindful awareness is brought to the body too soon in a person's journey towards recovery from trauma, it can be very frightening, and may trigger an abreaction in the form of a psychological or physiological response. Also, for people who have experienced trauma, exercises that require the person to relate to processes inside their body such as thoughts or feelings can also be very problematic, and again may act as a trigger for intense emotional reactions or even flashbacks or dissociation. Using the primary principles of pendulation and titration, Peter Levine has developed as staged model of working somatically with clients to release trapped trauma energy in the body. Table 7.6 (overleaf) is a brief summary of Levine's (2010b) criteria for working with the principles of safety and titration with people who still hold the physical impact of trauma in their bodies.

For those who have experienced trauma, current external reminders of the initial trauma experienced in the here and now through sight, sound, smell, taste or touch may in turn trigger corresponding internal responses that could be experienced as unpleasant, painful or unbearable. Knowing the link between how exteroceptive and interoceptive senses correlate with, and trigger one another, can be very helpful when working with people who have experienced particular types of trauma where there have

Table 7.6: Levine's (2010a; 2010b) building block principles of titrating

	Building block	Description
1.	Safety	Create *relative* safety within the environment of the therapy room. Stay calm and present as the therapist and adopt an accepting neutral physical and emotional stance
2.	Exploration and acceptance of body sensations	Support the client in an initial exploration and acceptance of physical sensations. Help the client to experience positive sensations
3.	Pendulation	Create a rhythm of moving between dipping into the area just outside the window of tolerance and back in. Follow the natural rhythm of the body between expansion and contraction, as awareness of the rhythm helps the client relax
4.	Titration	Use titration to connect with the slightest amount of physical sensation that feels challenging in order to prevent re-traumatisation. Use titration to create an increase in organisation, resilience and stability. Only work with one sensation at a time to avoid further overwhelm of the nervous system
5.	Provide a corrective experience of defence responses	Replace learned passive reactions of helplessness and collapse with *empowered* active defence responses
6.	Separate conditioned association	De-couple the learned helpless and fear responses from the physical response of immobility. Support the client to experience the physical sensations of immobility without being automatically paired with the emotion of fear

7.	Encourage energy discharge	Gently discharge the trapped survival energy within the body and support its redistribution to supporting higher-level brain function. The energy release may happen through trembling, shaking, or changes in breathing or temperature, and usually happens in cycles
8.	Restore self-regulation	Support the restoration of relaxed alertness and 'dynamic equilibrium' in the body. The energy discharge helps to bring equilibrium back to the nervous system, and clients feel calmer and more able to self-regulate
9.	Re-orientation to here and now	Reconnect with the physical environment and re-establish social connections

been natural or conditioned physiological responses to external triggers or stimuli. Thus, although this chapter advocates the use of a titration process starting with practices that focus on sensations proximally *outside* the body, it is equally important to be aware of the potential for internal reactivity if the stimulus is particularly closely related to the experience of the initial trauma.

Titration
Titration refers to the process of grading the exercises and skills practiced in a way that is appropriate to the client's difficulties, symptoms, preference, and level of skill. There are two options available in relation to which aspects of a client's skills practice can be titrated as described in table 7.7 (overleaf).

Table 7.7: The three types of titration in Trauma-Informed Mindfulness

Type of Titration	Description
Time	The length of time that the mindfulness skills are practiced for is the simplest and easiest decision to make in terms of titration. One of the main characteristics of TIM is that it uses very short timeframes for its exercises. Typically a starting point would be to engage in a mindfulness skills practice for just one minute. When you are thinking about appropriate levels of titration for a particular client, you may need to reduce this to 30 seconds if they struggle with attention, or increase it to two or three minutes if a longer timeframe seems to be valuable for the client to practice the particular skill on which you are focusing properly. You will need a clock, or stopwatch or timer of some kind to measure this accurately
Proximity	Proximity is the term used in TIM to refer to whether the mindfulness exercise that is most suitable for this particular client at this time is outside the body in the physical environment, whether the exercise relates specifically to concrete sensations experienced by the body itself, or whether the exercise is focused on a more abstract internal experience such as emotions. TIM is designed so that you can make these choices sensibly based on what you know about the kind of trauma your client has experienced. For example, if there has been physical trauma to the body, exercises focused on the body may overwhelm the client with memories of the event, and so it may be safer to titrate the exercises to start with those that are clearly external in the physical environment. If in doubt, it is probably wise to use an external stimulus for your first few TIM exercises, just in case

In chapter one the third component of the TIM process chart (figure 1.3) after introducing the client to the TIM attitudes and skills and agreeing goals, was to decide on the initial exercise, titration and skill (see figure 7.3 for a 'close up' of the third stage of the process chart).

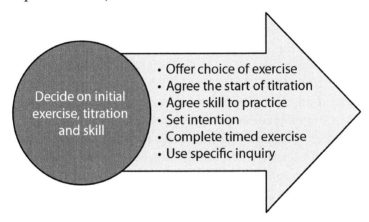

Figure 7.3: Deciding on the initial exercise, titration and skill for TIM

The ways in which any single TIM practice can be structured involves deciding on a number of components, starting with the choice of exercise. Choosing the kind of exercise will relate to the second type of titration, that of proximity. As suggested, using an exercise that is external in the physical environment is usually the safest option to start with, so as not to risk any kind of abreaction in the initial stages (bearing in mind the caveat mentioned earlier about the link between exteroception and interoception). For example, if the client has experienced torture or other physical trauma, initially only offering a choice of exercises that are in the environment and external to the client's body may be sensible. Where a person has experienced physical trauma, if mindful attention is focused on a part of the body that may have been subject to abuse or injury too soon, drawing attention to that area may be sufficient to trigger an adverse reaction in the client.

Remembering always the importance of safety and choice for individuals who have had traumatic experiences, it can be beneficial to offer your client a choice of suitable exercises. For example choosing between a flower or a toy car for the focus of the exercise. Simply offering the choice of two options will allow your client to feel some control over the process. Providing too many choices can just make things confusing. Additionally, individuals suffering from the effects of complex and/or extended trauma may be very unpracticed in making choices for themselves, and could find too much choice overwhelming. So, be sensible and offer a small number of choices, as appropriate to your client.

Suggesting a level of time titration at this point would also be part of agreeing together what exactly the practice will involve. It is recommended that when using TIM, facilitators suggest a one-minute exercise to start with. Only after trying this level a few times, and collecting focused feedback from the client during the inquiry stage, can the timing of the exercise be appropriately adjusted up or down to suit the client's ability at this particular stage of their TIM training. A timer will need to be set that has a bell when the time is complete, so that the titration can be accurate. Alternatively, as facilitator, you could have a clock with a second hand on it, and you ring a bell at the start and end of the minute of practice. After agreeing titration of practice proximity and time, the next decision to make is the specific mindfulness skill that will be practiced during the exercise. Again, balance offering choice with making suggestions, so that the client does not feel too overwhelmed with options, but also does not feel dictated to.

You could have a printed list of the seven TIM skills to recap which one to choose to practice first, as that may be helpful to both you and your client. Once the client is very clear on what is expected of them during the exercise, you can set that as your intention and start the clock. When the time ends, the exercise also stops, and it is time to start the inquiry. This is led by the facilitator, and involves asking *very specific* questions of the client about how well they managed their practice of the *specific skill* that was agreed at the start and set as the intention for that practice. The information gained from this inquiry discussion will help you to design the next practice. These do not have to be long drawn out discussions, and can be as simple as the client saying that they got distracted by something, and could not attend to practicing the skill at all. In which case you may decide to repeat the same exercise again to see if the client is able to concentrate better, or reduce the time of the exercise to 30 seconds so there is more chance of the client maintaining concentration and focus throughout. If the client reports that they were triggered or distressed by the exercise itself, you may need to change the exercise.

Titrating proximity from outside to inside
The TIM model proposes a staged approach whereby exercises are proximally ordered, starting with a focus of exercises that relate to the external environment, then those that are more focused on the physical body, and then finally, those practices that encourage the client to be drawn more into internal processes. This model allows for greater flexibility with regard to titration, and allows a cautionary approach to be taken with people who have experienced trauma. Obviously, it is important to be client-centred, but as a rule for working in a trauma-informed way, the principle of working from the outside to the inside can be helpful. In practice, this means starting initial practices with tasks that involve the use of exteroceptors, before moving on to tasks that predominantly require focus on proprioceptor mechanisms, before moving on to interoceptor related practices.

Stage 1: Outside the body – experienced via exteroceptors
Stage 2: The body – experienced via proprioceptors
Stage 3: Inside the body – experienced by interoceptors

Examples of practices suitable for stage 1: Outside the body – experienced via exteroceptors:

- Mindfulness practices that suit this stage: are anything that uses the five senses to bring awareness to what is outside in the world around us
- Smelling fruit, flowers, tea, essential oils or bread for example
- The 'raisin' exercise is suitable for this stage

Examples of practices suitable for stage 2: The body – experienced via proprioceptors:

- Mindfulness practices that suit this stage involve focusing on the body itself
- Mindful movement is suitable for this stage: breathing, or a careful body scan focusing on the outer layer of the body – skin, muscles
- Looking in a mirror or at another person may be suitable at this stage

Examples of practices suitable for stage 3: Inside the body – experienced by interoceptors:

- Mindfulness practices that suit this stage are those that bring awareness inside to thoughts and emotions and associated inner bodily sensations
- Sitting practices, directed visualisation meditations or loving-kindness practice may be suitable

When working with the body, it is common that people who have experienced physical trauma will have certain parts of their body in which they work hard to avoid experiencing any physical sensations, as this automatically triggers a reactive response. However, there may be other parts of the body that are relatively safe to start working with. In the trauma processing modality Comprehensive Resource Model (CRM) (Schwarz et al., 2016), one of the initial practices in which a client is asked to participate is called 'building a grid'. During this exercise, the client is asked to find one part of their body, even if it is as small as a grain of sand, that feels secure or safe or grounded. In CRM a network or 'grid' of several of these points is built up, as points are connected together to enable the client to have a felt sense of stability within their body. Although mindfulness practice does not involve this kind of grid-building, a lesson that can be taken from this model is that even a client who has experienced extreme physical trauma can find *somewhere* in their body, even if it is only a tiny speck that feels OK to place their awareness on.

Titration of time

One of the defining features of TIM in comparison to other mindfulness models is that it utilises very short timed exercises, typically between 30 seconds and three minutes. The philosophy behind this is that people who have experienced trauma find extended mindfulness exercises extremely difficult to tolerate, and may experience abreactions or dissociate. When one has never engaged in practices designed to focus the attention in a very deliberate way, it can be very challenging. It is therefore proposed in TIM that with much shorter and more focused exercises, clients can experience a degree of success immediately. When moving through each of the stages, remember to start with short practice sessions, and if necessary build up to longer ones. Discuss with your client how long they would like each exercise to be, so that the client has the greatest chance of achieving a positive outcome.

Summary

The concept of titration as it relates to trauma therapy has been introduced and explained in this chapter, including the two primary methods of titration used in TIM, which are proximity and time. The relationship between the importance of titration and the window of tolerance has been described in relation to the importance of maintaining client safety and not engaging in practices that would be overwhelming and re-traumatising. Using the window of tolerance model a rationale has been provided for the need to identify and avoid extreme hyper- and hypo-aroused states in the client, which is facilitated by attending to the provision of a relatively safe and contained environment and therapeutic relationship. This chapter has also introduced the idea of the link between awareness and dissociation, which is conceptualised as two ends of a continuum, with the possibility of awareness building through mindfulness training to support movement towards a more balanced position on that continuum. This sets the scene for the following chapter, which addresses in more detail how the stages of trauma work relate to the application of TIM in practice.

References

Braun, B. G. (1988). The BASK model of dissociation. *Dissociation, 1*(1), 4–23.

Brorstrom, L. (2009). *Portfolio of academic, therapeutic practice and research work including an investigation of trauma therapy in a landscape of suffering: Towards a grounded theory* (Unpublished doctoral thesis). University of Surrey, United Kingdom.

Brown, K. W., Ryan, R. M., & Creswell, J. D. (2007) Mindfulness: Theoretical foundations and evidence for its salutary effects. *Psychological Inquiry, 18*(4), 211–237.

Chiesa, A., & Malinowski, P. (2011). Mindfulness-based approaches: Are they all the same? *Journal of Clinical Psychology, 67*, 404–424.

Cioffi, D., & Holloway, J. (1993). Delayed costs of suppressed pain. *Journal of Personality and Social Psychology, 64*(2), 274–282.

Clark, D. M., Ball, S., & Pape, D. (1991). An experimental investigation of thought suppression. *Behavior Research and Therapy, 29*, 253–257.

Duerden, T. (2018). *Teaching mindfulness: Potentially traumatising or detraumatising. Teaching mindfulness safely.* Minding the Gaps conference, Brighton, United Kingdom. Retrieved from http://integratedmindfulness.com/mindingthegap2017/.

Farb N. A., Segal Z. V., & Anderson, A. K. (2013). Mindfulness meditation training alters cortical representations of interoceptive attention. *Social Cognitive and Affective Neuroscience, 8,* 15–26.

Follette, V., Palm, K. M., & Pearson, A. N. (2006). Mindfulness and trauma: Implications for treatment. *Journal of Rational-Emotive and Cognitive-Behavior Therapy, 24*(1), 45–61.

Kiyimba, N., Lester, J. N., & O'Reilly, M. (2018). *Using naturally occurring data in qualitative health research: A practical guide.* London, United Kingdom: Springer.

Lazarus, R. S. (1974). Psychological stress and coping in adaptation and illness. *The International Journal of Psychiatry in Medicine, 5*(4), 321–333.

Levine, P. A. (2010a). *In an unspoken voice: How the body releases trauma and restores goodness.* Berkeley, CA: North Atlantic Books.

Levine, P. A. (2010b). *Instructor's Manual for resolving trauma in psychotherapy: A somatic approach.* Instructors' manual. Retrieved from
https://www.psychotherapy.net/data/uploads/5113e38c831c3.pdf

Marchand, W. R. (2012). Mindfulness-based stress reduction, mindfulness-based cognitive therapy, and Zen meditation for depression, anxiety, pain, and psychological distress. *Journal of Psychiatric Practice, 18,* 233–252.

Marchand, W. R. (2014, 28 July). Neural mechanisms of mindfulness and meditation: Evidence from neuroimaging studies. *World Journal of Radiology, 6*(7), 471–479.

Ogden, P., Pain, C., & Fisher, J. (2006). A sensorimotor approach to the treatment of trauma and dissociation. *Psychiatric Clinics of North America, 29*(1), 263–279.

Palm, K. M., & Follette, V. M. (2000). Counseling strategies with adult survivors of sexual abuse as children. *Directions in Clinical and Counseling Psychology, 11,* 49–60.

Payne, P., Levine, P. A., & Crane-Godreau, M. A. (2015). Somatic experiencing: Using interoception and proprioception as core elements of trauma therapy. *Frontiers in Psychology, 6*, 93.

Perry, B. (2006). Applying principles of neurodevelopment to clinical work with maltreated and traumatized children. In N. Webb (Ed.), *Working with traumatized youth in child welfare* (pp. 27–52). New York, NY: Guilford Press.

Perry, B. D., Pollard, R. A., Blakley, T. L., Baker, W. L., & Vigilante, D. (1995). Childhood trauma, the neurobiology of adaptation, and "use-dependent" development of the brain: How "states" become "traits". *Infant Mental Health Journal, 16*(4), 271–291.

Raz, A., & Buhle, J. (2006). Typologies of attentional networks. *Nature Reviews Neuroscience, 7*, 367–379.

Resick, P. A. (2014). *Stress and trauma (Clinical psychology: A modular course)*. New York, NY: Psychology Press.

Rothschild, B. (1999). Making trauma therapy safe. *Self & Society, 27*(2), 17–23.

Rothschild, B. (2010). *Eight keys to safe trauma recovery. Take-charge strategies to empower your healing*. New York, NY: W. W. Norton & Company Inc.

Schwarz, L., Corrigan, F., Hull, A., & Raju, R. (2016). *The comprehensive resource model: Effective therapeutic techniques for the healing of complex trauma*. New York, NY: Taylor and Francis.

Selye, H. (1974). *Stress without distress* (p. 171). Philadelphia, PA: J. B. Lippincott Company.

Siegel, D. J. (1999). *The developing mind*. New York, NY: Guilford Press.

Spiegel, H. (1963). The dissociation-association continuum. *Journal of Nervous and Mental Disease, 136*(4), 374–378.

Tang, Y. Y., & Posner, M. I. (2009). Attention training and attention state training. *Trends in Cognitive Science, 13*, 222–227.

van der Kolk, B. A. (1996). The complexity of adaptation to trauma: Self-regulation, stimulus discrimination, and characterological development. In B. A. van der Kolk, A. C. McFarlane, & L. Weisaeth (Eds.), *Traumatic stress: The effects of overwhelming experience on mind, body, and society* (pp. 182–213). New York, NY: Guilford Press.

Wegner, D., & Zanakos, S. (1994). Chronic thought suppression. *Journal of Personality, 62*(4), 615–640.

Wegner, D. M., Shortt, J. W., Blake, A. W., & Page, M. S. (1990). The suppression of exciting thoughts. *Journal of Personality and Social Psychology, 58*(3), 409–418.

Yerkes, R. M., & Dodson, J. D. (1908). The relation of strength of stimulus to rapidity of habit-formation. *Journal of Comparative Neurology and Psychology, 18*(5), 459–482.

CHAPTER EIGHT
DYNAMIC STABILISATION AND INTEGRATION

Chapter contents
• The developmental relationship • Group versus individual mindfulness • A phased approach to trauma treatment • Readiness for change • Dynamic stabilisation and integration • Summary

A current issue within the clinical and research communities regarding safe, timely and effective trauma intervention is that of whether to use a phased approach. This debate will be engaged in this chapter, considering some of the arguments and evidence and locating TIM within that discussion. In brief, TIM is designed to be both a stand-alone intervention and a set of skills that can be integrated into other schemes of work. As such the existing structure of a phased approach as was initially proposed by Judith Herman, and later formally supported by the International Society for Traumatic Stress Studies (ISTSS), does not fit exactly (Cloitre et al., 2012). This is not to say that TIM does not agree with the need for stabilisation before active treatment, but it proposes to do that in a dynamic way, whereby the question of the need for stabilisation is one that is revisited iteratively throughout the intervention. The dynamic aspect of how the three phases of stabilisation, intervention and integration are employed in TIM will be explained later in this chapter. As a preliminary discussion to the introduction of this approach, the topic of the developmental relationship between facilitator and client is introduced theoretically and practically. This framework provides a helpful conceptual heuristic as it maps on to the intention behind TIM, which is to facilitate the client to grow gradually in their ability to need less

248

scaffolding as treatment progresses. The other topic that is introduced is a discussion of the comparative advantages and limitations of group work and individual mindfulness interventions, as this relates to the position of TIM as a primarily individual mindfulness intervention.

In addition, an overview of the literature pertaining to the model of the phased approach will be covered as a precursor to a discussion about the readiness for change cycle and the potential advantages of adding a preliminary contemplation and psycho-education phase before initial stabilisation work. Finally, the possibility of a dynamic approach to working with aspects of stabilisation and integration will be considered in the context of working within a titration and window of tolerance framework. In chapter one (table 1.1) the full specification for learning requirements relating to the seven TIM characteristics was provided. Table 8.1 is a duplicate of the section of that table that relates to dynamic stabilisation and integration, and is provided here as a reminder for pedagogical purposes. This chapter explicates in more detail the descriptive elements that relate specifically to this characteristic.

Table 8.1: Trauma-Informed Mindfulness characteristic 7. 'Dynamic stabilisation and integration' learning aims

	TIM characteristic	Description
7.	Dynamic stabilisation and integration	• To understand the model of working in a phased way within a trauma treatment programme • To have a knowledge of the existing recommended phases of stabilisation, intervention and integration in trauma work

		• To be able to work dynamically within these phases and to work backwards and forwards between them when necessary • To critically assess the potential value of including a readiness for change pre-treatment phase

The developmental relationship

Before any effective intervention can be commenced with a person who has experienced single or multiple traumatic events from which they are continuing to suffer symptoms of post-traumatic stress, it is valuable to revisit and consider the issues of safety and choice discussed in chapter six. A primary consideration in trauma work is for the client to feel enough of a sense of safety to reduce their hyper-aroused, hyper-vigilant behaviour sufficiently to facilitate engagement in the practice exercises. This level of safety is usually established within a secure environment and therapeutic relationship. The kind of relationship that is potentially most conducive to positive growth is one in which the dialectics of acceptance and change are both kept in balance. In other words, the client knows that who they are, what has happened to them, and how they are managing their current situation, both inside and outside the therapy room, is accepted for what it is. What is meant by the term acceptance in this context is as defined by the general mindfulness literature: that the behaviour may not be condoned, but it is 'accepted' as reflecting the current situation. There is no need for change to happen in order for a client to be accepted. However, the other aspect of the dialectic is that change is collaboratively agreed as something that will be worked towards for the benefit of the client. The see-saw of balance between the need for both acceptance and change is illustrated in figure 8.1.

Dynamic stabilisation and integration

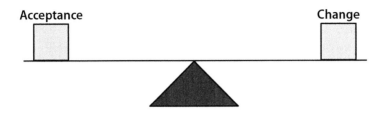

Figure 8.1: The dialectic of acceptance and change

The particular kind of relationship that supports and fosters positive change is what Bronfenbrenner (1979) described as a 'developmental relationship'. It is characterised by "reciprocal human interactions that embody an enduring emotional attachment, progressively more complex patterns of joint activity, and a balance of power that gradually shifts from the developed person in favour of the developing person" (Li and Julian, 2012). This concept that includes 'progressively more complex patterns of joint activity' and 'gradual shifts' in the balance of power from one to another was used by Li and Julian to discuss the scaffolding of supporting children towards independence by adults. The gradation of competence building as described in the model of the developmental relationship is a good way to describe the ethos behind the titrated processes in TIM. Adult facilitators of TIM may be either working in adult-child, or adult-adult dyads, where one is supporting the other to perform ever more complex tasks with gradually less and less support and input. Both adult and child clients are gradually taught through incrementally titrated practice to succeed, gain mastery and to grow in confidence in performing those practices independently.

The concept of the 'zone of proximal development' (ZPD) is defined as "the distance between the actual developmental level as determined by independent problem solving and the level of potential development as determined through problem solving under adult guidance, or in collaboration with more capable peers" (Vygotsky, 1978, p. 86). Within that zone, and under the guidance of a facilitator, the learner is able to attempt progressively more complex tasks, as the proximal distance between the 'actual' and 'potential' development of skills is gradually and incrementally bridged. Due to the one-to-one context of TIM where mindfulness exercises are being introduced, the facilitator is able to gauge the appropriate level of the practice that is within the client's zone of proximal development and to adjust their level of support dynamically. This kind of titration of support has also been referred to in the literature as 'fading' by gradually lessening the support or 'scaffolding' needing to be provided by the person in the dyad with initially more developed skills (Collins, Brown and Newman, 1990). In terms of the developmental relationship, as the client becomes progressively more competent in being able to engage in the different aspects of TIM practice successfully, the balance of power can move across from the facilitator to the client. The ultimate objective is to enable the client to be able to engage in different kinds of mindfulness practices in ways that support their overall wellbeing completely independently of the facilitator.

For those readers working with young people, a helpful study that demonstrates the value of engaging in developmental relationships with clients involved eight Big Brothers/Big Sisters of America (BB/BSA) adult-mentor and youth-mentee pairing programmes in the United States. In a study of the BB/BSA programme Morrow and Styles (1995) differentiated between developmental relationships and prescriptive relationships. Prescriptive relationships were those characterised by a high level of adult control where the adult mentors typically unilaterally decided on what topics of conversation and activities the pairing would engage in. Prescriptive relationships were apparently un-collaborative, not responsive to the mentee, and did not fade over time. The results were that the mentees were less likely to discuss their difficulties with their mentors, there was more tension than in developmental relationships, and overall the quality of the relationship deteriorated with time (Li and Julian, 2012). This study shows the value and importance of working collaboratively within a developmentally supportive framework when facilitating TIM practice. The Morrow and Styles (1995) mentoring study also highlights the value and need for shared decision-making, whereby the client is able to make choices about the process, and to be afforded an appropriate level of control and choice that is gradually increased as competence grows. The developmental relationship, in contrast to the prescriptive relationship, offers greater support and direction initially, but gradually 'fades' or lessens the amount of scaffolding needed, as the client grows in confidence and competence. The key 'ingredients' of a developmental relationship are listed in table 8.2.

Table 8.2: Key ingredients of a developmental relationship (adapted from Li and Julian, 2012; and Bath, 2016)

	Aspect of the developmental relationship	Description
1.	Attachment	This term is used to refer to any positive, natural, emotional connection that is appropriate to the context
2.	Reciprocity	This refers to the interactivity of the relationship, including providing support by scaffolding within the zone of proximal development, and gradually removing that scaffolding through fading
3.	Progressive complexity	This refers to the way that developmental skill is acquired, through supporting mastery of progressively more complex or challenging activities

4.	Balance of power	This refers to the importance of progressively allowing control within the relationship to move from the facilitator to the learner

The developmental relationship model is a helpful guideline for thinking about how to approach working with a client to facilitate learning of TIM practices. Aspect one of developing attachment in the relationship matches with the fundamental premise of TIM that the client needs to feel safe. Relational safety, as discussed in chapter five, is essential for a traumatised client to feel secure enough to reduce their hyper-vigilance sufficiently to be able to engage in the beneficial activities of mindfulness. Aspect two of reciprocity relates in TIM to the essential nature of the relationship being collaborative, whereby the client has as much choice within the process as is sensible. Collaboration also relates to the way in which TIM practices are titrated carefully so that the client is scaffolded with support to work on both the edge of their zone of proximal development for skills acquisition, and the edge of their window of tolerance for emotional regulation. This is important because engaging in mindfulness practices in a way that is inappropriate to an individual's needs can be traumatising or re-traumatising rather than de-traumatising (Duerden, 2018).

Aspect three relates both to progressive complexity and to the concept of fading in the developmental relationship model. This aspect maps on to the TIM philosophy of gradually building the client's competency to use mindfulness practices in their daily life in a way that best suits their own personal path towards recovery and growth. Aspect four of the balance of power also fits well with the TIM model; although reframed as 'choice' rather than power, this relates again to the importance of allowing someone who has experienced trauma not to feel *powerless* again in the therapeutic relationship. In contrast, clients are facilitated to gain personal control and autonomy, giving a sense of purpose and independence as they gain greater mastery of the TIM skills. Consequently this helps them to manage their thoughts and regulate their emotions more effectively.

Make a few notes or discuss with peers or colleagues the idea of titrating TIM practices to be tailored to the client in each of these two ways:

1. To work on skills at the edge of their zone of proximal development
2. To work within or at the edge of their window of tolerance for emotional regulation

Group versus individual mindfulness

Mindfulness in the West has so far been predominantly the domain of group teaching settings. Despite its proponents, and the evidence of its efficacy for those who have experienced trauma, some of the critiques that have been proposed regarding the use of mindfulness are: that it is usually undertaken in groups, which may be threatening to those with post-trauma symptoms; and that the focus of the training is teaching skills which may not appropriate for the client at their stage (Braer, 2003). Furthermore, it has been argued that as the training is brief (usually eight weeks, 2.5 hours per week with a whole day's retreat), this may not fit the needs of the individual (Courtois and Ford, 2012). Some group facilitators who have started to encounter problems in groups where people experience trauma triggers during the mindfulness practices have further confirmed concerns about the appropriateness of standard mindfulness group programmes for people with current trauma-related symptoms. A couple of solutions have bubbled up from experts in mindfulness and trauma. The first is simply to screen out people who have trauma-related symptoms to avoid these challenges and the risks of re-traumatisation, de-compensation or abreaction. Whilst this is one possible solution, and probably a much better solution than keeping traumatised people in a group where their specific needs cannot be supported adequately, it does also exclude them from an intervention that may be very beneficial. A further problem with the screening approach is that often people feel reluctant to disclose their experiences of trauma to mindfulness group facilitators (Burrows, 2017), especially if they feel shamed by their experiences. Therefore, people struggling with trauma-symptoms may be present in the group unbeknown to the facilitator. The second solution that is gaining popularity is to find a way to bring mindfulness to traumatised individuals by adapting the standard MBSR group programme to make it more trauma-sensitive and responsive (Magyari, 2015). Adaptations can include having a predictable structure, smaller classes, psycho-education and additional practices to help participants to 'stay with' their experiences. Another suggested solution has been to offer individual therapy alongside the group work (Magyari, 2015) to help tailor and apply the skills learned in the group programme and address any problems that arise.

As the majority of mindfulness-based programmes that have been studied in Western therapeutic use have been delivered in group situations, the literature struggles to differentiate between the benefits gained from being with other clients in a group setting, and the benefits of the practices themselves. These two variables are sometimes referred to as the 'specific' (the mindfulness practice), and the 'non-specific' (the group processes) (Allen et al., 2009). Clients report that it can be very validating to be in a group context where there are other people who are also struggling with similar experiences to themselves, such as in MBCT groups for people with recurrent depression. Having the opportunity to see first-hand that other people also may feel inferior or isolated as a result of their symptoms can be helpful for individuals, and can lead them to becoming less self-critical. Being part of such a group may assist in alleviating feelings of being less able to cope than other people or not feeling good enough

So we know that there is an interrelationship between the specific and non-specific factors of group therapeutic interventions of any kind, but as yet are unclear as to exactly how these variables affect one another, and affect the overall treatment outcomes. What we do know from qualitative research is that participants in mindfulness groups compare themselves to others in ways that can decrease self-depreciating cognitions. For example a participant in a study by Alan and colleagues said that "'we're all sort of in the same boat' and ... we aren't mad, and we ain't stupid" (Allen et al., 2009, p. 424). This is a good use of qualitative research, to illuminate not just whether there are positive or negative outcomes from an intervention, but what exactly about that intervention it was that participants found beneficial. In the case of this participant, the reassurance of not being 'mad' or 'stupid' that was derived from being in a group of people with similar experiences was highlighted as one of the major gains of the intervention. In other words the 'non-specific' group processes were in themselves a benefit to the participant.

It seems therefore that when comparing group mindfulness for trauma with individual mindfulness there may be pros and cons on each side. There are gains from the reassurance of group interventions that are additional to the intervention itself, and at the same time there may be challenges to adequately understand or meet the needs of individuals in group settings. For example, many studies have highlighted the mediating role of a positive therapeutic alliance and its relationship to positive outcomes (Watson and Geller, 2005). The 'common factors' of therapist warmth, empathy and congruence, rather than the intervention itself, are arguably most significant in affecting positive outcomes (Lambert and Barley, 2001). In my work with clients with severe and enduring mental health problems, I have observed that many struggle to engage with groups for a variety of reasons, and so individual work, at least to start with, is the only viable option.[x] Additionally, I have found that when working with clients who have enduring complex psychological difficulties, there is a need to integrate a number of skill sets from different therapeutic models in order to effectively address their individual needs. Thus, my own experience has been that whilst I really wanted my clients to engage in mindfulness, there was a necessity to find a way to adapt existing mindfulness protocols to provide a much more individual, flexible approach so that they could still benefit from its advantages without having to attend a group programme. TIM was consequently primarily developed as an approach to using mindfulness with clients on an individual basis. The advantages of individual application of mindfulness in this way have not yet been empirically tested in the same way that group interventions have, and so data about its efficacy cannot be claimed. At this point I am offering a workable way to facilitate mindfulness for those clients who cannot cope with groups, especially those who have experienced trauma and need to be treated with compassion, dignity and uniqueness as individuals on their own particular path towards recovery.

A phased approach to trauma treatment
Judith Herman proposed a phased approach model for treating psychological trauma based on three interdependent sequentially organised stages. The inclusion of the initial 'stabilisation' phase was proposed to be the best way to work with complex trauma.

- Phase 1: Safety and stabilisation
- Phase 2: Remembering and mourning
- Phase 3: Reconnection (Herman, 2015, p. 3)

---

[x] A discussion of arguments about contra-indications is presented in chapter nine.

258

Dynamic stabilisation and integration

This phased-based approach has consistently been adopted in a wide range of settings for the treatment of PTSD and Complex PTSD (CPTSD), and is also recommended by the International Society for Traumatic Stress Studies (ISTSS) as the most appropriate way to work with complex PTSD (Cloitre et al., 2012). Typically, the stabilisation phase involves elements of psycho-education about trauma, and the treatment options. It also includes teaching skills such as grounding and affect regulation, so that by using these skills, the client is able to safely manage any emotional dysregulation during the treatment phase. A sequential or phased-based approach was endorsed by 84% of fifty expert clinicians for the treatment of complex PTSD (Cloitre et al., 2011). This consensus model phased approach, whereby a period of symptom management and 'stabilisation' precedes an active trauma therapy 'processing' phase has been generally accepted as good practice (Herman, 1998) and has been fairly standard in the treatment of psychological trauma. Figure 8.2 (overleaf) gives a bit more detail about what each of these phases encompasses.

Research evidence suggests that when treating PTSD related to childhood abuse, the development of therapeutic alliance and stabilisation in phase one has significance in determining positive outcomes for the therapy (Cloitre et al., 2004). A phased approach has also been recommended for working with refugees and asylum seekers, as this approach recognises that clients have experienced prolonged and repeated trauma, and are often still in situations where there is ongoing threat and uncertainty (Gorman, 2001; Nickerson et al., 2011). An example of a successful phased-based treatment protocol is provided in table 8.3 (on p. 261), which is a replication of the phases used in a creative arts programme for children who have experienced trauma (van Westrhenen et al., 2017).

 **Safety and stabilisation**

This is an initial phase of treatment that focuses on establishing client safety, and to reduce trauma symptoms through developing skills to manage overwhelming cognitions and affect, and severe disruptions in social relationships. This phase also includes the facilitator normalising the client's experiences by offering explanations for their symptoms, and to offer hope through psycho-education.

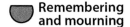 **Remembering and mourning**

The second phase is essentially the part of the intervention which directly addresses the trauma memories. The goal is to 'process' these memories so that they are more manageable and controlled, and less somatically experienced. Literally, remembering what has happened and allowing the grief of what has been lost to be experienced. Typically this is the phase that relates to the implementation of interventions that are recommended to be appropriate and effective according to evidence-based practice.

 Reconnection

The reconnection phase is also now sometimes referred to as integration. It relates to the post-treatment stage of therapy where new cognitions and experiences are consolidated and become more established. The focus of this phase is on thinking about moving forward, and living life having been able to accept what has happened. It may involve thinking about relapse prevention, self-care in relation to stress-vulnerability, and new ways of self-conceptualisation. This can also mean reconnecting with relationships and work.

Figure 8.2 (above): The consensus model of trauma therapy three-phase approach to trauma work

Table 8.3 (opposite): Example of a phased approach group creative arts treatment protocol for children who have experienced trauma (adapted from van Westrhenen et al., 2017)

Herman's consensus model phase	Arts therapy phase	Session	Theme	Goal or purpose
Safety and stabilisation	Creating a safe space	1.	Introduction	Group rules, meeting each other
		2.	Psycho-education	Relaxation practice, normalisation
		3.	Safe space	Develop self-control, self-soothe and mindfulness
Remembering and mourning	The trauma story	4.	Emotion identification	Identify and validate emotions
		5.	Emotion regulation	Understand emotion regulation
		6.	The trauma story	Disclosure of trauma
Reconnection	Returning to the community	7.	Strength finder	Use strengths and favourite things as coping strategies
		8.	Community support	Discuss social networks and group connection
		9.	Meaning making	Reflection on learning and growth
		10.	Goodbye	Leaving the group with hope and good memories

Interestingly in this model, as in many similar protocols, the processing of the actual 'trauma story' makes up a small proportion of the whole intervention, consisting of three weeks of this ten-week programme. The importance of the stabilisation and reconnection phases is represented by the amount of time that is allocated to these aspects. In this model, mindfulness is introduced in week three as part of the stabilisation phase along with self-control and self-soothe. It is interesting to consider further, in relation to a phased-based model, where in the process mindfulness is currently used, and where it could be used.

- **In which 'phase' of treatment might mindfulness be used?**
'The Mindfulness Initiative' is a document that was written by a UK all-party parliamentary group (MAPPG, 2015). The aims of this group were to review and evaluate the current empirical evidence and best practice in mindfulness training, in order to develop recommendations for government in developing public policy relating to the implementation of mindfulness training. At the time of writing, mindfulness has not been recognised in the UK as an evidence-based intervention singularly recommended as an intervention for psychological trauma (NICE, 2018). However, mindfulness is a core component of DBT, which is recommended for clients with emotionally unstable (borderline) personality disorder, many of whom have experienced early childhood trauma (Herman, Perry and van der Kolk, 1989; van der Kolk et al., 1994). In line with PTSD treatment guidelines, those clients with co-morbid PTSD, borderline personality disorder and deliberate self-harm are typically referred for 'stabilisation' prioritising treatments such as DBT either as a preliminary or an alternative to trauma-focused treatments (Harned, Korslund and Linehan, 2014). In DBT a phased approach is used whereby an extended initial period of stabilisation is devoted to training the client in emotion regulation and distress tolerance skills, including mindfulness. This initial phase tends to be recommended to last for two complete cycles of skills training. Each module of skills is usually 10–12 weeks and there are four modules per cycle, so to

262

complete the whole of the training twice would take approximately two years. During this extended stabilisation phase, mindfulness is taught as a core skill alongside skills in emotion regulation, distress tolerance and interpersonal effectiveness. It is intended that this extended stabilisation phase, which incorporates mindfulness training, will provide the client with sufficient resources to manage any emotional dysregulation that may be precipitated by actively engaging in the phase of treatment which is more specifically directed at treating any underlying trauma.

Having said this, there is current research that is seeking to understand whether those clients appropriate for DBT programmes who also have co-morbid PTSD, may benefit from a much shorter stabilisation phase before a prolonged exposure PTSD treatment element is introduced. One example is a pilot randomised controlled trial consisting of a control group of DBT only, and an intervention group of DBT plus DBT prolonged exposure (DBT PE) based on Foa, Hembree and Rothbaum's prolonged exposure (2007) for a period of one year. In this study, the treatment group were required to achieve an assessed level of stabilisation before the DBT PE was introduced. This stabilisation threshold consists of: not having had any suicide attempts or self-harm for two months; demonstration of the ability to control urges to self-harm; no indication of serious behaviours deemed to be 'therapy interfering'; no indication of imminent suicide risk; a willingness to tolerate intense emotions; with the PTSD treatment being regarded as the most important treatment priority. During the trial, clients were on average able to achieve this level of stabilisation within five months of entering the programme (Harned, Korslund and Linehan, 2014). The researchers in this project report that in terms of risk, the DBT + DBT PE group scored lower on suicidal urges post-treatment, indicating that the integration of a prolonged exposure form of PTSD treatment alongside DBT was more effective than DBT alone for this client group.

Although these trials show some promising results that may indicate that stabilisation can be achieved more quickly than the initial DBT programme might suggest, research also shows that the introduction of trauma-focused treatments during the 'active' stage of therapy such as tf-CBT or EMDR can be extremely challenging for clients. There is wisdom therefore in the premise that for client safety (especially when working with suicidal clients) the development of confidence in having some skills in being able to manage the additional distress that is typically stirred up by re-engaging with trauma memories is essential. However, it is also the case that when clients are suffering from trauma symptoms, the stabilisation skills alone are often not sufficient to alleviate the symptoms fully. Although in the DBT model mindfulness is taught as part of the stabilisation phase, there is some evidence of the efficacy of combining mindfulness at the active trauma-processing phase such as in support of EMDR (Tounsi et al., 2017). In the work by Tounsi and colleagues for example, mindfulness was used with a client with complex trauma as a way to minimise the anxiety caused by engaging in the EMDR part of the therapy, and at times to allow new material to come forward. In this case study, mindfulness was successfully used for stabilisation in parallel to processing during phase two, the desensitisation and cognitive restructuring part of the therapy (Tounsi et al., 2017).

Critique of the need for a stabilisation phase

A recent movement has begun to critique the phase-based model for complex trauma interventions, claiming that the pre-processing phase of stabilisation is unnecessary, delays treatment, and can be demotivating for clients (de Jongh et al., 2016). The rationale for introducing trauma interventions at an earlier stage than has previously been felt to be appropriate, is that the overall treatment length is reduced, in turn reducing the resource burden for service providers, and the length of time that the client has to live with the PTSD symptoms (Kredlow et al., 2017). Proponents of this position claim that implementing 'first-line trauma-focused treatments' without prior stabilisation or emotion regulation training are effective in treating people with symptoms of PTSD and trauma histories of childhood sexual abuse (Wagenmans et al., 2018). For example, Kredlow and colleagues (2015) assert that for clients with co-morbid PTSD and borderline personality disorder, trauma-focused CBT can effectively be implemented without adherence to the usual phased approach. They argue that within a CBT programme of 12–16 hours, cognitive restructuring can effectively commence at session four (Kredlow et al., 2017). Although the authors argue that the relatively low drop-out rates in this study evidence the validity of being able to provide trauma-focused treatments without a prior stabilisation phase, they do acknowledge that all of the participants in their study had previously been receiving some form of community mental health support or treatment which may have served to provide stabilisation (Kredlow et al., 2017).

Critics of the reduced stabilisation position argue that the extremely limited evidence for trauma-focused therapy only does not afford a "solid logical reason to modify current guidelines" (Rydberg, 2017, p. 98), and therefore treatment recommendations for a phased-based approach should still be maintained. Additionally, even those who might entertain the possibility of a move towards the removal or reduction of pre-trauma therapy stabilisation suggest that there may be exceptions that need to be considered when clients engage in dissociative responses. As clients who dissociate during treatment tend to have less positive treatment outcomes, it has been argued that a phased approach may be more appropriate whenever dissociation is observed regardless of diagnosis (Dorahy et al., 2017). Dorahy and colleagues (2017) noted in their research that when dissociation was evident experienced therapists tended to prefer to use a phase-based approach, perhaps because of their experience in detecting negative treatment responses and their sensitivity to a wide range of dissociative symptoms. They also note however, that client distress levels need to be closely monitored during treatment, whether a phased or exposure approach is being used, especially when the client uses dissociation as a protective mechanism (Dorahy et al., 2017). Despite phase-based approaches being commonly advocated by trauma practitioners, and also being ISTSS recommended in treating complex PTSD, there is little empirical evidence as to the efficacy of separating out the different elements of these phases to see whether they can be safely and effectively utilised independently of one another. A different approach to this argument is to look at those therapies that might be regarded as 'stabilisation only'.

- **Stabilisation only**

In contrast to the proposition of negating the stabilisation phase of treatment for complex trauma presentations, some writers argue for the benefits of stabilisation only as a viable and effective intervention in its own right. The advantage proposed for stabilisation-only as a viable intervention is that it is very flexible, making it possible to adapt stabilisation interventions to be spiritually and culturally sensitive (Eichfeld et al., 2019). Additionally, as stabilisation can serve to reduce severe post-traumatic symptoms to some degree, it can be extremely valuable to offer in countries where longer term therapy may be limited or unavailable (Wöller and Mattheß, 2016). Although some authors have cautioned against therapists offering stabilisation techniques unnecessarily, or for longer than recommended by ISTSS guidelines (Rydberg, 2017), there is a wide consensus about its value. Notably, within this field there may be variations in what might be labelled as, or included in a 'stabilisation' phase. For example, in a recent stabilisation-only project, the stabilisation techniques taught included resource activation, imaginative distancing and attention focusing (Eichfeld et al., 2019). These techniques were found to reduce PTSD symptoms effectively in both sub-clinical and clinical groups and are described further:

- **Resource activation:** Invoking memories of personal successes, positive role models, relationships and positive memories to reduce negative affect
- **Imaginative distancing:** Using techniques such as imagining being in a 'safe place' or putting the trauma memory in a 'container' to develop feelings of safety and control
- **Attention focusing:** Directing attention towards positive or neutral external stimuli and away from internal trauma-related experiences

The resources for stabilisation used in this study were based on the ROTATE model (Resource-Oriented Trauma Therapy and Resource Installation with Eye-movement desensitization and reprocessing), a brief (typically 5–10 x 50-minute sessions) psychodynamically informed intervention designed for use with clients with complex trauma presentations. The aims of the ROTATE model are not to activate or work on trauma material directly, but to enhance resilience and coping potential through the activation of personal resources within a safe therapeutic relationship (Wöller and Mattheß, 2016). Using these resources for stabilisation Eichfeld and colleagues (2019) reported that they observed over 90% remission rates for PTSD including effective reduction of intrusions, avoidance, arousal and negative mood alterations. Thus, the value of stabilisation either as part of a phased-based approach or as a stand-alone treatment is well supported in the empirical literature.

Readiness for change pre-treatment group

Even where the work is done in a phased way, with a good therapeutic relationship, and the client is willing at each stage to proceed with the next part of the trauma memory processing, the need to revisit horrific and terrifying events is an essential part of the treatment protocol. Although there is a substantial amount of evidence that indicates the efficacy of reliving and reprocessing treatments, the process can nevertheless often be quite gruelling for the client. Some authors suggest that one way to balance the dichotomy between the client's desire to have the memories 'just go away' and feel better, and the therapist's need to revisit the trauma memories to process them, is through an initial phase of education and preparation of the client before treatment begins (d'Ardenne and Heke, 2014). I would suggest that this may operate in a similar way to the 'readiness for change' model (Prochaska and DiClemente, 1982), which is illustrated in figure 8.3.

When Prochaska and DiClemente first developed this model, they identified five basic processes of change, which they divided into three verbal processes (pre-contemplation, contemplation and preparation) and two behavioural processes (action and maintenance). The sixth stage of 'relapse' has since been added. Although this model has predominantly been applied to health management interventions such as in drug and alcohol services and weight management or smoking cessation clinics, its basic principles apply fairly universally across a wide range of settings. What I propose is a potential benefit in offering a short group programme designed to work with people considering engaging in psychological treatment for PTSD or CPTSD. I suggest that this may benefit clients by giving them space to properly consider what will be involved in the treatment protocol. Adopting the readiness for change model as a guideline for a pre-treatment group would also largely remove the stigma attached to relapse, as the model incorporates it as a normal part of any change process. With this in

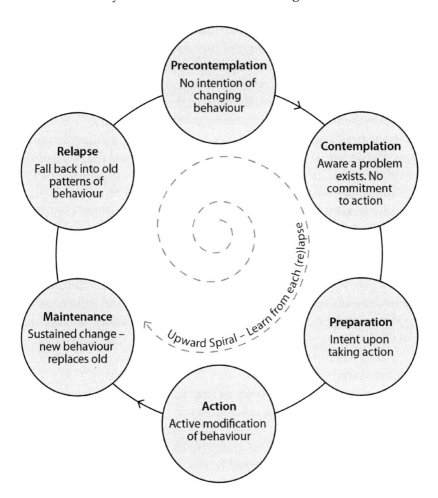

Figure 8.3: The readiness for change cycle (Prochaska and DiClemente, 1982, practice 010b) building block principles of titrating somatic work with people who have experienced trauma

mind, if a client does need to stop therapy at any point, the door remains open to re-engage when they feel more stable and ready to re-commence treatment.

I have successfully set up and run readiness for change groups, pre-DBT treatment, for borderline personality disorder clients. This opportunity to explore the pros and cons of engaging in the treatment and to carefully think through what it will involve does seem to help anecdotally in ensuring that clients engage and stay with the programme once they do decide to start. This kind of pre-treatment approach may be considered to be a helpful adjunct prior to the initial affect 'stabilisation' phase, and could usefully cover symptom normalisation, trauma psycho-education, and an explanation of treatment options. Clients would be encouraged to consider the impact that treatment may have in the short and long term, and to consider their current life circumstances, responsibilities and support network, together with motivation. Given the evidence at this point about non-engagement and drop out, my suggestion is that for some client groups a pre-stabilisation phase that involves more information-giving and relationship-building would enhance the client's feelings of safety and control, as well as giving opportunity to fully explore what stage they are at in the readiness for change cycle. This proposed model is illustrated in figure 8.4.

Having worked in both statutory and private contexts, I understand that the demands of matching resources to client needs are not always an easy fit, and that timing interventions to be accessible at the same time that clients are ready is not always possible. However, the introduction of a readiness for change group run by staff whose time is less pressured than those qualified to engage in trauma treatment interventions, may alleviate some of the resource bottle-necking that can occur.

Figure 8.4: Proposed four-phase psycho-trauma intervention model

Dynamic stabilisation and integration

Even where therapists work within a phased treatment approach model, it is widely recognised that flexibility is needed in moving back and forth between the stabilisation and processing as clients become agitated or distressed during processing. This use of a dynamic phased approach has been shown to be valuable also for clients who have experienced childhood sexual abuse, and who are suffering from with complex PTSD (Cloitre et al., 2012). With regards to the implementation of TIM as a stand-alone or integrated modality, I suggest that such flexibility for dynamic movement between the components of an intervention is advisable. By renaming the 'phases' as 'components' the linearity of the phase-based approach is softened and more fluidity of movement is encouraged. The seventh and final TIM characteristic of 'dynamic stabilisation and integration' speaks to this position. Mindfulness is primarily not a processing treatment modality, but has frequently been used in what has been referred to as the stabilisation phase to provide clients with the skills to manage the emotional dysregulation stirred up by the processing component of treatment. Additionally, mindfulness has been utilised as a way to accept and integrate new beliefs and cognitions post trauma-processing in what might be referred to as the integration component. With TIM, my recommendation is that because it is fundamentally designed as an individual titrated modality, it can be used very flexibly across all stages/phases/components of a client's trauma healing journey. It can be used pre-processing, as a 'time-out' strategy during processing or as a separate adjunctive intervention and/or as a post-processing approach to support integration. The details of how this may be worked out will be described in more detail in chapter nine.

Summary

This chapter began with a discussion of the developmental relationship model between client and facilitator as being closely aligned to the philosophy and ethos of TIM. This alignment operates such that the facilitator role is to scaffold the client's ability to work within their zone of proximal development and their window of tolerance, and is achieved incrementally through an individually tailored and titrated approach. Having carefully laid out the argument for a phased approach to trauma treatment, some attention has been given to discussing possible alternative solutions, including the argument for treatment without stabilisation, and the argument for stabilisation only treatment. Additionally, the introduction of the possible benefits for clients engaging with a readiness for change pre-treatment group has been unpacked. I have made it clear that my position is that stabilisation is an essential part of trauma treatment especially in the treatment of complex trauma, and in cases where dissociation is a significant client coping strategy. With regards to the position of TIM in relation to the phase-based argument, I have explained the value of taking a dynamic and iterative approach to weaving stabilisation and integration throughout the treatment process.

References

Allen, M., Bromley, A., Kuyken, W., & Sonnenberg, S. J. (2009). Participants' experiences of mindfulness-based cognitive therapy: "It changed me in just about every way possible". *Behavioural and Cognitive Psychotherapy*, 37(4), 413–430.

Bath, H. (2016, August). The three pillars of transforming care: Healing in the 'other 23 hours'. Retrieved from http://www.twi.org.au/3PHealingInTheOther23Hours.pdf

Braer, R. A. (2003). Mindfulness training as a clinical intervention: A conceptual and empirical review. *Clinical Psychology: Science and Practice, 10*, 125–143.

Bronfenbrenner, U. (1979). *The ecology of human development: Experiments by nature and design*. Cambridge, MA: Harvard University Press.

Brown, K. W., Ryan, R. M., & Creswell, J. D. (2007) Mindfulness: Theoretical foundations and evidence for its salutary effects. *Psychological Inquiry, 18*(4), 211–237.

Burrows, L. (2017). "I feel proud we are moving forward": Safeguarding mindfulness for vulnerable student and teacher wellbeing in a community college. *The Journal of Adult Protection, 19*(1), 33–46.

Cloitre, M., Chase Stovall-McClough, K., Miranda, R., & Chemtob, C. M. (2004). Therapeutic alliance, negative mood regulation, and treatment outcome in child abuse-related posttraumatic stress disorder. *Journal of Consulting and Clinical Psychology, 72*(3), 411.

Cloitre, M., Courtois, C. A., Charuvastra, A., Carapezza, R., Stolbach, B. C., & Green, B. L. (2011). Treatment of complex PTSD: Results of the ISTSS expert clinician survey on best practices. *Journal of Traumatic Stress, 24*(6), 615–627.

Cloitre, M., Courtois, C. A., Ford, J. D., Green, B. L., Alexander, P., Briere, J., & van der Hart, O. (2012). The ISTSS expert consensus treatment guidelines for complex PTSD in adults. Retrieved from https://www.istss.org/ISTSS_Main/media/Documents/ISTSS-Expert-Concesnsus-Guidelines-for-Complex-PTSD-Updated-060315.pdf

Collins, A., Brown, J. S., & Newman, S. E. (1990). Cognitive apprenticeship: Teaching the crafts of reading, writing, and mathematics. In L. B. Resnick (Ed.), *Knowing, learning, and instruction: Essays in honor of Robert Glaser* (pp. 453–494). Hillsdale, NJ: Lawrence Erlbaum.

Courtois, C. A., & Ford, J. D. (2012). *Treatment of complex trauma: A sequenced, relationship-based approach.* London, United Kingdom: Guilford Press.

d'Ardenne, P., & Heke, S. (2014). Patient-reported outcomes in post-traumatic stress disorder Part I: Focus on psychological treatment. *Dialogues in Clinical Neuroscience, 16*(2), 213.

de Jongh, A., Resick, P. A., Zoellner, L. A., Van Minnen, A., Lee, C. W., Monson, C. M., Foa, E. B., Wheeler, K., Broeke, E. T., Feeny, N., & Rauch, S. A. (2016). Critical analysis of the current treatment guidelines for complex PTSD in adults. *Depression and Anxiety, 33*(5), 359–369.

Dorahy, M. J., Lewis-Fernández, R., Krüger, C., Brand, B. L., Şar, V., Ewing, J., Martínez-Taboas, A., Stavropoulos, P., & Middleton, W. (2017). The role of clinical experience, diagnosis, and theoretical orientation in the treatment of posttraumatic and dissociative disorders: A vignette and survey investigation. *Journal of Trauma and Dissociation*, *18*(2), 206–222.

Duerden, T. (2018). *Teaching mindfulness: Potentially traumatising or detraumatising. Teaching mindfulness safely.* Minding the Gaps conference, Brighton, United Kingdom. Retrieved from http://integratedmindfulness.com/mindingthegap2017/

Eichfeld, C., Farrell, D., Mattheß, M., Bumke, P., Sodemann, U., Ean, N., Phoeun, B., Direzkia, Y., Firmansyah, F., Sumampouw, N. E., & Matheß, H. (2019). Trauma stabilisation as a sole treatment intervention for post-traumatic stress disorder in Southeast Asia. *Psychiatric Quarterly*, *90*(1), 63–88.

Foa, E. B., Hembree, E. A., & Rothbaum, B. O. (2007). *Prolonged exposure therapy for PTSD: Emotional processing of traumatic experiences, therapist guide.* New York, NY: Oxford University Press.

Gorman, W. (2001). Refugee survivors of torture: Trauma and treatment. *Professional Psychology: Research and Practice*, *32*, 443–451.

Harned, M. S., Korslund, K. E., & Linehan, M. M. (2014). A pilot randomized controlled trial of Dialectical Behavior Therapy with and without the Dialectical Behavior Therapy Prolonged Exposure protocol for suicidal and self-injuring women with borderline personality disorder and PTSD. *Behaviour Research and Therapy*, *55*, 7–17.

Herman, J. L. (1992). Complex PTSD: A syndrome in survivors of prolonged and repeated trauma. *Journal of Traumatic Stress*, *5*(3), 377–391.

Herman, J. L. (1998). Recovery from psychological trauma. *Psychiatry and Clinical Neurosciences*, *52*(S1), S98–S103.

Herman, J. L. (2015). *Trauma and recovery: The aftermath of violence--from domestic abuse to political terror.* London, UK: Hachette UK.

Herman, J. L., Perry, C., & van der Kolk, B. A. (1989). Childhood trauma in borderline personality disorder. *The American Journal of Psychiatry*, *146*(4), 490.

Kredlow, M. A., Szuhany, K. L., Lo, S., Xie, H., Gottlieb, J. D., Rosenberg, S. D., & Mueser, K. T. (2017). Cognitive behavioral therapy for posttraumatic stress disorder in individuals with severe mental illness and borderline personality disorder. *Psychiatry Research, 249*, 86–93.

Lambert, M. J., & Barley, D. E. (2001). Research summary on the therapeutic relationship and psychotherapy outcome. *Psychotherapy: Theory, Research, Practice, Training, 38*(4), 357.

Li, J., & Julian, M. M. (2012). Developmental relationships as the active ingredient: A unifying working hypothesis of "what works" across intervention settings. *American Journal of Orthopsychiatry, 82*(2), 157.

Magyari, T. (2015). Teaching MBSR and mindfulness to women with trauma. In V. M Follette, J. Briere, D. Rozelle, J. W. Hopper, & D. I. Rome (Eds.), *Mindfulness-oriented interventions for trauma: Integrating contemplative practices* (pp. 140–156). London, United Kingdom: Guilford Press.

MAPPG (2015). Mindful Nation United Kingdom: Report by the Mindfulness All-Party Parliamentary Group (MAPPG). October 2015. Retrieved from https://www.themindfulnessinitiative.org.uk/publications/mindful-nation-uk-report

Morrow, K. V., & Styles, M. B. (1995). *Building relationships with youth in program settings: A study of Big Brothers/Big Sisters.* Philadelphia, PA: Public/Private Ventures.

NICE (2018). National Institute for Clinical Excellence. Post-traumatic stress disorder (PTSD): The management of PTSD in adults and children in primary and secondary care. (Clinical Guideline). https://www.nice.org.uk/guidance/ng116

Nickerson, A., Bryant, R. A., Silove, D., & Steel, Z. (2011). A critical review of psychological treatments of posttraumatic stress disorder in refugees. *Clinical Psychology Review, 31*(3), 399–417.

Prochaska, J. O., & DiClemente, C. C. (1982). Transtheoretical therapy: Toward a more integrative model of change. *Psychotherapy: Theory, Research & Practice, 19*(3), 276.

Rothschild, B. (2010). *Eight keys to safe trauma recovery. Take-charge strategies to empower your healing.* New York, NY: W. W. Norton & Company Inc.

Rydberg, J. A. (2017). Research and clinical issues in trauma and dissociation: Ethical and logical fallacies, myths, misreports, and misrepresentations. *European Journal of Trauma & Dissociation*, *1*(2), 89–99.

Shapiro, D. H. (1994). Examining the content and context of meditation: A challenge for psychology in the areas of stress management, psychotherapy, and religion/values. *Journal of Humanist Psychology*, *34*, 101–135.

Tounsi, H., Pacioselli, P., Riou, L., Gouret, C., Gross, L., Quaderi, A., & Palazzolo, J. (2017). Psychotherapies for complex trauma: A combination between EMDR and mindfulness. *European Psychiatry*, *41*, S726.

van der Kolk, B. A., Hostetler, A., Herron, N., & Fisler, R. E. (1994). Trauma and the development of borderline personality disorder. *Psychiatric Clinics*, *17*(4), 715–730.

van Westrhenen, N., Fritz, E., Oosthuizen, H., Lemont, S., Vermeer, A., & Kleber, R. J. (2017). Creative arts in psychotherapy treatment protocol for children after trauma. *The Arts in Psychotherapy*, *54*, 128–135.

Vygotsky, L. S. (1978). *Mind in society: The development of higher psychological processes* (pp. 79–91). Cambridge, MA: Harvard University Press.

Wagenmans, A., Van Minnen, A., Sleijpen, M., & De Jongh, A. (2018). The impact of childhood sexual abuse on the outcome of intensive trauma-focused treatment for PTSD. *European Journal of Psychotraumatology*, *9*(1), 1430962.

Watson, J. C., & Geller, S. M. (2005). The relation among the relationship conditions, working alliance, and outcome in both process-experiential and cognitive–behavioral psychotherapy. *Psychotherapy Research*, *15*(1–2), 25–33.

Wöller, W., & Mattheß, H. (2016). *Resource-oriented trauma therapy combined with EMDR resource installation treatment manual.* Version 1.0, July 2016. Germany: Trauma Aid.

CHAPTER NINE
INTEGRATING TIM INTO
YOUR CURRENT PRACTICE

Chapter contents
• The ripple effect of trauma • Cognitive distortions • Possible contra-indications • Adding mindfulness to your practice safely • Tips for trauma therapy work • Using SMART goals for titration • Matching intention to inquiry • Summary

This final chapter begins with a discussion about the 'ripple' effects of trauma. In other words the additional problems that are created by the coping strategies that people use to manage the symptoms of the original trauma, and which can further exacerbate those symptoms as circumstances and relationships are affected. This will be considered from the perspective of the individual with the disorder, as well as that of people surrounding the individual. The design of TIM has primarily been with its use for therapists, psychologists and counsellors and other healthcare professionals to draw upon as an integrative or adjunctive intervention to their current practice with individual clients. It can also be utilised by facilitators from a wider range of professions, and can be employed as a stand-alone intervention. After a discussion about cognitive distortions and the value of TIM for helping raise awareness and control of thoughts, the topic of appropriateness for certain client groups for working with TIM is addressed in light of a discussion around possible contra-indications. Following this, the rest of the chapter deals with some of the very practical details of implementing TIM and working with clients who have experienced trauma, including some advice and tips, and guidance about setting TIM SMART (specific, measurable, achievable, realistic and time-limited) goals. The important area of how to match effectively the intention-setting part of the practice with the inquiry afterwards is also explained and its necessity as part of the protocol is highlighted.

The ripple effect of trauma

The impact of the physical and mental sequelae of trauma affect the life of the person suffering from post-trauma symptoms in many more ways than might be immediately obvious. For example, if a person is suffering from terrifying intrusive thoughts or flashbacks, they may become quite reclusive in seeking to manage their symptoms. Alternatively, a person may turn to using substances such as drugs and alcohol to try to block out or numb the symptoms. In turn, the use of substances will have an impact on the person's finances, their social relationships, their diet and exercise, and physical health. By avoiding reminders of the traumatic event, a person may significantly reduce their previous activities, perhaps avoiding places and people that they previously enjoyed. This in turn may affect their opportunities for engaging in previously enjoyed activities, and connecting with people from whom they previously gained social and emotional support. Furthermore, changes in mood, and cognitions may distort a person's perception of themselves, others and the world to the extent that they retreat from engaging with others, reduce the places they might otherwise have enjoyed visiting, and pull away from relationships, or avoid starting new relationships. Conversely, a person suffering from trauma symptoms may become irritable, short-tempered or aggressive with people in which they are in relationships if they have had little sleep and suffer from terrifying flashbacks that affect their patience and tolerance. Many people who have experienced trauma may also choose not to share what has happened to them with those closest to them, due to fear of causing harm or distress, or evoking negative judgements. In relationships where a sufferer does not feel able to speak to their partner, for example, about their abuse or their combat experiences, the partner may feel excluded and confused and not understand their behaviour as trauma-related. These coping strategies that are designed in the short term to help manage the distress caused by the post-trauma symptoms, which can in themselves start to become problems in their own right, creating further problems interpersonally and in terms of self-concept, self-respect and self-compassion. Figure 9.1 is an attempt to capture in a visual form how some of these 'ripples' can damage large areas of a person's life.

In the case of a psychological trauma resulting from a traumatic accident in which there was also a physical trauma to the body, there may be both what are referred to as 'primary' or direct trauma, and 'secondary' or indirect trauma (Scott, 2013). In this circumstance, *direct* impairment relates to the immediate psychological effects and symptoms of being exposed to a life-threatening traumatic situation and *indirect* impairment relates to the pain, head injury or disfigurement that accompanies the physical damage caused, which when chronic or permanent, can serve as a constant reminder of the accident. When considering treatment and rehabilitation, both would need to be addressed for the person to find relief, as if either is left untreated it can act as a trigger to the other, creating a constant vicious circle.

Cognitive distortions

When working with clients who have experienced trauma, there might be a number of different reasons for suggesting TIM as an intervention. Typically, when mindfulness approaches have been introduced therapeutically, it has been as a way to manage stress

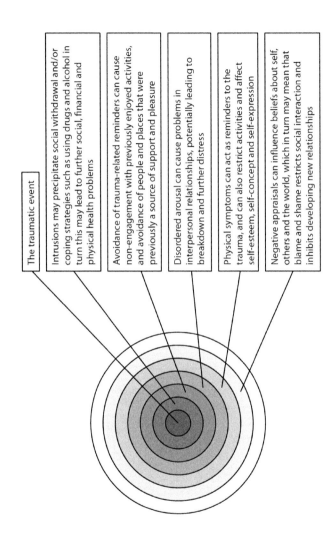

The traumatic event

Intrusions may precipitate social withdrawal and/or coping strategies such as using drugs and alcohol in turn this may lead to further social, financial and physical health problems

Avoidance of trauma-related reminders can cause non-engagement with previously enjoyed activities, and avoidance of people and places that were previously a source of support and pleasure

Disordered arousal can cause problems in interpersonal relationships, potentially leading to breakdown and further distress

Physical symptoms can act as reminders to the trauma, and can also restrict activities and affect self-esteem, self-concept and self-expression

Negative appraisals can influence beliefs about self, others and the world, which in turn may mean that blame and shame restricts social interaction and inhibits developing new relationships

Figure 9.1: The ripple effect of post-trauma symptom impact

or depression, both of which are perpetuated by negative rumination and/or anticipatory anxiety. When mindfulness is used in these situations, it helps train the individual not to get so caught up with and entangled in their thoughts. Without intervention, these kinds of thoughts can often quickly spiral out of control along well-worn negative pathways. Figure 9.2 is a simple illustration of how these thought patterns can spiral downwards into very negative places that can in turn exacerbate emotions and beliefs that are very painful to the individual.

From the thought spiral diagram, you can see how quickly an initial negative thought can become extremely serious and may then lead to a harmful behaviour. TIM helps a client to notice first of all what kinds of thoughts they are having at an early stage, and then offers strategies to let go of those thoughts or not to consider giving them further attention (by keeping attention focused elsewhere). The value of learning to control one's thoughts can

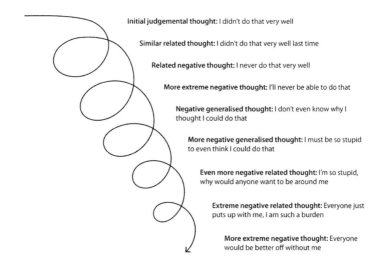

Figure 9.2: A negative downward thought spiral

perhaps be seen through this example. Learning to control thoughts that have less emotional content and less momentum behind them tends to be easier than trying to control thoughts that have snowballed. TIM teaches ways to be more self-aware, and also to take control of thoughts that may have a problematic trajectory at an early stage. As an adjunct to using TIM, it may be useful to discuss with a client what their thinking biases might be more generally, as often people have particular unhelpful patterns in the way that they think. In CBT, therapists use a list of common 'cognitive distortions' to help clients to see the inaccuracy of that thinking bias, so that it can be corrected to something more realistic. A list of the most common cognitive distortions is provided in table 9.1.

Table 9.1: Common cognitive distortions

Cognitive distortion	Description
Magical thinking	The mistaken belief that performing particular actions will have an influence on completely unrelated events or situations. For example, thinking that placing a red mat outside the door will deter terrorist attack, or that performing unusual rituals will protect family members, or that wearing a particular sweater will stop someone else shouting
Black and white thinking	Thinking in distorted absolutes or extremes. This is also called all-or-nothing thinking. For example, "I *always* mess things up", "people *never* talk to me", "*everyone* thinks I'm stupid", "I can't trust *anyone*". It also relates to achievements in terms of having the inaccurate thinking that unless something is done perfectly it is not good enough
Disqualifying the positive	This is a common cognitive bias, whereby a person tends to 'filter' positive and negative situations or comments from others. The person

	places far more emphasis on thinking about and believing the negative (even if it is tiny in comparison to the positive), and either ignores the positive, or rationalises it as insincere or undeserved
'Should' beliefs	A belief that there is a right way to act or think or feel or respond, regardless of what a person actually thinks or wants. Being driven by what a person thinks they 'should' do puts the emphasis on trying to ascertain what other people want, and seeking to align with that, rather than allowing and validating one's own feelings and thoughts
Magnification or minimisation	Exaggerating or overestimating the importance or meaning of some experiences and underestimating the importance or meaning of others. Commonly this might be to minimise or underestimate the value of one's own achievements, whilst also overestimating and placing too much importance on one's own perceived mistakes or faults
Over-generalisation	Making broad or sweeping generalisations (usually negative) from one situation. For example, a person might on one occasion drop something, and then over-generalise a distorted self-perception of *always* being clumsy and useless. Over-generalisations can also be about other people or negative situations, inaccurately over-estimating their prevalence
Catastrophising	This is very often a quick succession of thoughts in a chain that form a downward negative spiral. These unrealistic and distorted thought patterns quickly reach a conclusion that the outcome of any situation will be the worst possible scenario
Personalisation	This is a mistaken belief of being overly responsible for situations and other people.

	For example, believing that if someone else is upset, it must be because I have said or done something to make them upset. This cognitive distortion is very narrow and does not take into account the multitude of other explanations for why another person might be feeling the way that they do
Jumping to conclusions	This relates to being in a situation in which a person very quickly makes a judgement on the basis of very little or no actual evidence to support that conclusion (usually negative). Conclusions might be based on past experiences or negative beliefs about self, rather than the current situation
Emotional reasoning	This is the inaccurate conclusion that the reality of a situation can be gauged on the basis of how a person feels. For example, if a person has a negative feeling that they are a bad person, there is an associated belief that because they feel like that, it must be true
Fortune telling	Usually relating to a negative bias, this thinking distortion is about predicting that a situation is going to go wrong or turn out badly, even if there is insufficient evidence to support that pessimistic view

This list of cognitive distortions can be a helpful way to identify in which ways a client has become dis-aligned with how things are in reality. Identifying one's own tendencies towards particular cognitive distortions can be the first step in seeking to gain a more realistic perspective.

Possible contra-indications
There have been a number of authors who have argued that care should be taken when proposing mindfulness for certain groups

of people, and have proposed particular categories for whom mindfulness training would be contra-indicated. In 1994 Shapiro suggested that mindfulness was contra-indicated for people who are psychotic, schizoid, dissociated or hypochondriacal. Later, Magyari (2015) suggested that mindfulness is contra-indicated for those who are actively suicidal, have active addictions, or are actively psychotic. Furthermore, Germer, Siegal and Fulton (2005) advised caution in introducing mindfulness to those who struggle with reality testing, who have ego-based difficulties, who struggle to maintain boundaries or experience empathy, or who have rigid self-control (both physically and emotionally). Whilst taking on board these cautionary messages about the possible contra-indicators of mindfulness for certain groups, there is some evidence for the value of mindfulness for at least one of these categories of potentially 'excluded' participants; those with psychosis. In a dissertation study by Brorstrom (2009) of online discussion forum posts and blogs by people self-identified as having a diagnosis of schizophrenia and also using or previously having used mindfulness-based practices, participants reported positive benefits for managing intrusive thoughts. For example, one blog participant said he "used a simple form of mindfulness to regain control of my mind" (p. 33), with the results that "I now live in a wonderful place called now!" (p. 38). Another participant in the same study stated "once you get good at mindfulness it is with you every moment and is an antidote to the voices" (Brorstrom, 2009, p. 40).

Regarding considerations for screening people for appropriateness to engage in mindfulness practice, Briere (2015) recommends particularly screening for those factors that will influence potential distress levels, including:

a) Level of intrusive thoughts
b) Frequency of flashbacks

c) Level of rumination

d) How easily trigger memories are activated

Although it has been common for trainers of mindfulness groups and courses to 'screen out' people with trauma due to the many concerns that it raises, some mindfulness experts argue that this practice risks further marginalising people who are already marginalised. Additionally, it is known that many people do not disclose their trauma experiences to their mindfulness teachers unless explicitly asked (Burrows, 2017). An alternative approach therefore, is for teachers and facilitators of mindfulness groups to become more trauma-informed and trauma-responsive in their practices. There have been some recommendations about adaptations that can be made for MBSR groups to make them more trauma-sensitive (Magyari, 2015); these include having smaller group sizes and a predictable class structure, assessing symptoms and triggers at enrolment, finding out what has helped so far, informing participants that symptoms normally increase at first, being more flexible and having gradually longer process time, including additional practice of staying in contact with the self, and taking three breaths breaks between dyad debriefs. Magyari (2015) also recommends that it is helpful if individual therapy is offered as an adjunct to group mindfulness training. Perhaps what might be taken from these discussions and recommendations is that if the client group is not one that you have experience of working with (such as those with psychosis, personality disorder, suicidality or who deliberately self-harm) or if the symptoms of dissociation or flashbacks are more severe than you feel that you have the skills to safely manage, then it is probably wise not to attempt to introduce TIM with those clients. However, for facilitators who have existing skills and experience of working with clients with these symptom presentations, then TIM may be an option to add to your existing repertoire of interventions and skills training. For me personally, as a clinical psychologist working in both community and inpatient settings in the UK, I have successfully introduced TIM practices in a carefully titrated way to clients with these symptoms in order to help them manage or stabilise their dysregulation. However, I acknowledge that having additional training and experience of working with people who have experienced complex psychological trauma does offer a wider set of skills to support clients, in addition to the use of TIM skills. Therefore it is both wise and professionally ethical to only work with client presentations in which you are appropriately trained and experienced in working.

Adding mindfulness to your practice safely

The term 'practice' is used in mindfulness, and is a good word, because the skills of focusing attention away from what is harmful or distressing towards something that is bearable, do take considerable time and patience to practice. It is this element of practice that is one of the four pillars of the Sanctuary Model (Bloom, 2019):

- **Knowledge**: Of trauma, adversity and attachment
- **Values**: Sanctuary commitments to emotional intelligence, social learning, open communication, social responsibility, democracy, growth and change and nonviolence
- **Language**: The S.E.L.F. model of safety, emotion, loss and future
- **Practice:** Sanctuary toolkit of resources to support implementation of the model in organisations

The mechanism by which it has been thought that mindfulness may act to help reduce some of the symptoms experienced by those with trauma reactions, is that clients are able to develop a new relationship with their negative thoughts. Through mindfulness practice, thoughts are no longer experienced as frightening, they are just thoughts that can be observed, and the person can then process these thoughts more easily. An inability to remain present without engaging in avoidance can be conceptualised as a skills deficit (Follette, Palm and Pearson, 2006), therefore mindfulness practice may be seen as enabling exposure. Bessel van der Kolk (2014) argues that the process of recovery from trauma involves a number of elements, and that the primary challenge of trauma recovery is to 're-establish ownership' of one's body and mind, of the 'self'. This means that a person learns to experience their thoughts and feelings without becoming enraged, ashamed, overwhelmed or collapsed. In my own clinical experience, and in talking to other professionals, I have found that one of the biggest impacts of trauma, especially complex trauma sustained over a period of time and/or from a young age, is a lack of trust in self. In the words of a colleague who also expressed this point,

> any traumatic experience explodes a person's sense of reality, to such an extent that trust in reality itself is profoundly challenged. The resultant numbing seen in traumatised individuals is a disconnect from their own sense of ground. Mindfulness and its 'realness rooted in the present' seeks to reconnect the individual to themselves through trusting again in their own senses. Trust in self is slowly re-established within the frame of reference of the client's own present felt senses. (Woollams, 2019)

The way that this kind of acceptance and tolerance of thoughts and feelings is accomplished for the majority of people is through a number of steps:

- Discovering ways to become focused and remain calm
- Learning to maintain that state of calm even in the face of thoughts, images and physical sensations that trigger reminders of a traumatic past experience
- Discovering ways to be fully present, engaged, and feeling alive and connected to other people (van der Kolk, 2014)

TIM can be added to your practice safely if you take care about each of the components described in chapter two, with special attention to safety and choice and titration of exercises. The following section is a discussion of some of the 'traps' that inexperienced practitioners working with people who have experienced complex trauma may fall into, and some tips for how to manage these potential pitfalls.

Tips for trauma therapy work
The importance of the therapeutic relationship in determining positive outcomes is well documented, and one of the reasons that has been suggested that this is the case is that therapists who are accepting, congruent and empathetic are able to agree suitable goals and tasks with their clients more effectively and collaboratively (Watson and Geller, 2005). However, Chu (1988) proposed ten 'traps' that therapists may fall into when working with people who have experienced complex trauma. These are really helpful clinical observations that are worth bearing in mind, to maintain your own wellbeing when working with complex trauma. A précised list is presented in table 9.2.

Table 9.2: Lessons for therapists working with survivors of complex trauma (from Chu, 1998)

	Lesson	Description
1.	Trust	Chu argues that trust can take months or years to develop and that during this time clients will repeatedly 'test' their therapist. The difficulty is that the client expects trust to be broken, and this causes them to look for evidence that the therapist is not trustworthy constantly, to confirm their belief
2.	Distance	In times of crisis a client may be seen by the therapist as being inappropriately needy and may be concerned about over-dependency. At these times, the tendency may be for the therapist to distance themselves from the

		client. However, Chu argues that at these times it may be more advantageous for the therapist to stay in contact with the client rather than distance themselves, as this can often result in reducing or ending the time of crisis
3.	Boundaries	Having boundaries is essential for both the client and the therapist. The boundaries need to be comfortable for the therapist to work within, and where they are placed needs to be the therapist's decision, so that their privacy is protected and they can work effectively. Clients with complex trauma will feel a need for reassurance and will struggle with issues of trust wherever the boundaries are placed. Therefore, it is best for the therapist to be clear about boundaries, as this will help stabilise the client in the longer term
4.	Limits	Often therapists make a great deal of effort to avoid conflict with their clients and to manage their demands. This can mean that therapists risk neglecting their own needs, and may over-commit. Knowing your own limits as a therapist is essential for maintaining your own wellbeing, and working within those limits is just as important as being flexible. Having limits to what you can and cannot do is part of making a safe environment for both the therapist and the client
5.	Responsibility	The process of therapy is undeniably very challenging for clients, and there are times when they may feel unable to go on. At these times, the therapist my feel a great responsibility to urge the client to remain in therapy for their own safety. Although it is often the case that the therapist needs to hold

		hope for the client when the client does not have any for themselves, during these particularly difficult stages of therapy, it can feel that the therapist is holding all the responsibility for the client's life. Having empathy for the client is important, and it is also important for the therapist to know and to emphasise to the client that the responsibility for their progress is shared
6.	Control	Often clients who have experienced trauma, exist alternately in either a state of overwhelming feelings of not having control, or of trying to maintain a rigid control of their feelings or themselves. Having had no control over what happened to them during the trauma or abuse, grasping efforts to control external events or their own lives can be a compensatory strategy. As a therapist working with such a client, it is necessary to negotiate loosening the grasp on some areas of control and perhaps taking a bit more control in other areas. The aim is to work through this polemic of over control/loss of control to make more balanced choices
7.	Denial	One of the defence mechanisms for people who have experienced trauma is denial that certain experiences ever happened. However, this can lead to dissociation or repression. Similarly, clients may acknowledge that certain events have happened, but may deny its impact or significance. A therapist should take care not to collude with the denial of the trauma that has happened, or fail to validate its significance, so that work can be done to address the difficulties arising from what has happened

8.	Projection	The person who has experienced psychological trauma finds different ways to defend themselves against the unbearable effects. One such defence mechanism is the dissociation and fragmentation of parts of the self. The unbearable aspects of self can then be 'projected' on to others, so that the person doing the projecting experiences the other person as containing those features rather than themselves. The therapist working with a client who uses these unconscious defences needs to be highly alert to disentangling reactions that are transference-provoked
9.	Idealisation	One of the things that can happen with traumatised clients is that they split their perceptions of people in extreme ways. This can manifest by them having a perception of the therapist as being exceptional. The therapist who is the object of such idealisation needs to be wary that this idealisation is a fragile projection of a fragmented part. The challenge is to help the client to develop a more integrated experience of themselves and to withdraw these projections. Meanwhile, the therapist must keep a level head and be aware of any personal gratification from experiencing such projections, knowing that the idealised position can quickly be shattered
10.	Motivation	The therapeutic process for people who have experienced trauma can be extremely painful, and motivation to continue past these challenges is essential. Where there is deeply ingrained and severe pathology, and particularly rigid coping strategies, there is a need for sustained motivation to pull through. There will inevitably be a degree of ambivalence from the client, but those who get

		'stuck' may settle for using the therapist as an external ego resource to help them manage their day-to-day lives. With variability of motivation, it is prudent for the therapist to set realistic goals

Using SMART goals for titration

As mentioned already, when teaching someone new to mindfulness it is better to start with exercises that they can complete comfortably whilst they are already in their optimal zone (if possible). Also, it is best to choose exercises that you anticipate will not challenge them too much or act as a trigger. Getting to know the person will be necessary to gauge this accurately, as well as putting in place agreements between you about how these conditions can be negotiated and communicated effectively. In relation to a child's development of new skills, Vygotsky used the term 'zone of proximal development' (ZPD) to refer to "the distance between the actual development ... and the level of potential development as determined" (Vygotsky, 1978, p. 86). Guided by a sensitive facilitator the child is able to learn to master progressively more challenging practices. The same principle also applies with adults, as the proximal distance between the 'actual' and 'potential' development of skills is gradually and incrementally bridged. Once a person has gained a steady practice within their optimal zone (both in terms of their arousal level, and their skill level), it may be possible to start to introduce exercises that are more challenging. The best way forward is to start by ensuring your client has the feeling of success, of achievement and of benefit through simple 'low titration' exercises, before moving on to anything more challenging. The advantages of agreeing SMART practices are:

- Collaborative
- Predictable timeframe

- Achievable, so less likelihood of failure and discouragement
- Gives opportunity to explore possible triggers
- More client control

Very often people who have experienced trauma are particularly sensitive to feeling shamed or feeling inadequate or a failure. If you can present the practices for TIM in a titrated and individually tailored way, then they are also more likely to benefit from the increased personal satisfaction of gaining a sense of 'mastery' as well as the intrinsic benefits of the practice itself. Being able to agree together beforehand what a practice should be and for how long, and making sure the goals are SMART is another way to ensure that the practices are being effectively managed. What we are aiming for when we are thinking about scaffolding are two things. First, increasing the client's tolerance of distressing arousal by expanding the optimal area of the 'window of tolerance' and keeping within it, and second, to keep working on skill development within the 'zone of proximal development', so that the practice has some challenge but is achievable. These two principles are the cornerstones of titration in TIM, and are going to help you to be more effective in supporting your client to stay with the process. Making the goal 'realistic' is also a way in which achievability can be increased. The other SMART goals of being specific, measurable and time-limited are the mechanisms through which the practice can be made to be achievable. Using SMART goals also increases the probability of clients engaging and succeeding because they have been involved in doing so, as long as there has been support and guidance in creating them (Armitage, 2009). Table 9.3 gives a clearer picture of how SMART goals apply to the titration of TIM practice.

Table 9.3: Using SMART goals to titrate Trauma-Informed Mindfulness practice

SMART goal	Description of how this relates to the process of titration in TIM
Specific	This relates to setting a very specific intention about exactly which of the seven TIM skills is being practiced in any given exercise (Curiosity, Observation, Factual description, Non-judgement, Non-resistance, Turning towards and Letting go). Unlike other mindfulness-based interventions that do not make such a distinction, TIM asks clients to just focus on practicing one skill at a time
Measurable	In TIM, it is emphasised that the intention and inquiry need to match. What is being measured after each TIM practice exercise is how the client experienced the particular skill that they were practicing. During the inquiry phase after the completion of the exercise the facilitator and client measure how successful the client was in practicing the specific skill chosen collaboratively
Achievable	**The primary goal of the TIM exercise should be that it is achievable for the client. In other words, it should be designed and titrated in such a way as to be within their zone of proximal development. If the client is successful they are less likely to feel shame and to reconfirm negative core beliefs about themselves.**
Realistic	This relates to the stage of titration for the client. At what stage of the process of skills acquisition and development are they? TIM exercises are titrated in such a way as to build incrementally one to the next in a way that is individually suited to each client. The current 'level' of titration needs to be realistic for the particular stage that the client has reached, so that it is still achievable
Time-limited	This part of the goal setting mnemonic relates to timing the exercise. In TIM emphasis is placed on practicing very short exercises of a minute or two. In order for the exercises to be contained and predictable

	(important for people who have experienced trauma), each exercise should be timed with a bell, or buzzer, stopwatch or timer app

The whole ethos of developing SMART goals together is "to work collaboratively with patients to give them ownership of goals created" (Shaw et al., 2015, p. 1). So, the collaborative nature of using SMART goals serves the functions of both facilitating involvement (Borrelli et al., 2005) and thus *choice* for the client, as well as making the task clear and manageable so that progress and achievement is easy to identify, celebrate and build on.

Matching intention to inquiry

The intention for a practice is vitally important when training a client to learn TIM. In relation to a client being able to make incremental progress and to build mastery gradually and systematically, the intention is the place where the exercise can be titrated, and expectations of the practice are clearly delineated. The term 'intention' is used in TIM to describe the specificity of the intended practice that is planned with the client. One of the most recognisable features of TIM is that the intention part of setting up the practice is done very carefully and deliberately, so that it is very clear which of the seven TIM skills is to be practiced during any of the exercises. It is not reasonable to expect people during their mindfulness training to be able to focus on every aspect of mindfulness practice at the same time, which is why the intention helps to pick out just one or two at most to start with. An example might be to ask the client during a particular practice to notice any judgemental thoughts that they have whilst they are engaged in the focused task. Then after the practice, the inquiry component is where the therapist or trainer will inquire about how the client got on during the practice *specifically in relation to the set-up task* of just noticing judgements. I cannot emphasis enough how important it is to ensure when teaching and learning TIM, that careful attention and thought is given to working with the intention and inquiry components, so that the client is really clear about what is expected of them during the practice, and very clear progress can be monitored and incremental changes be made in accordance with that progress. This exercise is completely integral to the practice and not just an 'add on' – in fact it is a crucial part of the learning cycle.

In Buddhism, intention-setting differs from goal-setting in the sense that it is 'present moment' rather than 'future outcome' focused (Moffitt, 2003). This emphasis on being present is a familiar part of mindfulness practice, as is the notion of acting 'on purpose'. Intentionality therefore is the practice of consciously doing or thinking something on purpose in the present moment. For those who have experienced trauma, there has been a feeling of having no control or volition over what was happening. In a traumatic situation, the person has no choice, they are helpless in that moment. By contrast, when starting mindfulness practice, setting an intention about the practice immediately gives back that personal power and control. So, as a facilitator who is introducing mindfulness to someone else, our role is to *offer* the practice exercises. As we do, it is important in TIM always to allow the client a reasonable amount of choice (too much choice can be overwhelming) about how and when, for how long, and what the intentional focus of the practice will be. We collaborate with them, not do to them.

Take notes or read this section again and/or discuss with a colleague or peer to make really sure that you understand what is meant by 'matching the intention to the inquiry'.

In TIM, practice exercises are typically only a minute or a couple of minutes long, and so the emphasis is very much on quality over quantity. In conjunction with the pre-exercise intention setting, the post-exercise 'inquiry' is used to gather very *specific* feedback on how well the client managed to keep their focused attention on the particular task at hand. In my experience, it is common for the facilitator to ask rather generic questions such as 'how was that?' For example, you might choose to focus a particular practice on asking the client to notice any negative judgement thoughts they have about themselves during an exercise. It is really important to make it very clear before the practice that in addition to engaging in the activity itself, the client is expected to notice carefully their negative self-judgements on this particular exercise. This makes it much easier after the practice, during the inquiry or feedback segment, for you to inquire specifically about whether the client noticed themselves having any judgemental thoughts and if so what they did with those thoughts (i.e. were they able to 'let go' of the thoughts, or did they hold on to them and think about them more?). If the actual mindfulness practice is the central part of the exercise, the two extra components of 'intention' and 'inquiry' are like the bookends that come before and after the practice respectively.

- *The intention* is the specific instructions you give before the client engages in the practice
- *The inquiry* is the reflective discussion after the practice to establish what was learned

Figure 9.3 (overleaf) is a visual representation of how the intention and inquiry components relate to either side of the practice itself.

The most important thing to remember about the relationship between the intention and the inquiry is that they should match. For example:

Figure 9.3: Intention – practice – inquiry

- If the intention asks to focus on observing, the inquiry should ask about what was observed
- If the intention asks to focus on proprioception, the inquiry should ask about what was experienced by the spatial positioning of the body
- If the intention asks to focus on non-judgement, the inquiry should ask about what judgemental thoughts were experienced and whether they could be 'let go'

The following section offers some more specific examples of how to work with intention and inquiry either side of the practice exercise at different 'stages' of titration. The big advantage of short sessions is that there is a lot of opportunity for feedback, repeating the same practice several times, fine-tuning practices, gaining mastery and client choice about extending sessions. Before presenting the examples however, I have reproduced in figure 9.4 part of the 777 model introduced in chapter two for reference to the TIM attitudes and skills.

It is important to differentiate the attitudes and skills from the actual practice exercises. A list of ideas for possible exercises is provided in table 9.4 at the end of this chapter (on p. 309). The resources needed to start a TIM practice are:

1. The resources for the practice exercise
2. A timer
3. A 'Subjective Units of Success' (SUS) scale if used for inquiry (see below). You can draw or photocopy these as needed, or just use verbally

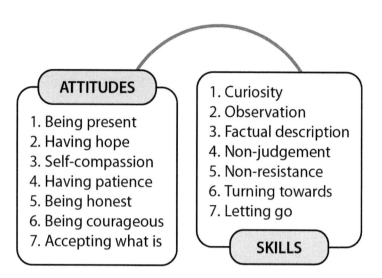

Figure 9.4: TIM attitudes and skills

The agreements about intention that need to be discussed collaboratively and decided on with the client are:

1. Proximity level of titration (external, body, internal)
2. Time level of titration (small)
3. The skill (from the list of seven provided) to be practiced

For clients who have had some practice, also bear in mind some or all of the seven TIM attitudes during the practice. When working one-to-one with TIM, you can tailor the set-up and inquiry to focus on particular aspects that are individually relevant, such as more work on non-judgement or self-compassion as needed.

Example one for proximity titration level 1: Outside the body
- **Intention:** Practice the *skill* of just 'observing' without describing or labelling (skill 1.) by giving focused attention to the *exercise* of listening to the sound of the traffic outside. If the client is able this could also be done with the *attitude* of 'being present' (attitude 1.)
- **Practice:** Complete one minute of silence (time titration) during the practice exercise of listening to the sound of the traffic outside with a timer
- **Inquiry:** Reflect on how well the practice went *specifically* in relation to just observing the sound of the traffic outside without describing, labelling or judging. To quantify this, a Subjective Units of Success (SUS) scale can be used

SMART goal	Description in this exercise
Specific	TIM skill 1. Observe
Measurable	Measure success in practicing the skills of just observing via qualitative verbal inquiry and/or a quantitative measurement tool
Achievable	Choice of skill to practice, length of time, proximity and exercise are all set at a low enough level that the client can succeed
Realistic	Starting at the lowest level and only building incrementally when the client has experienced some success at this level
Time-limited	One minute

SUS scale

0	1	2	3	4	5	6	7	8	9	10

Question example: On a scale of 0–10 with 0 being 'not at all' and 10 being 'completely', how successful do you feel you were during that practice in just observing the sound of the traffic outside without describing or labelling?

Example two for stage 1: Outside the body

- **Intention:** Practice the *skill* of 'letting go' (skill 7.) of thoughts as they pop up whilst engaged in the *exercise* of looking at a candle flame. If the client is able this could also be done with the *attitudes* of 'being present' (attitude 1.) and/or 'having patience' (attitude 4.)
- **Practice:** Complete two minutes of silence (time titration) during the practice exercise of looking at a candle flame with a timer
- **Inquiry:** Reflect on how well the practice went *specifically* in relation to being able to let go of thoughts as they came up during the practice exercise. To quantify this, a Subjective Unit of Success' (SUS) scale can be used

SMART goal	Description in this exercise
Specific	TIM skill 7. Letting go
Measurable	Measure success in practicing the skills of letting go of thoughts via qualitative verbal inquiry and/or a quantitative measurement tool
Achievable	Choice of skill to practice, length of time, proximity and exercise are all set at a low enough level that the client can succeed
Realistic	Starting at the lowest level and only building incrementally when the client has experienced some success at this level
Time-limited	Two minutes

SUS scale

0	1	2	3	4	5	6	7	8	9	10

Question example: On a scale of 0–10 with 0 being 'not at all' and 10 being 'completely', how successful do you feel you were during that practice in letting go of thoughts?

Example one for stage 2: The body
- **Intention:** Practice the *skill* of 'non-judgement' (skill 4.) whilst engaged in the *exercise* of looking at your own hand. If the client is able this could also be done with the attitude of 'self-compassion' (attitude 3.) and/or 'accepting what is' (attitude 7.)
- **Practice:** Complete three minutes of silence (time titration) during the practice of looking at your own hand with a timer
- **Inquiry:** Reflect on how well the practice went *specifically* in relation to practicing the skill of being able to be non-judgemental. You may also inquire about how well the client was able to maintain an attitude of self-compassion or accepting what is, if that was also used. To quantify this, an SUS scale can be used

SMART goal	Description in this exercise
Specific	TIM skill 4. Non-judgement
Measurable	Measure success in practicing the skills of being non-judgemental via qualitative verbal inquiry and/or a quantitative measurement tool
Achievable	Choice of skill to practice, length of time, proximity and exercise are all set at a low enough level that the client can succeed
Realistic	Starting at the lowest level and only building incrementally when the client has experienced some success at this level
Time-limited	Three minutes

SUS scale

0	1	2	3	4	5	6	7	8	9	10

Question example: On a scale of 0–10 with 0 being 'not at all' and 10 being 'completely', how successful do you feel you were during that practice in being non-judgemental?

Example two for stage 2: The body
- **Intention:** Practice the *skill* of 'non-resistance' (skill 5.) whilst engaged in the *exercise* of pressing your feet on the floor and being aware of the physical sensations. If the client is able this could also be done with the *attitude* of 'being present' (attitude 1.)
- **Practice:** Complete two minutes of silence (time titration) during the practice of pressing your feet on the floor and being aware of the physical sensations with a timer
- **Inquiry:** Reflect on how well the practice went specifically in relation to practicing the skill of being able to be non-resistant. You may also inquire about how well the client was able to maintain an attitude of being present, if that was also used. To quantify this, an SUS scale can be used

SMART goal	Description in this exercise
Specific	TIM skill 5. Non-resistance
Measurable	Measure success in practicing the skills of being non-resistant via qualitative verbal inquiry and/or a quantitative measurement tool
Achievable	Choice of skill to practice, length of time, proximity and exercise are all set at a low enough level that the client can succeed
Realistic	Starting at the lowest level and only building incrementally when the client has experienced some success at this level

Time-limited	Two minutes

SUS scale

0	1	2	3	4	5	6	7	8	9	10

Question example: On a scale of 0–10 with 0 being 'not at all' and 10 being 'completely', how successful do you feel you were during that practice in being non-resistant? You might also inquire how aware were you of the physical sensations in your feet?

Example one for stage 3: Inside the body
- **Intention:** Practice the *skill* of 'turning towards' (skill 6.) whilst engaged in the exercise of focusing back on your breath. If the client is able this could also be done with the attitude of 'being courageous' (attitude 6.)
- **Practice:** Complete two minutes of silence (time titration) during the practice of focusing on your breath with a timer
- **Inquiry:** Reflect on how well the practice went *specifically* in relation to practicing the skill of turning towards. You may also inquire about how well the client was able to maintain an attitude of being courageous, if that was also used. To quantify this, an SUS scale can be used if preferred

SMART goal	Description in this exercise
Specific	TIM skill 6. Turning towards
Measurable	Measure success in practicing the skills of turning towards via qualitative verbal inquiry and/or a quantitative measurement tool
Achievable	Choice of skill to practice, length of time, proximity and exercise are all set at a low enough level that the client can succeed

Realistic	Starting at the lowest level and only building incrementally when the client has experienced some success at this level
Time-limited	Two minutes

SUS scale

0	1	2	3	4	5	6	7	8	9	10

Question example: On a scale of 0–10 with 0 being 'not at all' and 10 being 'completely', how successful do you feel you were during that practice in turning towards a focus on your breath?

Example two for stage 3: Inside the body

- **Intention:** Practice the *skill* of 'curiosity' (skill 1.) whilst engaged in the *exercise* of paying attention to the physical sensations in your tummy. If the client is able this could also be done with the attitude of 'being honest' (attitude 5.)
- **Practice:** Complete three minutes of silence (time titration) during the practice of focusing on the physical sensations in your tummy with a timer
- **Inquiry:** Reflect on how well the practice went *specifically* in relation to practicing the skill of curiosity. You may also inquire about how well the client was able to maintain an attitude of being honest, if that was also used. To quantify this, an SUS scale can be used if preferred

SMART goal	Description in this exercise
Specific	TIM skill 1. Curiosity
Measurable	Measure success in practicing the skills of curiosity via qualitative verbal inquiry and/or a quantitative measurement tool

Achievable	Choice of skill to practice, length of time, proximity and exercise are all set at a low enough level that the client can succeed
Realistic	Starting at the lowest level and only building incrementally when the client has experienced some success at this level
Time-limited	Three minutes

SUS scale

| 0 | 1 | 2 | 3 | 4 | 5 | 6 | 7 | 8 | 9 | 10 |

Question example: On a scale of 0–10 with 0 being 'not at all' and 10 being 'completely', how successful do you feel you were during that practice in being curious about the physical sensations in your tummy?

*****

Table 9.4 is a list of a few ideas that you might find helpful to get started with TIM exercises. This is only a starting point, and can be adapted and built on in innumerable ways to fit your context, cultural setting and the clients you are working with.

Table 9.4: A list of ideas for TIM exercises

Watch	Look at
A flame (candle/fireplace)	Your own hand
A fish tank	Someone else's hand
Traffic passing	Your face in a mirror
The sea	Someone else's face
Trees moving in the breeze	Your foot
Clouds in the sky	A vegetable

Listen to	Write
Music	A poem
Traffic	Song lyrics
Air conditioning	Your name
Insects	Something copied
Rain	In large writing on a white/black board
Waves	In the sand
Singing	With a paintbrush
Drums	With chalk on the pavement
An instrument	With non-dominant hand
Draw	**Touch**
An animal	A shell
A tree	A piece of fruit
A flower	A toy
A person	A ball
A place	A piece of office equipment
A boat/car	A tool
A series of shapes	A lump of ice
A country/planets	Something textured
Moving your body	**Taste**
Put your hands/feet in water	A piece of bread
Stand on one leg	A drink
walk slowly	Something very spicy or minty
Close your eyes and touch your nose	Something very sour
Turn around in a circle	Something sweet
Stretch out flat on the floor	Something you have not tried before
Open arms wide to the sides	Something salty

Make	Smell
Origami	An essential oil
A paper plane	Tea or coffee
A bead bracelet	Something minty
A cardboard robot	A flower or bush
Soup	The sea/ocean air
Toast	The grass

Summary

This chapter has acknowledged that building mindfulness skills takes effort and commitment and needs to be done slowly and incrementally. The word used throughout this book to explain this process of incremental building of skills, combined with graded exposure to something that is feared or challenging is 'titration'. The skills of mindful awareness and focus take time to build and need to be used frequently to have effect. This chapter has explained the 'ripple' effects of trauma, where additional problems become created through the use of coping strategies, which in turn can affect others. Some detailed examples have been provided of how to set up an intention for a practice and how to engage in a focused inquiry. These scenarios draw together the information provided throughout the book, and in particular make the information about the model provided in chapter two clearer through examples.

References

Armitage C. (2009). Effectiveness of experimenter-provided and self-generated implementation intentions to reduce alcohol consumption in a sample of the general population: A randomized exploratory trial. *Health Psychology, 28*(5), 545–553.

Bath, H. (2016, August). The three pillars of transforming care: Healing in the 'other 23 hours'. Retrieved from http://www.twi.org.au/3PHealingInTheOther23Hours.pdf

Bloom, S. A. (2019). *What qualities characterize a certified Sanctuary organization? The Sanctuary Model.* Retrieved from http://sanctuaryweb.com/TheSanctuaryModel.aspx

Borrelli, B., Sepinwall, D., Ernst, D., Bellg, A. J., Czajkowski, S., Breger, R., DeFrancesco, C., Levesque, C., Sharp, D. L., Ogedegbe, G., & Resnick, B. (2005). A new tool to assess treatment fidelity and evaluation of treatment fidelity across 10 years of health behavior research. *Journal of Consulting and Clinical Psychology, 73*(5), 852.

Briere, J. (2015). Pain and suffering. A synthesis of Buddhist and Western approaches to trauma. In M. Folette, J. Briere, D. Rozelle, J. W. Hopper, & D. I. Rome (Eds.). *Mindfulness oriented interventions for trauma* (pp. 11–30). New York, NY: Guilford Press.

Bronfenbrenner, U. (1979). *The ecology of human development: Experiments by nature and design.* Cambridge, MA: Harvard University Press.

Brorstrom, L. (2009). *Portfolio of academic, therapeutic practice and research work including an investigation of trauma therapy in a landscape of suffering: Towards a grounded theory* (Doctoral dissertation). University of Surrey, United Kingdom.

Burrows, L. (2017). "I feel proud we are moving forward": Safeguarding mindfulness for vulnerable student and teacher wellbeing in a community college. *The Journal of Adult Protection, 19*(1), 33–46.

Chu, J. A. (1988). Ten traps for therapists in the treatment of trauma survivors. *Dissociation, 1*(4), 24–32.

Follette, V., Palm, K. M., & Pearson, A. N. (2006). Mindfulness and trauma: Implications for treatment. *Journal of Rational-emotive and Cognitive-behavior Therapy, 24*(1), 45–61.

Germer, C. K., Siegal, R. D., & Fulton, P. R. (2005). *Mindfulness and psychotherapy.* New York, NY: Guilford Press.

Li, J., & Julian, M. M. (2012). Developmental relationships as the active ingredient: A unifying working hypothesis of "what works" across intervention settings. *American Journal of Orthopsychiatry, 82*(2), 157.

Magyari, T. (2015) Teaching MBSR and mindfulness to women with trauma. In V. M. Follette, J. Briere, D. Rozelle, J. W. Hopper, & D. I. Rome, (Eds.). *Mindfulness-oriented interventions for trauma: Integrating contemplative practices* (pp. 140–156). London, United Kingdom: Guilford Press.

Moffitt, P. (2003). The heart's intention. *Yoga Journal,* 67–70.

Scott, M. (2013). *CBT for common trauma responses*. London, United Kingdom: Sage.

Shaw, R. L., Pattison, H. M., Holland, C., & Cooke, R. (2015). Be SMART: examining the experience of implementing the NHS Health Check in UK primary care. *BMC Family Practice, 16*(1), 1.

van der Kolk, B. (2014). *The body keeps the score*. New York, NY: Penguin.

Vygotsky, L. S. (1978). *Mind in society: The development of higher psychological processes* (pp. 79–91). Cambridge, MA: Harvard University Press.

Watson, J. C., & Geller, S. M. (2005). The relation among the relationship conditions, working alliance, and outcome in both process-experiential and cognitive–behavioral psychotherapy. *Psychotherapy Research, 15*(1–2), 25–33.

Wegner, D. M., Shortt, J. W., Blake, A. W., & Page, M. S. (1990). The suppression of exciting thoughts. *Journal of Personality and Social Psychology, 58*(3), 409–418.

Wegner, D., & Zanakos, S. (1994). Chronic thought suppression. *Journal of Personality, 62*(4), 615–640.

Woollams, I. (2019). Personal correspondence.